ALEXANDER FINDLAY

THE PHASE RULE

AND ITS APPLICATIONS

NINTH EDITION

By **A. N. CAMPBELL,** *Professor of Chemistry
the University of Manitoba; and* **N. O. SMITH,**
*Associate Professor of Physical Chemistry in
Fordham University.*

DOVER PUBLICATIONS, INC.

Printed and bound in the United States of America.

PREFACE TO THE FIRST EDITION

Although we are indebted to the late Professor Willard Gibbs for the first enunciation of the Phase Rule, it was not till 1887 that its practical applicability to the study of Chemical Equilibria was made apparent. In that year Roozeboom disclosed the great generalisation, which for upwards of ten years had remained hidden and unknown save to a very few, by stripping from it the garb of abstract Mathematics in which it had been clothed by its first discoverer. The Phase Rule was thus made generally accessible; and its adoption by Roozeboom as the basis of classification of the different cases of chemical equilibrium then known established its value, not only as a means of co-ordinating the large number of isolated cases of equilibrium and of giving a deeper insight into the relationships existing between the different systems, but also as a guide in the investigation of unknown systems.

While the revelation of the principle embedded in the Phase Rule is primarily due to Roozeboom, it should not be forgotten that, some years previously, van't Hoff, in ignorance of the work of Willard Gibbs, had enunciated his "law of the incompatibility of condensed systems," which in some respects coincides with the Phase Rule; and it is only owing to the more general applicability of the latter that the very important generalisation of van't Hoff has been somewhat lost sight of.

The exposition of the Phase Rule and its applications given in the following pages has been made entirely non-mathematical, the desire having been to explain as clearly as possible the principles underlying the Phase Rule, and to illustrate their application to the classification and investigation of equilibria, by means of a number of cases actually studied. While it has been sought to make the treatment sufficiently elementary to be understood by the student just commencing the study of chemical equilibria, an attempt has been made to advance his knowledge to such a stage as to enable him to study with profit the larger works on the subject, and to follow with intelligence the course of investigation in this department of Physical Chemisty. It is also hoped that the volume may be of use, not only to the student of Physical Chemistry, or of the other branches of that science, but also to the student of Metallurgy and of Geology, for whom an acquaintance with at least the principles of the Phase Rule is becoming increasingly important.

In writing the following account of the Phase Rule, it is scarcely necessary to say that I have been greatly indebted to the larger works on Chemical Equilibria by Ostwald *(Lehrbuch)* Roozeboom *(Die Heterogenen Gleichgewichte)*, and Bancroft *(The Phase Rule)*; and in the case of the first-named, to the inspiration also of personal teaching. My indebtedness to these and other authors I have indicated in the following pages.

In conclusion, I would express my thanks to Sir William Ramsay, whose guidance and counsel have been constantly at my disposal; and to my colleagues, Dr. T. Slater Price and Dr. A. McKenzie, for their friendly criticism and advice. To Messrs. J. N. Friend, M.Sc., and W. E. S. Turner, B.Sc., I am also indebted for their assistance in reading the proof-sheets.

A. F.

November, 1903.

PREFACE TO THE NINTH EDITION

For this edition Professor Findlay's "The Phase Rule and its Applications" has been largely rewritten by the present authors. Such imperfections as may be found are therefore their sole responsibility. One criticism we anticipate is that the book has lost its former delightful simplicity and become something of a work of reference. While we hope that this criticism is not entirely justified it is admitted that the design of the book has been changed. We have felt in teaching this subject that while "Phase Rule" made many things abundantly clear it left some important subjects untouched, presumably because it was felt that these subjects were too difficult for the undergraduate reader. In short, the book lacked, to some extent, continuity and systematic treatment. These defects, if they are such, we have endeavoured to rectify. We have constantly had in mind, when doing this, the systematic treatment of Roozeboom (and Schreinemakers) in his famous "Heterogene Gleichgewichte". Schreinemakers, indeed, in his treatment of the problem of liquid — vapour equilibrium has carried systematisation to a wearisome limit and we have endeavoured to avoid such an insistence on every possible variant.

The subject of heterogeneous equilibria is receiving ever increasing attention in undergraduate courses, and this is reflected in the space devoted to the subject in the ordinary undergraduate text-book of physical chemistry. In most modern text-books the subject is very well treated, within the limits of a general text. We therefore feel that the function of a special book devoted to Phase Rule is rather to serve the needs of graduate students and those engaged in research in the subject, while still remaining essentially a text-book and not a work of reference.

From this edition we have removed most of the data which can readily be found in works of reference, for instance, about a page of tables giving the vapour pressures of water and of ice. In addition, we have eliminated extensive reference to intensive drying and to Smits' theory of allotopy, which, if it was not founded on the effects, real or supposed, of intensive drying, at least received considerable support from these effects. Intensive drying aroused great interest some twenty-five years ago, but the general opinion now seems to be that if these effects, such as Brereton Baker's observation of an abnormal boiling-point for very dry benzene, are real, they are due to such secondary causes as superheating, and do not represent fundamental phenomena. Repetitive experimental studies of the same type of equilibrium have for the the most part been removed. In some cases, where the experimental studies were old and had not recently been repeated, the examples have been replaced by more modern ones. Some errors of long standing have been removed but new ones will inevitably have crept in, and for the notification of such errors the authors will be obliged.

Several new sections have been added, for example, one dealing with the experimental determination of the liquidus. This is written almost entirely from the practical experience of one author, extending over twenty years, and, while it may be incomplete, it is sound as far as it goes. Another section deals with the graphical thermodynamic deduction of some well-known equilibrium diagrams; this is chiefly an effort to show the reader that it is a matter of no great difficulty to arrive at those t,x diagrams which are usually produced in text-books without a word as to their deduction. The treatment of binary and ternary liquid-vapour equilibria is entirely new, as is that of solid solution in ternary systems. In the treatment of ternary equilibria, we have been sparing in our use of rectangular coordinates, preferring usually the equilateral triangle. Much more space has been devoted to the consideration of the solid model representing ternary solid — liquid equilibria at different temperatures, and to its isothermal sections. In general, in the discussion of systems of two and more components, generous use has been made of the solid model, since we believe that it is only in this way that the student can obtain a clear picture of the phenomena in their totality. About half of the original diagrams have been either redrawn or replaced by others.

With all these changes, excisions and additions, the book must be considered, for better or for worse, as largely a new book.

A.N.C.
N.O.S.

C O N T E N T S

SECTION ONE: INTRODUCTION

CHAPTER I. 1
General. Homogeneous and heterogeneous equilibrium. Real and apparent equilibrium.

CHAPTER II. 7
THE PHASE RULE. Phases. Components. Degrees of Freedom. Variance of a System. The Phase Rule. Classification of Systems according to the Phase Rule. Deduction of the Phase Rule.

SECTION TWO: ONE-COMPONENT SYSTEMS

CHAPTER III. 20
SYSTEMS OF ONE COMPONENT. Equilibrium between liquid and vapour. Vaporisation curve. Upper limit of vaporisation curve. Principle of Le Chatelier. The Clausius-Clapeyron equation. Presence of complex molecules. Equilibrium between solid and vapour. Sublimation curve. Equilibrium between solid and liquid. Curve of fusion. Equilibrium between solid, liquid, and vapour. The triple point. Bivariant systems. Changes at the triple point. Allotropy or polymorphism. Triple point $S_1 - S_2 - V$. Transition point. Transition curve. Enantiotropy combined with monotropy. Suspended transformation. Metastable equilibria. Pressure-temperature relations between stable and metastable forms. Velocity of transformation of metastable systems. "Law" of successive reactions.

CHAPTER IV. 61
TYPICAL SYSTEMS. Water. Other phases of the substance water. Other phases of deuterium oxide. Sulphur. Metastable systems. Bivariant systems. Tin. Transition point. Phosphorus. Liquid crystals or anisotropic liquids. Equilibrium relations in the case of liquid crystals. Ammonium nitrate.

SECTION THREE: TWO-COMPONENT SYSTEMS

CHAPTER V. 84
Different Systems of Two Components. Classification and Order of Treatment. Solutions.

CHAPTER VI. 90
A. SYSTEMS CONSISTING OF TWO LIQUID PHASES ONLY. Ideal Solutions and Raoult's law. Partial or limited miscibility. Phenol and water. Methylethylketone and water. Triethylamine and water. Completely closed solubility curves. Influence of pressure on the critical solution temperature. Influence of foreign substances on the critical solution temperature.

CHAPTER VII. 107
B. SYSTEMS CONSISTING OF LIQUID AND VAPOUR PHASES ONLY. Henry's law. Ideal solutions. Raoult's law. I. Completely Miscible Liquid Pairs. Isothermal distillation. Isobaric distillation. Boiling-point curves. Industrial fractional distillation. Fuming liquids. II. Two Partially Miscible Liquids in Equilibrium with Vapour. III. Two Immiscible Liquids. Distillation with Steam. Comparison of types.

CHAPTER VIII. 133
C. SYSTEMS CONSISTING OF SOLID AND LIQUID PHASES ONLY. I. The Components are Completely Miscible in the Liquid State. (a) The only Solid Phases are the Pure Components. Freezing mixtures. Method of mixed melting-points. Allotropy of components. Purification by partial liquefaction. (b) Compounds are Formed with a Congruent Melting-point. The indifferent point. Inevaporable solutions. (c) Compounds are Formed with an Incongruent Melting-point. Sodium sulphate and water. Suspended transformation. Dehydration by means of anhydrous sodium sulphate. Other systems. (d) Solid Solutions or "Mix-Crystals" are Formed. (i) The two components can form an unbroken series of solid solutions. (a) The freezing-points of all mixtures lie between the freezing-points of the pure components. (b) The freezing-point curve passes through a minimum. Fractional crystallisation of solid solutions. (ii) The two components do not form a continuous series of solid

solutions. (a) The freezing-point curve exhibits a transition point. (b) The freezing-point curve exhibits a eutectic point. (c) A sixth type. Changes in solid solutions with the temperature. II. The Components are Not Completely Miscible in the Liquid State. "Melting under the solvent." Suspended transformation. Binary equilibria at lower temperatures. III. Factors Affecting Solubility. The saturated solution. (a) The pressure factor. (b) The temperature factor. (c) The nature of the solid phases, (allotropy). Suspended transformation and supersaturation.

CHAPTER IX. 189
MISCELLANEOUS EXAMPLES OF FREEZING-POINT CURVES. I. Optically Active Substances. (a) The inactive substance is a dl-mixture. (b) The two components form a racemate. (c) The inactive substance is a pseudo-racemic mix-crystal (solid solution). Transformations. II. Alloys. (a) The components separate out in the pure state. (b) The two metals can form one or more compounds. (c) The two metals form solid solutions. The brasses. (d) Amalgams. The nature and formulae of intermetallic compounds. (e) The components are not completely miscible in the liquid state. III. Iron-Carbon alloys. IV. Minerals.

CHAPTER X. 212
D. SYSTEMS CONSISTING OF SOLID AND GAS PHASES ONLY. I. Two Volatile Solids which do not Interact Chemically or Form Solid Solutions. II. A Gaseous and a Solid Component which can only Form Compounds. Ammonia compounds of metal chlorides. Formation of oxy-carbonates. Salts with water of crystallisation. Efflorescence. Indefiniteness of the vapour pressure of a hydrate. Suspended transformation. Range of existence of hydrates. Constancy of vapour pressure and the formation of compounds. III. (a) The Gas is Absorbed by the Solid Component and No Compound is Formed. (b) The Gas is Absorbed by the Solid Component and a Compound is also Formed. Application of X-ray analysis to Phase Rule problems.

CHAPTER XI. 233
E. COEXISTENCE OF SOLID, LIQUID AND GAS PHASES.

I. Only One Component is Volatile. Pressure — temperature — concentration model. Changes at the quadruple point. Pressure — temperature plane diagram. Vapour pressure of solid—solution—vapour. Other univariant systems. Bivariant systems. Deliquescence. Separation of salt on evaporation. The system sodium sulphate—water. Potassium iodide and sulphur dioxide. II. Both Components are Volatile. General. (a) Iodine and Chlorine. Concentration-temperature diagram. Pressure — temperature diagram. Partial pressures of the components and the composition of the vapour phase. Bivariant systems. A generalised p,t,x model. Pressure — temperature — composition model for aniline and sulphur dioxide. III. Critical Phenomena in Binary Systems, in the Presence or Absence of Solid Phases.

CHAPTER XII 261
DYNAMIC ISOMERIDES AND PSEUDO-BINARY SYSTEMS.
Temperature-concentration diagram. Transformation of the unstable into the stable form. Examples. — Benzaldoximes. Acetaldehyde and paraldehyde. Sulphur. Melting-points of sulphur.

SECTION FOUR: THREE-COMPONENT SYSTEMS

CHAPTER XIII 277
General. Graphic representation.

CHAPTER XIV 282
A. SYSTEMS CONSISTING OF LIQUID PHASES ONLY. I. The Three Components Form Only One Pair of Partially Miscible Liquids. Retrograde solubility. The influence of temperature. II. The Three Components Can Form Two Pairs of Partially Miscible Liquids. III. The Three Components Form Three Pairs of Partially Miscible Liquids.

CHAPTER XV 296
B. SYSTEMS CONSISTING OF LIQUID AND VAPOUR PHASES ONLY. I. Systems with Only One Liquid Phase. (a) Each of the three binary systems has neither a maximum nor a minimum boiling-point. (b) One of the three binary systems exhibits a maximum boiling-point. (c) Two of the three binary systems exhibit minimum boiling-points. (d) All three binary systems

and the ternary system exhibit minimum boiling-points. II. Systems with More Than One Liquid Phase.

CHAPTER XVI.   314
C. SYSTEMS CONSISTING OF SOLID AND LIQUID PHASES ONLY. I. The Solid Phases are the Pure Components. II. A Congruently Melting Binary Compound Can Form. III. A Congruently Melting Ternary Compound Can Form. IV. An Incongruently Melting Binary Compound Can Form. V. An Incongruently Melting Ternary Compound Can Form. VI. Binary Solid Solutions Can Form. VII. Ternary Solid Solutions Can Form. VIII. Complex Types.

CHAPTER XVII.   340
AQUEOUS SYSTEMS. I. The Anhydrous Salts are the only Solids. II. Binary or Ternary Compounds are Formed. III. Transition Point and Transition Interval. Solubility curves at the transition point. IV. Presence of Vapour. V. Rectangular Coordinates. Application to the characterisation of racemates. The solid model. Space model for carnallite. VI. Formation of Solid Solutions or Mix-Crystals. VII. Indirect Identification of Solid Phases. VIII. Hydrolysis. IX. Two-Liquid Systems. Soap systems.

CHAPTER XVIII.   390
PRACTICAL APPLICATIONS OF EQUILIBRIUM DIAGRAMS The system sodium chloride-potassium chloride-water. Separation of salts by a temperature-cycle process. Potassium chloride-potassium sulphate-water. Ammonium perchlorate-ammonium sulphate-water. Ammonium sulphate-sodium sulphate-water.

SECTION FIVE: SYSTEMS OF MORE THAN THREE
COMPONENTS

CHAPTER XIX.   403
FOUR-COMPONENT SYSTEMS. I. Water and Three Salts with a Common Ion. Lithium sulphate-ammonium sulphate-ferrous sulphate-water. II. Reciprocal Salt-Pairs. Choice of components. Transition point. Solubility and transition point. Forma-

tion of double salts. Graphic representation. Isothermal evaporation. Conversion Saltpetre. General description of the method.
Ammonia-soda process. Oceanic salts.

CHAPTER XX. 446
SYSTEMS OF MORE THAN FOUR COMPONENTS. I. Five-
Component Systems. Oceanic salts. II. Six-Component Systems.

APPENDIX I. 455
SOME THERMODYNAMIC DEDUCTIONS. I. Solid Solutions
are Not Formed. (a) Two-Component Systems. (b) Three-Component Systems. (i) The components are the only solid phases.
(ii) Binary compounds as solid phases. (iii) Congruently melting ternary compounds as solid phases. II. Formation of Solid
Solutions. (a) Two-Component Systems. (i) The solid components form solid solutions in all proportions. Type I. The freezing-points of all mixtures lie between those of the two components. Type II. The freezing-point curve shows a maximum.
Type III. The continuous curve of freezing-points exhibits a
minimum. (ii) The solid components form solid solutions to a
limited extent. Type IV. The freezing curve shows a transition
point. Type V. The freezing curve has a eutectic point. (b)
Three-Component Systems.

APPENDIX II. 471
DETERMINATION OF BINARY SOLID-LIQUID EQUILIBRIA.
Thermal analysis. Types of cooling curve employed. (a) Free
cooling. (b) Graduated cooling. Formation of solid solutions.
The thaw-point – melting-point method. The quenching method.
The isothermal method.

AUTHOR INDEX 480
SUBJECT INDEX 486

SECTION 1: INTRODUCTION

CHAPTER I

General. Before proceeding to the more systematic treatment of the Phase Rule, it may, perhaps, be not amiss to give a brief forecast of the nature of the subject we are about to study, in order that we may gain some idea of what the Phase Rule is, of the kind of problem which it enables us to solve, and of the scope of its application.

It has long been known that if water is placed in a closed, exhausted space, vapour is given off and a certain pressure is created in the enclosing vessel. Thus, when water is placed in the Torricellian vacuum of the barometer, the mercury is depressed, and the amount of depression increases as the temperature is raised. But, although the pressure of the vapour increases as the temperature rises, its value at any given temperature is constant, no matter whether the amount of water present or the volume of the vapour is great or small; if the pressure on the vapour is altered while the temperature is maintained constant, either the water or the vapour will ultimately disappear; the former by evaporation, the latter by condensation. At any given temperature within certain limits, therefore, water and vapour can exist permanently in contact with each other—or, as it is said, be in equilibrium with each other—only when the pressure has a certain definite value. The same law of constancy of vapour pressure at a given temperature, quite irrespective of the volumes of liquid and vapour [1],* holds good also in the case of alcohol, ether, benzene, and other pure liquids. It is, therefore,

*Notes and references to the literature are collected at the end of each chapter.

1

not unnatural to ask the question, Does it hold good for all
liquids ? Is it valid, for example, in the case of solutions ?

We can find the answer to these questions by studying the
behaviour of a solution—say, a solution of common salt in water—
when placed in the Torricellian vacuum. In this case, also, it
is observed that the pressure of the vapour increases as the
temperature is raised, but the pressure is no longer independent
of the volume;   as the volume increases, the pressure slowly
diminishes. If, however, solid salt is present in contact with the
solution, then the pressure again becomes constant at constant
temperature, even when the volume of the vapour is altered. As
we see, therefore, solutions do not behave in the same way as
pure liquids.

Moreover, on lowering the temperature of water, a point is
reached at which ice begins to separate out;   and if heat be now
added to the system or withdrawn from it, no change will take
place in the temperature or vapour pressure of the latter until
either the ice or the water has disappeared.[2] Ice, water, and
vapour, therefore, can be in equilibrium with one another only
at one definite temperature and one definite pressure.

In the case of a solution of common salt, however, we may
have ice in contact with the solution at different temperatures
and pressures. Further, it is possible to have a solution in
equilibrium not only with anhydrous salt (NaCl), but also with the
hydrated salt (NaCl, $2H_2O$), as well as with ice, and the question,
therefore, arises: Is it possible to state in a general manner the
conditions under which such different systems can exist in
equilibrium;   or to obtain some insight into the relations which
exist between pure liquids and solutions ? As we shall learn,
the Phase Rule enables us to give an answer to this question.

The preceding examples belong to the class of so-called
"physical" equilibria, or equilibria depending on changes in the
physical state. More than a hundred years ago, however, it was
shown by Wenzel and Berthollet that "chemical" equilibria can
also exist;   that chemical reactions do not always take place
completely in one direction as indicated by the usual chemical

equation, but that before the reacting substances are all used up the reaction ceases, and there is a condition of equilibrium between the reacting substances and the products of reaction. As an example of this, there may be taken the process of lime-burning, which depends on the fact that when calcium carbonate is heated, carbon dioxide is given off and quicklime is produced. If, however, the carbonate is heated in a closed vessel, it will be found that it does not undergo complete decomposition. When the pressure of the carbon dioxide reaches a certain value (which is found to depend on the temperature), decomposition ceases, and calcium carbonate exists side by side with calcium oxide and carbon dioxide. Moreover, at any given temperature, the pressure of carbon dioxide is constant and independent of the amount of carbonate or oxide present, or of the volume of the gas; *nor does the addition of either of the products of dissociation, carbon dioxide or calcium oxide, cause any change in the equilibrium.* Here, then, we see that, although there are three different substances present, the equilibrium obeys the same law as the vapour pressure of a pure volatile liquid, such as water.

Again, it is well known that sulphur exists in two different crystalline forms, rhombic and monoclinic, each of which melts at a different temperature. The problem here is, therefore, more complicated than in the case of ice, for there is now a possibility not only of one solid form, but of two different forms of the same substance existing in contact with liquid. What are the conditions under which these two forms can exist in contact with liquid, either singly or together, and under what conditions can the two solid forms exist together without the presence of liquid sulphur ? To these questions an answer can also be given with the help of the Phase Rule.

These cases are, however, comparatively simple; but when we come, for instance, to study the conditions under which solutions are formed, and especially when we inquire into the solubility relations of salts capable of forming, perhaps, a series of crystalline hydrates; and when we seek to determine the conditions under which these different forms can exist in contact with the solution, the problem becomes more complicated, and the need for some general guide to the elucidation of the behaviour of these different systems becomes more urgent.

A condition of true equilibrium must be distinguished from a state of quiescence in which all action has apparently ceased. The latter states are common and do not necessarily represent equilibria. The following criteria are tests by means of which one may ascertain whether or not a given state is one of equilibrium: (1) A true equilibrium is sensitive to change of external conditions; (2) the equilibrium concentrations are independent of time; and (3) are independent of the masses of the phases; (4) the same equilibrium concentrations are obtained when the equilibrium is approached from at least two directions.

It is, now, to the study of such physical and chemical equilibria as those above-mentioned that the Phase Rule finds application; to the study, also, of the conditions regulating, for example, the formation of alloys from mixtures of the fused metals, or of the various salts of the Stassfurt deposits; the behaviour of iron and carbon in the formation of steel and the separation of different minerals from a fused rock-mass. With the help of the Phase Rule we can group together into classes the large number of different isolated cases of systems in equilibrium; with its aid we are able to state, in a general manner at least, the conditions under which a system can be in equilibrium, and by its means we can gain some insight into the relations existing between different kinds of systems.

Homogeneous and Heterogeneous Equilibrium. Before passing to the consideration of this generalisation, it will be well first to make mention of certain restrictions which must be placed on its treatment, and also of the limitations to which it is subject. If a system is uniform throughout its whole extent, and possesses in every part identical physical properties and chemical composition, it is said to be *homogeneous*. This term does not imply that a homogeneous system consists of only one atomic or molecular species, but rather that our methods of investigation only allow us to detect in the system portions of matter of greater than atomic or molecular dimensions. Thus, for example, a solution of sodium chloride in water is said to be homogeneous. An equilibrium occurring in such a homogeneous system (such as the equilibrium occurring in the formation of an ester in alcoholic solution) is called *homogeneous equilibrium*. If, however, the system consists of parts which have different physical properties, perhaps also different chemical properties, and which are marked off and separated from one another by bounding surfaces, the system is said to be *heterogeneous*. Such a system is formed by ice, water, and vapour, in which the three portions, each in itself homogeneous, can be mechanically separated from one another. When equilibrium exists between different, physically distinct parts, it is known as *heterogeneous equilibrium*. It is with heterogeneous equilibria, with the conditions under which a heterogeneous system can exist, that we shall deal here.

A certain degree of restriction must, however, be introduced, and we shall not take into account changes of equilibrium due to the action of electrical, magnetic, or capillary forces, or of gravity; but shall discuss only those which are due to changes of pressure, temperature, and volume (or concentration).

Real and Apparent Equilibrium. In discussing equilibria, we have seen (p. 4) that a distinction must be drawn between real and apparent equilibria. In the former case there is a state of rest which undergoes continuous change with change of the conditions *(e.g.* change of temperature or of pressure), and for which the chief criterion is that *the same condition of equilibrium is reached from whichever side it is approached.* Thus in the case of a solution, if the temperature is maintained constant, the same concentration will be obtained, no matter whether we start with an unsaturated solution to which we add more solid, or with a supersaturated solution from which we allow solid to crystallise out; or, in the case of water in contact with vapour, the same vapour pressure will be obtained, no matter whether we heat the water up to the given temperature or cool it down from a higher temperature. In this case, water and vapour are in *real* equilibrium. On the other hand, water in contact with hydrogen and oxygen at the ordinary temperature is a case only of *apparent* equilibrium; on changing the pressure and temperature continuously within certain limits there is no continuous change observed in the relative amounts of the two gases. On heating beyond these limits there is a sudden and not a continuous change, and the system no longer regains its former condition on being cooled to the ordinary temperature. In all such cases the system may be regarded, formally, at least, as undergoing change and as tending towards a state of true or real equilibrium, but with such slowness that no change is observed.

Although the case of water in contact with hydrogen and oxygen is an extreme one, it must be borne in mind that the condition of true equilibrium may not be reached instantaneously or even with measureable velocity, and in all cases it is necessary to be on one's guard against mistaking apparent (or false) for real (or true) equilibrium. The importance of this will be fully illustrated in the sequel.

NOTES

1. Except when the volume of the liquid becomes exceedingly small, in which case the surface tension exerts an influence on the vapour pressure.

2. For reasons which will appear later (Chap. III), the volume of the vapour is supposed to be large in comparison with that of the solid and liquid.

CHAPTER II

THE PHASE RULE

Ten years after the law of mass action was propounded by Guldberg and Waage, Willard Gibbs (died April, 1903), Professor of Physics in Yale University, showed how, in a perfectly general manner, free from all hypothetical assumptions as to the molecular condition of the participating substances, all cases of equilibrium could be surveyed and grouped into classes, and how similarities in the behaviour of apparently different kinds of systems, and differences in apparently similar systems, could be explained.

As the basis of his theory of equilibria, Gibbs adopted the laws of thermodynamics.[1] In deducing the law of equilibrium, Gibbs regarded a system as possessing only three independently variable factors[2]—temperature, pressure, and the concentration of the components of the system—and he enunciated the general theorem now usually known as the *Phase Rule*, by which he defined the conditions of equilibrium as a relationship between the number of what are called the phases and the components of the system.

Phases. We have already seen (p. 5) that a heterogeneous system is made up of different portions, each in itself homogeneous but marked off in space and separated from the other portions by bounding surfaces. These homogeneous, physically distinct and and mechanically separable portions are called *phases*. Thus ice, water, and vapour are three phases of the same chemical substance—water. A phase, however, whilst it must be physically and chemically homogeneous, need not necessarily be chemically simple. Thus, a gaseous mixture or a solution may form a phase; but a heterogeneous mixture of solid substances comprises as

7

many phases as there are substances present. Thus when calcium carbonate dissociates under the influence of heat, calcium oxide and carbon dioxide are formed. There are then *two* solid phases present, viz. calcium carbonate and oxide, and one gas phase, carbon dioxide. Although a phase is homogeneous, it is not necessarily continuous. It may be broken up into numerous crystals or drops.

The *number of phases* which can exist side by side may vary greatly in different systems. In all cases, however, there can be but one gas or vapour phase on account of the fact that gases are miscible with one another in all proportions. In the case of liquid and solid phases, the number is indefinite, since the property of complete miscibility does not apply to them. The number of phases which can be formed by any given substance or group of substances also differs greatly, and in general increases with the number of participating substances. The Phase Rule shows, however, that the number of solid phases in equilibrium can never be greater than $C + 2$, where C is the number of components (vide infra); whereas, in the case of liquid phases, it is empirically observed that the number of liquid phases never exceeds the number of components.

Even in the case of a single substance the number may be considerable; in the case of water, for example, at least six different solid phases are known (*v.* Chap. IV). All the solid phases of a given substance, known as allotropes or polymorphs, cannot however in general be in equilibrium under a given set of external conditions, the maximum number being limited by the Phase Rule itself. Thus, in the one-component system, water, only three solid phases can coexist, and only then under certain conditions: it is impossible, under any conditions, for four phases of a one-component system to be in equilibrium.

It is of importance to bear in mind that equilibrium is *independent of the amounts* of the phases present. Thus it is a familiar fact that the pressure of a vapour in contact with a liquid (*i.e.* the pressure of the saturated vapour) is unaffected by the amounts, whether relative or absolute, of the liquid and vapour; also, the amount of a substance dissolved by a liquid is independent of the amount of solid in contact with the solution. It is true that deviations from this general law occur when the amount of liquid or the size of the solid particles is reduced beyond a certain point,[3] owing to the influence of surface energy; but we have already (p. 5) excluded such cases from consideration. (Cf., however, the section on metastable equilibria,(p. 42).

As the Phase Rule is a direct deduction from thermodynamics, it is not surprising that it possesses all the strength and all the weakness of the parent science. Its strength is its rigid exactness, there being no exceptions to it for systems of dimensions larger than molecular. To apply the Phase Rule no knowledge is required of the molecular state of a phase. This is often an advantage, but, conversely, Phase Rule is powerless of itself to give us any information about molecular states. In common with other thermodynamic deductions, it is unable to throw any light on mechanism, and the internal structure of a phase necessarily involves a mechanistic view-point. Another disadvantage is that, though Phase Rule informs us of the equilibrium conditions, it tells us nothing as to the rate of attainment of equilibrium.

Components. Although the conception of phases is one which is readily understood, somewhat greater difficulty is experienced when we come to consider what is meant by the term *component;* for the components of a system are not synonymous with the chemical elements or compounds present, *i.e.* with the *constituents* of the system, although both elements and compounds may be components. By the latter term there are meant only those constituents the concentration of which can undergo *independent* variation in the different phases, and it is only with these that we are concerned here.

To understand the meaning of this term we shall consider briefly some cases with which the reader will be familiar, and at the outset it must be emphasised that the Phase Rule is concerned merely with those constituents which take part in the state of real equilibrium (p. 5); for it is only to the final state, not to the processes by which that state is reached, that the Phase Rule applies.

Consider now the case of the system water—vapour, or ice—water—vapour. The number of constituents taking part in the equilibrium here is only one, viz. the chemical substance, water. Hydrogen and oxygen, the constituents of water, are not to be regarded as components, because, in the first place, they are not present in the system in a state of real equilibrium (p. 5); in the second place, they are combined in definite proportions to form water, and their amounts, therefore, cannot be varied independently. A variation in the amount of hydrogen necessitates a definite variation in the amount of oxygen.

In the case, already referred to, in which hydrogen and oxygen are present along with water at the ordinary temperature, we are not dealing with a condition of true equilibrium. If, however, the temperature is raised to a certain point, a state of true equilibrium between hydrogen, oxygen, and water vapour will be possible. In this case hydrogen and oxygen will be components, because now they do take part in the equilibrium; also, they need no longer be present in definite proportions, but excess of one or the other may be added. Of course, if the restriction be arbitrarily made that the free hydrogen and oxygen shall be present always and only in the proportions in which they are combined to form water, there will be, as before, only one component, water. From this, then, we see that a change in the conditions of the experiment (in the present case a rise of temperature) may necessitate a change in the number of the components.

It is, however, only in the case of systems of more than one component that any difficulty will be found; for only in this case will a choice of components be possible. Take, for example, the dissociation of calcium carbonate into calcium oxide and carbon dioxide. At each temperature, as we have seen, there is a definite state of equilibrium. When equilibrium has been established, there are three different substances present — calcium carbonate, calcium oxide, and carbon dioxide; and these are the constituents of the system between which equilibrium exists. Although these constituents take part in the equilibrium, they are not all to be regarded as components, for they are not mutually independent. On the contrary, the different phases are related to one another, and if *two* of these are taken, the composition of the third is defined by the equation

$$CaCO_3 = CaO + CO_2.$$

In deciding the number of components in any given system, not only must the constituents chosen be capable of independent variation, but a further restriction is imposed, and we obtain the following rule: *As the components of a system there are to be chosen the smallest number of independently variable constituents by means of which the composition of each phase participating in the state of equilibrium can be expressed in the form of a chemical equation.*[4]

Applying this rule to the case under consideration, we see that of the three constituents present when the system is in a state of equilibrium, only two are independently variable. It will further be seen that in order to express the composition of each phase present, two of these constituents are necessary. The system is, therefore, one of *two components*, or a system of the second order.

When we proceed to the actual choice of components, it is evident that any two of the constituents can be selected. Thus, if we choose as components $CaCO_3$ and CaO, the composition of each phase can be expressed by the following equations:

$$CaCO_3 = CaCO_3 + oCaO$$
$$CaO = CaO + oCaCO_3$$
$$CO_2 = CaCO_3 - CaO.$$

As we see, then, both zero and negative quantities of the components have been introduced; and similar expressions would be obtained if $CaCO_3$ and CO_2 were chosen as components. The matter can, however, be simplified and the use of negative quantities avoided if CaO and CO_2 are chosen; and it is, therefore, customary to select these as the components.

While it is possible in the case of systems of the second order to choose the two components in such a way that the composition of each phase can be expressed by positive quantities of these, such a choice is not always possible when dealing with systems of a higher order (containing three or four components).

From the example which has just been discussed, it might appear as if the choice of the components was rather arbitrary. On examining the point, however, it will be seen that the arbitrariness affects only the *nature*, not the *number*, of the components; a choice could be made with respect to which, not to how many, constituents were to be regarded as components. As we shall see presently, however, it is only the number, not the nature of the components, that is of importance.

Although the examples to be considered in the sequel will afford sufficient illustration of the application of the rules given above, one case may perhaps be discussed to show the application of the method just given for determining the number of components.

Consider the system consisting of Glauber's salt in equilibrium with solution and vapour. If these three phases are analysed, the composition of the solid will be expressed by $Na_2SO_4, 10H_2O$; that of the solution by $Na_2SO_4 + xH_2O$, while the vapour phase will be H_2O. The system evidently cannot be a one-component system, for the phases have not all the same composition. By varying the amounts of two phases, however (*e.g.* $Na_2SO_4, 10H_2O$ and H_2O), the composition of the third phase—the solution—can be obtained. The system is, therefore, one of *two components*.

But sodium sulphate can also exist in the anhydrous form and as the hydrate $Na_2SO_4, 7H_2O$. In these cases there may be chosen as components Na_2SO_4 and H_2O, and $Na_2SO_4, 7H_2O$ and H_2O respectively. In both cases, therefore, there are *two components*. The two systems ($Na_2SO_4, 10H_2O—H_2O$, and $Na_2SO_4, 7H_2O—H_2O$) can, however, be regarded as special cases of the system $Na_2SO_4—H_2O$, and these two components will apply to all systems made up of sodium sulphate and water, no matter whether the solid phase is anhydrous salt or one of the hydrates. In all three cases, of course, the *number* of components is the same; but by choosing Na_2SO_4 and H_2O as components, the possible occurrence of negative quantities of components in expressing the composition of the phases is avoided; and further, these components apply over a much larger range of experimental conditions. Again, therefore, we see that, although the number of the components of a system is definite, a certain amount of liberty is allowed in the choice of the substances; and we also see that the choice will be influenced by the conditions of experiment.

Summing up, now, we may say:

(1) The components are to be chosen from among the constituents which are present when the system is in a state of true equilibrium, and which take part in that equilibrium.

(2) As components are to be chosen the *smallest number* of such constituents necessary to express the composition of each phase participating in the equilibrium, zero and negative quantities of the components being permissible.

(3) In any given system the *number* of the components is definite, but may alter with alteration of the conditions of experiment. A certain freedom of choice, however, is allowed in the (qualitative, not quantitative) selection of the components, the choice being influenced by considerations of simplicity, suitability, or generality of application.

Degree of Freedom. Variance of a System. It is well known that in dealing with a certain mass of gas or vapour, *e.g.* water vapour, if only one of the independently variable factors — temperature, pressure, and concentration (or volume) — is fixed, the state of the gas or vapour is undefined; while occupying the same volume (the concentration, therefore, remaining unchanged), the temperature and the pressure may be altered; at a given temperature, a gas can exist under different pressures and occupy different volumes, and under any given pressure the temperature and volume may vary. If, however, two of the factors are arbitrarily fixed, then the third factor can only have a certain definite value; at any given values of temperature and pressure a given mass of gas can occupy only a definite volume.

Suppose, however, that the system consists of a liquid in contact with its own vapour. The condition of the system then becomes perfectly defined on arbitrarily giving one of the variables a certain value. If the temperature is fixed, the pressure under which liquid and vapour can coexist is also determined; and conversely, if a definite pressure is chosen, the temperature is also defined. Liquid and vapour can coexist under a given pressure only at a definite temperature.

Finally, let the liquid and vapour be cooled down until solid begins to separate out. As soon as the third phase, solid, appears, the state of the system as regards temperature and pressure is perfectly defined, and none of the variables can be arbitrarily changed without causing the disappearance of one of the phases— solid, liquid or vapour.

We see, therefore, that in the case of some systems two, in other cases, only one of the independent variables (temperature, pressure, concentration) can be altered without destroying the nature of the system; while in other systems, again, these variables have all fixed and definite values. We shall therefore define the number of degrees of freedom[5] of a system as the *number of the variable factors, temperature, pressure, and concentration of the components, which must be arbitrarily fixed in order that the condition of the system may be perfectly defined.* From what has been said, therefore, we shall describe a gas or vapour as having two degrees of freedom; the system liquid– vapour as having only one; and the system solid – liquid –vapour as having no degrees of freedom. We may also speak of the *variance* of a system, and describe a system as being invariant, univariant, bivariant, multivariant,[6] according as the number of degrees of freedom is nought, one, two, or more than two.

A knowledge of its variance is, therefore, of essential importance in studying the condition and behaviour of a system, and it is the great merit of the Phase Rule that *the state of a system is defined entirely by the relation existing between the number of the components and the phases present,* no account being taken of the molecular complexity of the participating substances, nor any assumption made with regard to the constitution of matter. It is, further, as we see, quite immaterial whether we are dealing with "physical" or "chemical" equilibrium; in principle, indeed, no distinction need be drawn between the two classes, although it is nevertheless often convenient to make use of the terms, in spite of a certain amount of indefiniteness which attaches to them — an indefiniteness, indeed, which attaches equally to the terms "physical" and "chemical" process.

The Phase Rule. The Phase Rule of Gibbs, which defines the condition of equilibrium by the relation between the number of co-existing phases and components, may be stated as follows: A system consisting of C components can exist in C + 2 phases only when the temperature, total pressure of the system, and concentration of each phase have fixed and definite values; if there are C components in C + 1 phases, only one of the factors may be arbitrarily fixed, and if there are only C phases, two of the varying factors may be arbitrarily fixed. This rule, the application of which, it is hoped, will become clear in the sequel, may be very concisely and conveniently summarised in the form of the equation

$$F = C - P + 2 \,,$$

where F denotes the variance or number of degrees of freedom of the system, C the number of the components, and P the number of phases. From the equation it can readily be seen that the greater the number of the phases, the fewer are the degrees of freedom, for a fixed number of components. With increase in the number of the phases, therefore, the condition of the system becomes more and more defined, or less and less variable.

Classification of Systems according to the Phase Rule. We have already learned in the introductory chapter that systems which are apparently quite different in character may behave in a very similar manner. Thus it was stated that the laws which govern the equilibrium between a liquid and its vapour are quite analogous to those which are obeyed by the dissociation of calcium carbonate into carbon dioxide and calcium oxide; in each case a certain temperature is associated with a definite pressure, no matter what the relative or absolute amounts of the respective substances may be. And other examples were given of systems which were apparently similar in character, but which nevertheless behaved in a different manner. The relations between the various systems, however, become perfectly clear and intelligible in the light of the Phase Rule. In the case first mentioned, that of a liquid in equilibrium with its vapour, we have one component present in two phases, *i.e.* in two physically distinct forms, viz. liquid and vapour. According to the Phase Rule, therefore, since $C = 1$ and $P = 2$, the variance F is equal to $1 - 2 + 2 = 1$; the system possesses one degree of freedom, as has already been stated. But in the case of the second system mentioned above there are two components, viz. calcium oxide and carbon dioxide (p. 11), and three phases, viz. two solid phases, CaO and $CaCO_3$, and the gaseous phase, CO_2. The number of degrees of freedom of the system, therefore, is $2 - 3 + 2 = 1$; this system, therefore, also possesses one degree of freedom. We can now understand why these two systems behave in a similar manner; both are univariant or possess only one degree of freedom. We shall therefore expect a similar behaviour in the case of all univariant systems, no matter how dissimilar the systems may outwardly appear. Similarly, all bivariant systems will exhibit analogous behaviour; and generally, systems possessing the same degree of freedom will show a like behaviour. In accordance with the Phase Rule, therefore, we may classify the different systems which may be found into invariant, univariant, bivariant, multivariant, according to the relation which obtains between the number of the components and the number of coexisting phases; and we shall expect that in each case the members of any particular group will exhibit a uniform behaviour. By this means we are enabled to obtain an insight into the general behaviour of any system, so soon as we have determined the number of the components and the number of the coexisting phases. Moreover, knowing the number of the components and the degree of freedom of a system, one can determine the number of coexisting phases. In this way it is possible to decide whether a given body is a single homogeneous substance (a single phase) or a heterogeneous mixture.[7]

The adoption of the Phase Rule for the purposes of classification has been of great importance in studying changes in the equilibrium existing between different substances; for not only does it render possible the grouping together of a large number of isolated phenomena, but the guidance it affords has led to the discovery of new substances, has given the clue to the conditions under which these substances can exist, and has led to the recognition of otherwise unobserved resemblances existing between different systems.

Deduction of the Phase Rule. In the preceding pages we have restricted ourselves to the statement of the Phase Rule, without giving any indication of how it has been deduced. At the close of this chapter, therefore, the mathematical deduction of the generalisation will be given, but in brief outline only, the reader being referred to works on Thermodynamics for a fuller treatment of the subject.[8]

All forms of energy can be resolved into two factors, the *capacity* factor and the *intensity* factor; but for the production of equilibrium, only the intensity factor is of importance. Thus, if two bodies having the same temperature are brought in contact with each other, they will be in equilibrium as regards heat energy, no matter what may be the amounts of heat (capacity factor) contained in either, because the intensity factor — the temperature — is the same. But if the temperature of the two bodies is different, *i.e.* if the intensity factor of heat energy is different, the two bodies will no longer be in equilibrium; heat will pass from the hotter to the colder until both have the same temperature.

As with heat energy, so with chemical energy. If we have a substance existing in two different states, or in two different phases of a system, equilibrium can occur only when the intensity factor of chemical energy is the same. This intensity factor may be called the *chemical potential*; and we can therefore say that a system will be in equilibrium when the chemical potential of each component is the same in all phases in which the the component occurs. Thus, for example, ice, water, and vapour have, at the triple point, the same chemical potential.

The potential of a component in any phase depends not only on the composition of the phase, but also on the temperature and the pressure (or volume). If, therefore, we have a system of C components existing in P phases, then, in order to fix the composition of unit mass of each phase, it is necessary to know the masses of (C - 1) components in each of the phases. As regards the composition, therefore, each phase possesses (C—1) independent variables. Since there are P phases, it follows that, as regards composition, the whole system possesses P(C—1) independent variables. Besides these there are, however, two other variables, viz. temperature and pressure, so that altogether a system of C components in P phases possesses P(C - 1) + 2 independent variables.

In order to define the state of the system completely, it will be necessary to have as many equations as there are variables. If, therefore, there are fewer equations than there are variables, then, according to the deficiency in the number of the equations, one or more of the variables will have an undefined value; and values must be assigned to these variables before the system is entirely defined. The number of these undefined values gives us the variance or the degree of freedom of the system.

The equations by which the system is to be defined are obtained from the relationship between the potential of a component and the composition of the phase, the temperature and the pressure. Further, as has already been stated, equilibrium occurs when the potential of each component is the same in the different phases in which it is present. If, therefore, we choose as standard one of the phases in which all the components occur, then in any other phase in equilibrium with it, the potential of each component must be the same as in the standard phase. For each phase in equilibrium with the standard phase, therefore, there will be a definite equation of state for each component in the phase; so that, if there are P phases, we obtain for each component (P - 1) equations; and for C components, therefore, we obtain C(P - 1) equations.

But we have seen above that there are P(C - 1) + 2 variables, and as we have only C(P - 1) equations, there must be

$$P(C - 1) + 2 - C(P - 1) = C + 2 - P$$

variables undefined. That is to say, the variance (F) of a system consisting of C components in P phases is

$$F = C - P + 2.$$

NOTES

1. For a mathematical treatment of the Phase Rule, the reader is referred to MacDougall, *Physical Chemistry*, Ch. IX, (Macmillan).

2. The action of gravity and other forces being excluded (see p. 5).

3. The vapour pressure of water in small drops is greater than that of water in mass, and the solubility of a solid is greater when in a state of fine subdivision than when in large pieces (*cf.* Hulett, *Z. physikal. Chem.*, 1901, **37**, 385). The vapour pressure of small crystals is also greater than that of large ones (Pawloff, *Z. physikal. Chem.*, 1909, **68**, 316; Bigelow and Trimble, *J. Physical Chem.*, 1927, **31**, 1798).

4. This definition is as good as any of the numerous attempts which have been made to define a component. No really satisfactory definition can be given without reference to thermodynamics. For instance Gibbs (*Collected Works*, Vol. 1, p.63, Longmans, Green & Co., 1928), defining the conditions of equilibrium between phases, after stating the equation

$$d\epsilon = t\,d\eta - p\,dv + \mu_1\,dm_1 + \mu_2\,dm_2 + \cdots + \mu_n\,dm_n,$$

goes on to say: "The substances $S_1, S_2, \cdots, S_n$" (the components) "of which we consider the mass composed, must of course be such that the values of the differentials $dm_1, dm_2, \cdots, dm_n$ shall be independent, and shall express every possible variation in the composition of the homogeneous mass considered, including those produced by the absorption of substances different from any initially present."

5. The term "degree of freedom" employed here must not be confused with the same term used to denote the various movements of a gas molecule according to the kinetic theory.

6. Trevor, *J. Physical Chem.*, 1902, **6**, 136.

7. For an application of this principle, see Wegelius, *Z. physikal. Chem.*, 1911, **77**, 587.

8. See Butler, *Chemical Thermodynamics*, p. 320, Macmillan (1946); MacDougall, *Physical Chemistry*, p. 230, Macmillan (1943).

CHAPTER III

SYSTEMS OF ONE COMPONENT

Although it is possible to state, in the form of a mathematical equation, the conditions of equilibrium in different systems, the understanding and practical application of the Phase Rule are simplified and facilitated by graphic representation, From the expression $F = C - P + 2$, it follows that when one component

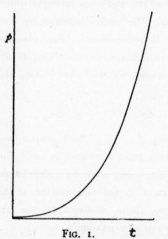

exists in only one phase, the degree of freedom is 2; and this must be the maximum degree of freedom possible. All systems of one component (unary systems) can, therefore, be perfectly defined by giving values to, at most, two variable factors; and the equilibrium conditions can be most conveniently represented graphically by a system of rectangular co-ordinates, the axes of which are pressure and tempera-

FIG. 1. t

ture (p - t diagram). In such a diagram, invariant systems will be represented by points, univariant systems by lines, and bivariant systems by areas.

Univariant systems are formed when one component exists as two phases in equilibrium. A single substance can, so far as is known, form only one gas phase and one liquid phase,[1] but it may exist in more than one crystalline solid phase.[2] Since any pair of phases will constitute a univariant system, the number of such systems may vary greatly and can be determined only by experiment.

Equilibrium between Liquid and Vapour.   Vaporisation Curve.
A volatile liquid in equilibrium with its vapour constitutes a univariant system, and the state of the system will be defined if one of the variable factors, pressure or temperature, be arbitrarily fixed. At a given temperature the pressure of the vapour will have a definite value; or, if a certain vapour pressure is maintained, coexistence of liquid and vapour will be possible only at a certain definite temperature. Each temperature, therefore, will correspond to a definite pressure; and if in the $p - t$ diagram we join by a continuous line all the points indicating the values of the pressure corresponding to the different temperatures, we shall obtain a curve (Fig. 1) representing the variation of the vapour pressure with the temperature. This is the curve of vapour pressure, or the *vaporisation curve*. The term "normal boiling-point" refers to the temperature at which the vapour pressure equals one standard atmosphere (760 mm. of mercury). In all $p - t$ diagrams, therefore, the boiling-point is the abscissa of the curve corresponding to an ordinate of one atmosphere.

The vapour pressure of a liquid is, of course, independent of the relative or absolute volumes of the liquid and vapour;[3] on increasing the volume at constant temperature, a certain amount of the liquid will pass into vapour, and the pressure will regain its former value. If, however, the pressure be permanently maintained at a value different from that corresponding to the temperature employed, then either all the liquid will pass into vapour, or all the vapour will pass into liquid, and we shall have either vapour alone or liquid alone.

As the result of a large number of determinations, it has been found that all vapour-pressure curves have the same general form as that shown in Fig. 1, the curve being convex towards the temperature axis in the ordinary $p - t$ diagram.

Upper Limit of Vaporisation Curve. On continuing to add heat to a liquid contained in a closed vessel, the pressure of the vapour will continuously increase. Since with increase of pressure the

density of the vapour must increase, and since with rise of temperature the density of the liquid must decrease, a point will be
reached at which the densities of the liquid and vapour become
identical, provided that sufficient liquid has been taken in the
first place, *i.e.* that the liquid is not merely exhausted by evaporation, before the critical temperature is reached. The system
ceases to be heterogeneous, and passes into one homogeneous
phase. The temperature at which this occurs is called the *critical
temperature*. To this temperature there will, of course, correspond
a certain definite pressure, called the *critical pressure*. The
curve representing the equilibrium between liquid and vapour must,
therefore, end abruptly at the critical point.[4] At temperatures
above this point no pressure, however great, can cause the formation of the liquid phase; at temperatures above the critical point
the vapour becomes a gas. In the case of water, the critical temperature is 374°, and the critical pressure 217.5 atm.; at the
point representing these conditions the vapour-pressure curve of
water must end. The lower limit of the curve is determined by the
range of the metastable state of the super-cooled liquid.

Principle of Le Chatelier. This principle can be stated as
follows: "If an attempt is made to change the pressure, temperature, or concentration of a system in equilibrium, then the
equilibrium will shift, if possible, in such a manner as to diminish
the magnitude of the alteration in the factor which is varied."[5]

This principle of Le Chatelier is of very great importance, for
it applies to all systems and changes of the condition of equilibrium,[6] whether physical or chemical; to vaporisation and
fusion, to solution and chemical action. In all cases, whenever
changes in the external condition of a system in equilibrium are
produced, processes also occur within the system which tend to
counteract the effect of the external changes.

By the introduction of the principle of Le Chatelier the scope
and practical utility of the Phase Rule are very greatly increased.

To illustrate the application of the principle of Le Chatelier,
let us consider the changes which take place in the system
liquid — vapour. If the volume is kept constant, addition of heat

will cause that reaction or process to take place which is accompanied by absorption of heat, for by so doing the magnitude of the temperature change is diminished. Since vaporisation is accompanied by absorption of heat, liquid will pass into vapour, and the pressure will increase. The vapour pressure increases with rise of temperature.

On the other hand, if transference of heat to or from the system is prevented, increase of volume (diminution of pressure) will cause that process to take place which is accompanied by increase of volume, *i.e.* vaporisation. Liquid will therefore pass into vapour, and since this process is accompanied by absorption of heat, the temperature will fall. This is exemplified in the well-known experiment with the cryophorus.

Addition or withdrawal of heat at constant pressure, and increase or diminution of the pressure at constant temperature, will cause the system to pass along lines parallel to the temperature and the pressure axis respectively. The working out of these changes may be left to the reader.

The Clausius-Clapeyron Equation. While the qualitative changes of equilibrium or the general direction of the equilibrium curve can be predicted by means of the principle of Le Chatelier, a quantitative formulation of the principle is given by the thermodynamic equation

$$\frac{dp}{dT} = \frac{q}{T(v_2 - v_1)}.$$

In this equation, known as the Clausius-Clapeyron equation, q represents the heat absorbed, per gram, in the transformation of one phase into the other, v_2 and v_1 are the specific volumes of the two phases, and T is the absolute temperature at which the change occurs. The above equation enables one to calculate only the slope of the curve at the given point, not the actual values of the pressure.[7] It is possible, however, to derive an expression by means of which the individual points on the vapour-pressure curve can be calculated approximately.

Referring all quantities to gram-molecular amounts of the

substance, and neglecting the volume of the liquid, which is small
compared with that of the vapour, we obtain the expression

$$\frac{dp}{dT} = \frac{Q}{TV}$$

where Q is the heat absorbed per gram-molecule and V is the
volume of a gram-molecule of the vapour. If it be now assumed
that the vapour obeys the gas laws, we may write $V = RT/p$. Sub-
stituting this value in the previous equation, we obtain

$$\frac{1}{p}\frac{dp}{dT} = \frac{Q}{RT^2}$$

or

$$\frac{d\log_e p}{dT} = \frac{Q}{RT^2}$$

Finally, if we assume that the heat of reaction (vaporisation)
remains constant over the temperature interval $(T_2 - T_1)$, the
equations just given yield, on integration,

$$\log_{10} p_2 - \log_{10} p_1 = \frac{Q(T_2 - T_1)}{(2.303)(1.985)\ T_1 T_2}$$

By means of this expression it is possible to calculate, approximately, individual values of the vapour pressure, if one such
value is known.

Presence of Complex Molecules. The Phase Rule, we have
seen, takes no account of molecular complexity, and so it is found
that the system water—vapour or the system acetic acid—vapour
behaves as a univariant system of one component, although in the
liquid and sometimes also in the vapour different molecular species
(simple and associated molecules) are present. Such systems,
however, it should be pointed out, can behave as one-component
systems *only if at each temperature there exists an equilibrium
between the different molecular species (pseudo-components) in
each phase separately and as between the two phases; and only
if these equilibria are established sufficiently rapidly.* By this
is meant that the time required for establishing equilibrium is
short compared with that required for determining vapour pressure.
When these conditions are satisfied, the system will behave as a

univariant system of one component.

If, however, a liquid consists of more than one molecular species, and if equilibrium between these species is not continuously and rapidly established, the system liquid — vapour will no longer show the behaviour of a one-component system; the vapour pressure will no longer be a function only of the temperature, but will depend on the relative proportion of the different molecular species in the liquid.

Equilibrium between Solid and Vapour. Sublimation Curve. Just as in the case of the system liquid — vapour, so also in the case of the system solid — vapour there will be, for each temperature, a certain definite pressure of the vapour; and this pressure will be independent of the relative or absolute amounts of the solid or vapour present, and will depend solely on the temperature. The curve representing the conditions of equilibrium between a solid and its vapour is called a *sublimation curve*; its general form is the same as that of the vaporisation curve.

The sublimation curve of all substances, so far as yet found, has its upper limit at the melting-point (triple point), although the possibility of the existence of a superheated solid is not excluded. The lower limit is, theoretically at least, at the absolute zero, provided no new phase, *e.g.* a different crystalline modification, is formed. If the sublimation pressure of a substance is greater than the atmospheric pressure at any temperature below the point of fusion, then the substance will *sublime without melting* when heated in an open vessel, and fusion will be possible only at a pressure higher than atmospheric. This is found, for example, in the case of violet phosphorus (p. 71). We may speak of the "boiling-point" of a solid in connection with these substances whose sublimation pressures exceed one atmosphere below the melting-point. If, however, the sublimation pressure of a substance at its melting-point is less than one atmosphere, then the substance will melt when heated in an open vessel.

Changes of sublimation pressure with temperature can be predicted and quantitatively calculated by means of the principle of Le Chatelier and the Clausius-Clapeyron equation, in the same way as changes of vapour pressure of a liquid (pp. 22 and 23).

Equilibrium between Solid and Liquid. Curve of Fusion. There is still another univariant system, the existence of which, at definite values of temperature and pressure, the Phase Rule allows us to predict. This is the system solid — liquid. A crystalline solid on being heated to a certain temperature melts and passes into the liquid state; and since this system solid — liquid is univariant, there will be for each temperature a certain definite pressure at which solid and liquid can coexist or be in equilibrium, independently of the amounts of the two phases present. Since the temperature at which the solid phase is in equilibrium with the liquid phase is known as the melting-point or point of fusion of the solid, the curve representing the temperatures and pressures at which the solid and liquid are in equilibrium will represent the change of the melting-point with the pressure. Such a curve is called the *curve of fusion*, or the melting-point curve.

It is easy to predict in a qualitative manner the effect of pressure on the melting-point if we consider the matter in the light of the principle of LeChatelier (p. 22). If the pressure on the system solid — liquid be increased, a change will take place which is accompanied by a diminution in volume. If, as in the case of ice and of bismuth,[8] the specific volume of the solid is greater than that of the liquid, increase of pressure will cause the solid to melt. Consequently, the temperature must be lowered in order to counteract the effect of pressure; or, in other words, the melting-point will be lowered by pressure. On the other hand, if, as is usually the case, the passage of the solid to the liquid state is accompanied by an increase of volume, increase of pressure will raise the melting-point.

Quantitatively, the effect of pressure on the melting-point may be calculated by means of the Clausius-Clapeyron equation,

$$\frac{d\mathrm{T}}{dp} = \frac{\mathrm{T}(v_2 - v_1)}{q}.$$

In the case of the system ice — water, for example, we have the following data: $\mathrm{T} = 273.18^{\circ}$; specific volume of water $(v_2) = 1.0002$;

specific volume of ice (v_1) = 1.0906; q = 79.67 calories = (79.67)(42670) gram-cm.; dp = 1 atm. = 1033.3 gm. per sq. cm. Hence,

$$dT = \frac{(273.18)(-0.0904)(1033.3)}{(79.67)(42670)} = -0.00750°$$

Increase of pressure by 1 atm. *lowers* the freezing-point by about 0.0075°. The effect of pressure on the melting-point of ice is therefore comparatively slight,[9] owing to the small volume change on fusion and the relatively large value of q. In the case of camphor, the change in the melting-point is much greater, namely, 0.13° per atm. As a general rule, increase of pressure by 1 atm. changes the melting-point by about 0.03°; or, in other words, an increase of pressure of more than 30 atm. is required, on an average, to produce a change in the melting-point of 1°.

The comparatively slight effect produced by pressure on the temperature of equilibrium is characteristic of all systems which are composed only of solid and liquid phases. Such systems are called *condensed systems*.[10]

The values of the fusion pressures of ice, benzene and potassium, given in the following tables (p. 28), will illustrate the course of the fusion curve.[11]

Investigations of the influence of pressure on the melting-point have shown that, up to pressures of several hundred atmospheres, the fusion curve is a straight line.[12] At higher pressures, however, it has been found[13] that the fusion curve no longer remains straight, but bends towards the pressure axis, so that, on sufficiently increasing the pressure, a maximum temperature might at length be reached.[14] This maximum has, so far, however, not been attained, although the melting-point curves of various substances have been studied by Bridgman up to pressures of 50,000 atm. This might be accounted for partly by the fact that the probable maximum temperature in the case of most substances lies at very great pressures, and also by the fact that other solid phases make their appearance, as, for example, in the case of ice (p. 61). It should, however, be pointed out that the existence of a maximum has not been proved.

FUSION PRESSURE OF ICE.

Temperature.	Pressure in kilogms. per sq. cm.[15]	Change of melting-point for an increase of pressure of 1 kilogm. per sq. cm.	Increase of pressure (kilogms. per sq. cm.) required to produce a change of melting-point of 1°.
0°	0	0.0072°	138.5
- 5°	610	0.0087°	115.5
-10°	1130	0.0102°	98.4
-15°	1590	0.0118°	84.8
-20°	1970	0.0135°	74.0

FUSION PRESSURE OF BENZENE.

FUSION PRESSURE OF POTASSIUM.

Pressure in kgm. per sq. cm.	Temperature.	Δ_v c.c. per gm. $\times 10^4$.	q in gm.-cm. per gm. $\times 10^5$.	Pressure in kgm. per sq. cm.	Temperature.	Δ_v c.c. per gm. $\times 10^5$.	q in gm. cm. per gm. 10^5.
1	5.4°	1317	12.88	1	62.5°	2680	5.51
1,000	32.5°	1026	12.94	1,000	78.7°	2368	5.81
2,000	56.5°	872	13.06	2,000	92.4°	2104	6.02
3,000	77.7°	759	13.24	3,000	104.7°	1877	6.15
4,000	96.6°	675	13.47	4,000	115.8°	1676	6.22
5,000	114.6°	614	13.70	5,000	126.0°	1504	6.21
6,000	131.2°	564	13.90	6,000	135.4°	1347	6.12
7,000	147.2°	522	14.05	7,000	144.1°	1205	6.00
8,000	162.2°	485	14.15	8,000	152.5°	1073	5.85
9,000	167.7°	451	14.20	9,000	160.1°	950	5.67
10,000	190.5°	422	14.21	10,000	167.0°	838	5.43
11,000	204.2°	394	14.20	11,000	173.6°	738	5.16
				12,000	179.6°	642	4.83

Although, as we have seen, the vaporisation curve ends at the critical point, the fusion curve may be followed continuously up to temperatures much above the critical temperature for liquid — vapour.[16] Thus the fusion curve of phosphonium chloride (critical point, 49°-50°) has been followed up to a temperature of over 100°: and the fusion curve of carbon dioxide (critical point, 31.4°) has been followed up to a temperature of 93.5°. For the course of the fusion curve, therefore, the critical temperature for liquid—vapour appears to have no special significance.

Equilibrium between Solid, Liquid and Vapour. The Triple Point. From the Phase Rule, $F = C - P + 2$ it follows that when one component is present in three coexisting phases, the system is invariant. Such a system can exist in stable equilibrium only at one definite temperature and one definite pressure. This definite temperature and pressure at which three phases coexist in equilibrium, as an invariant system, is called a *triple point*. Although the commonest triple point in a one-component system is the triple point, solid, liquid, vapour (S—L—V), other triple points are also possible when, as in the case of ice, sulphur, and other substances, allotropic forms occur. Whether or not all the triple points can be realised experimentally will, of course, depend on circumstances. We shall, in the first place, consider the triple point S—L—V.

We have already seen that the curve for S — V ends at the melting-point. At this point, liquid and solid are each in equilibrium with vapour at the same pressure, and they must also be in equilibrium with each other; and the particular value of temperature and vapour pressure must lie on the S—V as well as on the L—V curve. At one time it was thought that the S—V curve passes continuously into the L—V curve, but it follows quite clearly from the Clapeyron equation,

$$T \frac{dp}{dT} = \frac{q}{(v_2 - v_1)},$$

that this cannot be so. For the transformation solid $\rightarrow$ vapour the value of q is greater than for the transformation liquid $\rightarrow$ vapour, and since $(v_2 - v_1)$ is nearly the same in the two cases, it follows that

dp/dT must be greater in the former case than in the latter. That is, the curve S—V must, in the neighbourhood of the triple point, ascend more rapidly than the curve for L—V. In other words, the two curves must cut each other at the triple point. This is illustrated by the vapour pressure curves for ice and water (Fig. 2).

Since at the triple point S—L—V, solid and liquid must be in equilibrium, it follows that the curve for S — L must also pass through the triple point. We see, therefore, that the triple point is a point of intersection of three univariant curves.

As to the general arrangement of the three univariant curves around the triple point, the following rules may be given. (1) The prolongation of each of the curves beyond the triple point must lie between the other two curves. (2) The middle position, at one and the same temperature, in the neighbourhood of the triple point is taken by that curve (or its metastable prolongation) which represents the two phases of most widely differing specific volume. That is to say, if a line of constant temperature is drawn immediately above or below the triple point so as to cut the three curves— two stable curves and the metastable prolongation of the third—the position of the curves at that temperature will be such that the middle position is occupied by that curve (or its metastable prolongation) which represents the two phases of most widely differing specific volume.

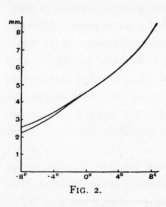

FIG. 2.

Although these rules admit of a considerable variety of possible arrangements of curves around the triple point, only two of these have been experimentally obtained in the case of the triple point solid—liquid—vapour. At present, therefore, we shall consider only these two cases. In Figs. 3 and 4 the curve AO is the sublimation curve, OB the vaporisation curve, and OC the fusion curve.

An examination of these two figures shows that they satisfy

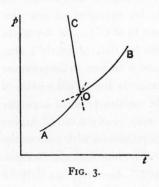

FIG. 3.

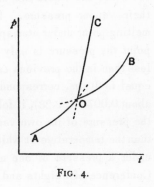

FIG. 4.

the rules laid down. Each of the curves on being prolonged passes between the other two curves. In the case of substances of the first type (Fig. 3), the specific volume of the solid is greater than that of the liquid (the substance contracts on fusion); the difference of specific volume will, therefore, be greatest between liquid and vapour. The curve, therefore, for liquid and vapour (or its prolongation) must lie between the other two curves; this is seen from the figure to be the case. Similarly, the rule is satisfied by the arrangement of curves in Fig. 4, where the difference of specific volumes is greatest between the solid and vapour. In this case the curve S—V occupies the intermediate position.

As we see, the two figures differ from each other only in that the fusion curve OC in one case slopes to the right away from the pressure axis, thus indicating that the melting-point is raised by increase of pressure; in the other case, the fusion curve slopes to the left, indicating a lowering of the melting-point with the pressure. These conditions are found exemplified in the case of sulphur and ice (pp. 66 and 61). We see further from the two figures that O in Fig. 3 gives the highest temperature at which the solid can exist, for the curve for solid — liquid slopes back to regions of lower temperature; in Fig. 4, O gives the lowest temperature at which the liquid phase can exist as stable phase.

It should be noted that the triple point S — L — V is not identical with the melting-point as ordinarily determined in an open vessel, that is, under atmospheric pressure. At the triple point, the solid and liquid are in equilibrium under a pressure equal to their vapour pressure. In the case, for example, of ice, the melting-point under atmospheric pressure is at $0°C$. At the triple point the pressure is only about 4.6 mm. (p. 61), or nearly 1 atm. less than in the previous case; and since a change in the pressure equal to 1 atm. corresponds with a change in the melting-point of about $0.0074°$ (p. 28), it follows that the melting-point of ice under the pressure of its own vapour will be very nearly $0.0074°$ higher than the temperature at which ice is in equilibrium with pure water under a pressure of one atmosphere. The International Seventh Conference of Weights and Measures (1927), however, has defined $0°C$ as the temperature at which ice and water saturated with air are in equilibrium, under a total pressure of one atmosphere. Saturation with air lowers the temperature of the equilibrium ice — water (p = 1 atm.) by $0.0024°$. Hence the true temperature of the triple point is $0.0024 + 0.0074 = 0.0098°$.[17]

Bivariant Systems. If we examine Figs. 3 and 4, we see that the curves OA, OB, OC, which represent diagrammatically the conditions under which the systems, solid and vapour, liquid and vapour, solid and liquid, are in equilibrium, form the boundaries of three "fields" or areas. These areas give the conditions of temperature and pressure under which the single phases, solid, liquid and vapour, are capable of stable existence. These different areas are the regions of stability of the phase common to the two curves by which the area is enclosed.[18] Thus, the phase common to the two systems represented by OA (solid and vapour) and OB (liquid and vapour) is the vapour phase; and the area enclosed by the curves OA and OB is therefore the area of the vapour phase. Similarly, the area AOC is the area of the solid phase, and BOC the area of the liquid phase.

Changes at the Triple Point. If we apply the principle of Le Chatelier to equilibria at the triple point S—L—V, and ask what changes will occur in such a system when the external conditions of pressure and temperature are altered, the general answer to the question will be: So long as the three phases are present, no change in the temperature or pressure of the system can occur, but *only changes in the relative amounts of the phases;* that is to say, the effect on the system of change in the external conditions is opposed and counterbalanced by the reactions or changes which take place within the system. In discussing these changes, conveniently spoken of as *phase reactions*, we shall consider first the effect of adding or withdrawing heat at constant volume.

When the volume is kept constant, the effect of the·addition of heat to a system at the triple point S —L ← V differs somewhat according as there is an increase or diminution of volume when the solid passes into the liquid state. In the former and most general case (Fig. 4), addition of heat will cause a certain amount of the solid phase to melt, whereby the heat which is added becomes latent; the temperature of the system therefore does not rise. Since, however, the melting of the solid is accompanied by an increase of volume, whereby an increase of pressure would result, a certain portion of the vapour must condense to liquid, in order that the pressure may remain constant. The total effect of addition of heat, therefore, is to cause both solid and vapour to pass into liquid, *i.e.* there occurs the change S + V→L. It will, therefore, depend on the relative quantities of solid and vapour, which will disappear first. If the solid disappears first, then we shall pass to the system L —V; if vapour disappears first, we shall obtain the system S—L. Withdrawal of heat causes the reverse change, L→S + V.

When fusion is accompanied by a diminution of volume (*e.g.* ice, Fig. 3), then, since the melting of the solid phase would decrease the total volume, *i.e.* would lower the pressure, a certain quantity of the solid must also pass into vapour in order that the pressure may be maintained constant. On addition of heat, therefore, there occurs the reaction S →L + V; withdrawal of heat causes the reverse change L + V →S. Above the temperature of the triple point the solid cannot exist. Below the triple point both systems, S —L and S —V, can exist, and it will therefore depend on the relative amounts of liquid and vapour which of these two systems is obtained on withdrawing heat from the system at constant volume. If, after obtaining the system S – L or S – V, one continues to remove heat at constant pressure, the system passes along OD′ (Fig. 5) into the region of solid; if heat is added

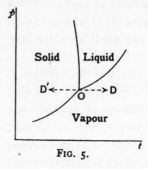

FIG. 5.

at constant pressure the liquid will disappear from the system L—V and we follow OD into the region of vapour.

Similar changes are produced when the volume of the system is altered at constant temperature. So long as the three phases are present, increase of volume must be compensated by the evaporation of liquid. As the result of increase of volume, therefore, the

process occurs L ➤ S + V. Diminution of volume without transference of heat, will bring about the opposite change, S + V ➤ L. In the former case there is ultimately obtained the univariant system S — V; in the latter case there will be obtained either S — L or L — V, according as the vapour or solid phase disappears first. This argument holds good for both types of triple point shown in Figs. 3 and 4 (p. 31). A glance at these figures will show that increase of volume (diminution of pressure) will lead ultimately to the system S—V. Decrease of volume on the other hand, will lead either to the system S — L or L — V. If the vapour phase disappears and we pass to the curve S — L, continued diminution of volume will be accompanied by a fall in temperature in the case of systems of the first type (Fig. 3), and by a rise in temperature in the case of systems of the second type (Fig. 4). If, however, the temperature is held constant, volume changes follow the dotted lines of Figs. 6 and 7, the interpretation of which is left to the student.

In discussing the alterations which may take place at the triple point with change of temperature and pressure, we have considered only the triple point S — L — V. The same reasoning, however, applies *mutatis mutandis*, to all other triple points, so that if the specific volumes of the phases are known, and the sign of the heat effects which accompany the transformation of one phase

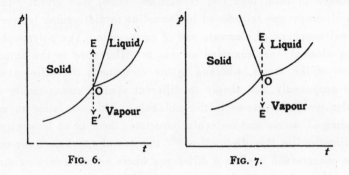

FIG. 6. FIG. 7.

into the other, it is possible to predict (by means of the principle of Le Chatelier) the changes which will be produced in the system by alteration of the pressure and temperature.

In all cases of transformation at the triple point, it should be noted that *all three phases are involved in the change,* and not two only; the fact that in the case, say, of the transformation from solid to liquid, or liquid to solid, at the melting-point with change of temperature, only these two phases appear to be affected, is due to the presence, as a rule, of a large excess of the vapour phase and to the prior disappearance therefore of the solid or liquid phase.

In the case of triple points at which two solid phases are in equilibrium with liquid, other arrangements of the curves around the triple point are found. It is, however, unnecessary to give a general treatment of these here, since the principles which have been applied to the triple point S—L—V can also be applied to the other triple points.[19]

Allotropy or Polymorphism. The fact that a solid can exist in more than one crystalline form was first observed by Mitscherlich in the case of sodium phosphate, and later with sulphur. To these two examples others were soon added, at first of inorganic, and later of organic substances, so that the property is now recognised as of very frequent occurrence indeed. To this phenomenon the name dimorphism, later changed to polymorphism to cover the existence of more than two crystalline forms, was given. The term allotropy was introduced by Berzelius to distinguish between the polymorphism of elements and of compounds. The polymorphs of an element were regarded as due to differences in the actual nature of the atoms, whereas in the compounds the differences were supposedly due simply to different spatial arrangements of similar groups of atoms in the molecule. With our fuller understanding of atomic and molecular structure, there is no longer any justification for this distinction;[20] the use of two names for the same phenomenon implies a difference where no difference exists. It would be better if the term polymorphism were abandoned in favour of the name allotropy to cover the phenomena in their totality. The various crystalline forms of a substance differ in the form of the crystal lattice or in the lattice dimensions, and this difference manifests itself not only in such physical properties as melting-point, specific gravity, etc., but in chemical properties as well, although the difference in chemical properties may not always be detectable. In the liquid state, however, the differences do not exist.

According to the definition of phases (p. 7), each of these allotropic forms constitutes a separate phase of the particular substance. As is readily apparent, the number of possible systems formed of one component may be considerably increased when that component is capable of existing in different crystalline forms. We have, therefore, to inquire what are the conditions under which different allotropic forms can coexist, either alone or in presence of the liquid and vapour phase.

From the equation $F = C - P + 2$, it is clear that zero variance is obtained when one component exists in three phases. From this it follows that one component cannot exist as a stable system in more than three phases, for in that case the system would have a negative variance, and this is impossible. Two different crystalline forms of a substance, therefore, can coexist in stable equilibrium only with vapour or with liquid, not with both vapour and liquid. Two new triple points, therefore, become possible, namely, $S_1 - S_2 - V$ and $S_1 - S_2 - L$, where S_1 and S_2 denote the two different crystalline forms.

Triple Point S_1—S_2—V. Transition Point. Just as the triple point S—L—V is the point of intersection of the two univariant curves S—V and L—V, so the triple point S_1—S_2—V is the point of intersection of the two curves S_1—V and S_2—V. Below the triple point only one of the solid phases (S_1) can exist in stable equilibrium with vapour; above the triple point only the other solid phase (S_2) will be stable. The triple point S_1—S_2—V is, therefore, a point at which the relative stability of the two solid phases undergoes change.

The triple point S_1—S_2—V is the point of intersection not only of the curves for the two univariant systems S_1—V and S_2—V, but the point of intersection also of a third curve, that for the system S_1—S_2. Since this is also a univariant system, the temperature at which the two solid phases can coexist will depend on the pressure. When the pressure is the atmospheric pressure, the temperature at which the two solid phases can coexist, and at which the relative stability of the two forms undergoes change, is known as the *transition point*. The transition point, therefore, bears the same relation to the triple point S_1—S_2—V as the melting-point does to the triple point S—L—V.

In the table (p. 38) is given a list of some of the more important allotropic substances, and the temperatures of the transition point. [21]

In the preceding discussion the transition point S_1—S_2—V has been regarded as the point of intersection of the vapour-pressure curves of the two solid forms, and equality of the vapour pressure has been taken as the condition for the stable coexistence of two crystalline forms of a substance. Were one dependent, however, on measurements of vapour pressure and temperature, the determination of the transition point would be a matter of great and in some cases of insuperable difficulty. When it is considered, however, that not only the vapour pressure but also the other physical properties of the solid phases, *e.g.* the density, undergo an abrupt change on passing through the transition point, owing to the transformation of one form into the other, then any method by which this abrupt change in the physical properties can be detected may be employed for determining the transition point.

Substance.					Transition temperature.
Ammonium nitrate					
α-rhombic $\rightarrow$ β-rhombic	.	.	.		32.3°
β-rhombic $\rightarrow$ rhombohedral		.	.		84.2°
Rhombohedral $\rightarrow$ cubic	.	.			125.2°
Mercuric iodide	.	.	.	.	126°
Potassium nitrate	.	.	.	.	129°
Silver iodide	.	.	.	.	145°
" nitrate	.	.	.	.	159.6°
Sulphur	.	.	.	.	95.5°
Tetrabrommethane	.	.	.	.	46.8°
Thallium nitrate					
Rhombic $\rightarrow$ rhombohedral	.	.	.		80°
Rhombohedral $\rightarrow$ regular	.	.	.		142.5°
Thallium picrate	.	.	.	.	44°
Tin	.	.	.	.	13.2°

Transition Curve. The transition point, like the melting-point, is influenced by pressure, and in this case also it is found that pressure may either raise or lower the transition point. The transition curve, therefore, may be inclined either away from or towards the pressure axis. The direction of the transition curve can be predicted, on the basis of the principle of Le Chatelier, if the change of volume accompanying the passage of one form into the other is known. The quantitative influence of pressure on the transition point can be calculated by means of the Clapeyron equation $dT/dp = T(v_2 - v_1)/q$. Since, as in the case of all condensed systems the value of $(v_2 - v_1)$ is small, the transition point, like the melting-point, is altered only to a relatively small extent by pressure.

The transformation, for example, of the α-rhombic to the β-rhombic form of ammonium nitrate is accompanied by an increase of volume ($v_\beta - v_\alpha = 0.0220$ c.c. per gram).[22] dT/dp has, therefore, a positive value, or the transition point is raised by increase of pressure, as shown by the numbers in the following table (p. 39):[23]

Pressure in kgm. per sq. cm.	Temperature.
1	$32.0°$
200	$38.5°$
400	$45.4°$
600	$52.9°$
800	$60.8°$

On the other hand, the passage of the β-rhombic into the rhombohedral form of ammonium nitrate is accompanied by a contraction, and the transition point is therefore lowered by increase of pressure, as shown by the following numbers:[24]

Pressure.	Temperature.
1 atm.	$85.85°$
100 ″	$84.38°$
200 ″	$83.03°$
250 ″	$82.29°$

The fairly numerous investigations which have been carried out show that over a range of pressure of a few hundred atmospheres the transition curve is practically a straight line. If, however, the range of pressure is extended considerably, up to say 12,000 atm., the transition curve ceases to be linear and shows a more or less marked curvature, being sometimes convex and sometimes concave to the pressure axis.[25]

In the case of mercuric iodide, as also in the case of Glauber's salt (a two-component system), it has been found that with increase of pressure the transition curve passes through a point of maximum temperature, and exhibits, therefore, a form similar to that assumed by Tammann for the fusion curve.[26]

In the following table (p. 40) are given the values of pressure and temperature for the transition point of red to yellow mercuric iodide:[27]

Enantiotropy and Monotropy. The triple point $S_1 - S_2 - V$ is one at which reversible transformation of the two crystalline forms can take place. Two cases must now be distinguished: (1) The transition point under atmospheric pressure lies below the melting-point of the solid; (2) the transition point lies above the melting-point. In the former case, each form possesses a definite range of

Pressure in kgm. per sq. cm.	Temperature.	$\triangle v$ c.c. per gm. $\times 10^5$.	q in gm.-cm. per gram $\times 10^5$	$\dfrac{dT}{dp}$.
1	127.0°	342	0.513	0.0267
1,000	149.8°	217	0.491	0.0187
2,000	165.2°	127	0.456	0.0122
3,000	174.9°	65	0.420	0.0069
4,000	179.9°	24	0.390	0.0028
5,000	181.2°	$-$ 8	0.365	-0.0010
6,000	178.2°	$-$ 45	0.345	-0.0059
7,000	169.7°	-100	0.330	-0.0134
8,000	152.4°	-175	0.318	-0.0234
9,000	122.3°	-270	0.296	-0.0361
10,000	79.4°	-390	0.278	-0.0495

stable existence, and is capable of undergoing reversible transformation into the other. In the latter case, only one of the solid forms is stable at all temperatures up to the melting-point, the other solid form being metastable. In this case there is no transition point realisable at atmospheric pressure, and transformation of crystalline forms can take place *only in one direction*. These two different kinds of behaviour are distinguished by the names *enantiotropy* and *monotropy;* enantiotropic substances being such that the change of one form into the other is a reversible process (*e.g.* rhombic sulphur into monoclinic, and monoclinic sulphur into rhombic), and monotropic substances, those in which the transformation of the crystalline forms is irreversible. This is found, for example, in the case of iodine monochloride and benzophenone.[28]

These differences of behaviour can be explained very well in many cases by supposing that in the case of enantiotropic substances the transition point lies below the melting-point, while in the case of monotropic substances, it lies above the melting-point. These conditions would be represented by the Figs. 8 and 9.

In these two figures, O_3 is the transition point, O_1 and O_2 the melting-points of the metastable and stable forms respectively. From Fig. 9 we see that the crystalline form I., at all temperatures up to its melting-point is metastable with respect to the form II.

In such cases the transition point could be reached only at higher pressures.

Although, as already stated, this explanation suffices for many cases, it does not prove that in all cases of monotropy the transi-

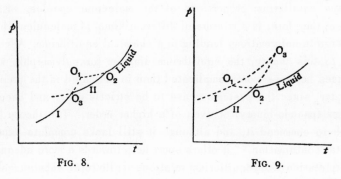

FIG. 8.   FIG. 9.

tion point is above the melting-point of the two forms. It is also quite possible that the transition point may lie below the melting-points;[29] in this case we have what is known as *pseudomonotropy*. It is possible that graphite and diamond,[30] perhaps also the two forms of phosphorus, stand in the relation of pseudomonotropy (*v.* p. 73). The possibility must also be recognised that there may be no transition point, real or imaginary, at all, but that the two crystalline forms may behave as dynamic isomerides. The system will then become a binary one (see Chap. XII).

The disposition of the curves in Figs. 8 and 9 also explains the phenomenon sometimes met with, especially in organic chemistry, that the substance first melts, then solidifies, and re-melts at a higher temperature. On again determining the melting-point after re-solidification, only the higher melting-point is obtained.

The explanation of such a behaviour is, that if the determination of the melting-point is carried out rapidly, the point O_1, the melting-point of the metastable solid form, may be realised. At this temperature, however, the liquid is metastable with respect to the stable solid form, and if the temperature is not allowed to rise above the melting-point of the latter, the liquid may solidify. The stable solid modification thus obtained will melt only at a higher temperature.

Another representation of enantiotropy and monotropy has been put forward by A. Smits,[31] on the basis of his theory of allotropy.

According to this theory, polymorphism and allotropy in general are explained as being due to the existence of two or more molecular species which coexist in equilibrium in each phase. Difference in crystalline form can then be explained as due to difference in the equilibrium proportions of the molecular species. Each phase, therefore, is a mixture of different kinds of molecules which undergo transformations leading to a chemical equilibrium. According to this theory, the equilibrium diagram for polymorphic substances becomes more complicated than is indicated in the present chapter, since the systems cease to be strictly unary and become binary (pseudo-binary) or even of a higher order. The theory has much to commend it, and although it still lacks complete experimental confirmation,[32] it offers some help towards a more adequate interpretation of the equilibrium relations of allotropic substances.[33] Pseudo-binary systems will be discussed more fully at a later point (Chap. XII).

Enantiotropy combined with Monotropy. Not only can allotropic substances exhibit enantiotropy or monotropy, but, if the substance is capable of existing in more than two crystalline forms, both relationships may be found, so that some of the forms may be enantiotropic to one another, while the other forms exhibit only monotropy. This behaviour is seen, for example, in the case of sulphur, which may exist in as many as eight different crystalline varities. Of these only monoclinic and rhombic sulphur exhibit the relationship of enantiotropy, *i.e.* they possess a definite transition point, while the other forms are all metastable with respect to rhombic and monoclinic sulphur, and remain so up to the melting-point; that is to say, they are monotropic modifications.[34]

Suspended Transformation. Metastable Equilibria. In the preceding pages we have considered only systems in stable equilibrium, and we have assumed that when the external conditions rendered a change of phase possible, that change took place. In actual fact, however, this is by no means always the case. Transformation may remain suspended.

It has, for example, long been known that water can be cooled below zero without solidification occurring. This was first discovered in 1724 by Fahrenheit, who found that water could be exposed to a temperature of -9.4° without solidifying; so soon, however, as a small particle of ice was brought in contact with the water, crystallisation commenced. Superfused or supercooled water—*i.e.* water cooled below 0°—is unstable only in respect of the solid phase; so long as the presence of the solid phase is carefully avoided, the water can be kept for any length of time without solidifying, and the system, supercooled water and vapour, behaves in every way like a stable system. A system which in itself is stable, and which becomes unstable only in contact with a particular phase, is said to be *metastable*, and the region throughout which this condition exists is called the metastable region.[35] Supercooled water, therefore, is in a metastable condition. If the supercooling be carried below a certain temperature, solidification takes place spontaneously without the addition of the solid phase; the system then ceases to be metastable, and becomes *unstable*.

Suspended transformation is likewise found to occur at the transition point for two crystalline forms of a substance. The transition point, as we have seen, is analogous to the melting-point of a solid. In both cases the change of phase is associated with a definite temperature and pressure in such a way that below the point the one phase, above the point the other phase, is stable. The transition point, however, differs in this respect from a point of fusion that while it is possible to supercool a liquid, no definite case is known where the solid has been heated above its melting-point without passing into the liquid state. Transformation, therefore, is suspended only on one side of the melting-point. In the case of two solid phases, however, the transition point can be overstepped in both directions, so that each phase can be obtained in the metastable condition. Thus, rhombic sulphur can be heated above the transition point, and monoclinic sulphur can be obtained at temperatures below the transition point, although in both cases transformation into a more stable form is possible; the system becomes metastable.[36]

The same reluctance to form a new phase is observed also in the phenomena of superheating of liquids, and the "hanging" of mercury in barometers, in which case the vapour phase is not formed. In general, then, we may say that *a new phase will not necessarily be formed immediately the system passes into such a condition that the existence of that phase is possible;* but rather, instead of the system undergoing transformation so as to pass into the most stable condition under the existing pressure and temperature, this transformation will be "suspended" or delayed, and the system will become metastable. Only in the case of the formation of the liquid from the solid phase, in a one-component system, has this reluctance to form a new phase not been observed.[37]

To ensure the formation of a new phase and to prevent the occurrence of suspended transformation, it is necessary to have that phase present. The presence of the solid phase will prevent the supercooling of a liquid (hence the efficacy of "inoculation" or "seeding"); and the presence of the vapour phase will prevent the superheating of a liquid. Suspended transformation takes place more readily in the case of the passage of an isotropic into an anisotropic phase (*e.g.* liquid into crystalline solid), where a definite arrangement of the molecules in a space lattice is necessary, than in the case of the transformation of one isotropic phase into another isotropic phase, where the molecules are in disarray.

When transformation of a less stable into a more stable phase occurs, the change does not take place at one moment throughout the whole phase, but proceeds from definite points or growth centres (nuclei). Such "nuclei" may form spontaneously in a supercooled phase, as is seen, for example, in the cloud formation produced on the cooling of a vapour by adiabatic expansion. The influence of dust particles and of gaseous ions in increasing the number of condensation nuclei, is well known.

In the case of a supercooled liquid, spontaneous formation of nuclei or crystal growth centres also takes place. Since, however, an anisotropic phase, with definite molecular arrangement, must now be formed from an isotropic phase, the number of nuclei formed in a given time per unit mass of the substance will be less than in the case of transformations between isotropic phases.

Spontaneous crystallisation from supercooled melts is subject to many influences, *e.g.* it can be brought about by a sharp blow,[38] by changing the material of the container,[39] by pounding and re-heating the vitrified melt, or by the application of an electric field.[40] It is a matter of everyday experience that crystallisation can be induced by scratching the inside of the containing vessel with a glass rod, or exposure to the dust of the atmosphere, although in this case the result is probably due to inoculation by the solid form or by some substance isomorphous with it.

The mechanism by means of which nuclei come into being has excited much interest. There is considerable evidence that after a solid has melted it still contains nuclei, that is fragmentary crystals, so that if such a liquid is cooled after a relatively short time, it will crystallise more readily than a liquid which has been raised to a high temperature or preserved for some time above the temperature of crystallisation.[41] Such nuclei will not persist indefinitely, however, as they are thermodynamically unstable.[42] Taylor, Eyring and Sherman[43] have attempted by methods of quantum mechanics, to trace the growth of a crystal lattice from the vapour phase.

Spontaneous crystallisation from supersaturated solutions, which are in this respect analogous to supercooled liquids, has been less frequently studied. On the whole the supersaturation is destroyed by much the same means as the supercooling of melts, but while supercooled melts can apparently be preserved indefinitely, there are indications that this is not the case with supersaturated solutions.

According to Miers,[44] if a solution is cooled more than $10°$ below the temperature at which it is saturated, it will eventually crystallise spontaneously, and the work of A. N. and A. J. R. Campbell[45] would seem to indicate that the nuclear number, in contradistinction to the velocity of crystallisation, is but little sensitive to outside influences, and is probably never zero.

In the case of spontaneous crystallisation from vapours, Volmer and Weber[46] have shown that a somewhat high degree of super-saturation is necessary to cause the spontaneous formation of nuclei, but further regularities are not known.

A peculiar type of metastability is observed when dealing with the solubility of a solid in a very fine state of division or with the vapour pressure of very small drops. It has long been known on theoretical grounds that the solubility of such a solid, or the vapour pressure of such a liquid, is greater than the equilibrium value, and this alone shows that the condition is one of metastability. The experimental observation of increased solubility, due to small particle size, was claimed by Hulett, but doubt has been cast upon the observations, in view of the relative coarseness of the particles obtained by grinding.[47] In any event, since a solution saturated with respect to fine particles is supersaturated with respect to coarse ones, such a solution will in time precipitate coarse particles, the fine particles dissolving, until the whole solid mass is converted to the coarsely crystalline form, having the normal solubility. The process is exactly the same as the conversion of a metastable to a stable allotrope when in contact with solution. The normal Phase Rule behaviour will therefore be observed provided sufficient time is allowed to elapse for the establishment of true equilibrium. It is worthy of note that whenever spontaneous crystallisation from a supersaturated solution takes place, this condition of enhanced solubility must prevail for a time, since the precipitated particles grow from molecular magnitudes through the size of colloidal particles, and eventually attain microscopic and macroscopic magnitude.[48]

That enhanced solubility can be obtained by mere grinding has recently been demonstrated by Cohen and Thönnessen,[49] in the case of salicylic acid and other organic substances. At higher temperatures, however, the solubility soon becomes normal,[50] in confirmation of the view expressed above.

Pressure-Temperature Relations between Stable and Metastable Forms. Since the possibility of the existence of a substance in a metastable state must be recognised, it becomes of importance to consider what relationship exists between the vapour pressure of the stable and metastable forms.

It has already (p. 30) been pointed out that in the neighbourhood of the triple point S —L— V, the curve for S—V must ascend more rapidly than the curve for L—V. It follows, therefore, that if the curve for $L-V$ be continued downwards to temperatures below the triple point, the continuation of the curve must lie above the curve for $S-V$. In other words, the vapour pressure of a supercooled liquid (metastable system) must be higher than the vapour pressure of the solid (stable system) at the same temperature. This conclusion is indicated by the curves for solid and liquid in Fig. 2 (p. 30), and is borne out by the numbers in the table below for water.

VAPOUR PRESSURE OF ICE AND OF SUPERCOOLED WATER.

Temperature.	Pressure in mm. mercury.		
	Water.	Ice.	Difference.
$0°$	4.579	4.579	0.000
$-2°$	3.952	3.879	0.073
$-4°$	3.404	3.277	0.127
$-8°$	2.509	2.322	0.187
$-10°$	2.144	1.947	0.197

It is now easy to understand why solid, liquid, and vapour cannot coexist in equilibrium at temperatures below the triple point. Since the vapour pressure of supercooled liquid is greater than that of solid, vapour will condense on the solid, and a process of distillation will take place from the liquid to the solid until all the liquid will have disappeared and only solid and vapour remain.

Since in the neighbourhood of the triple point S_1-S_2-V the curves S_1-V and S_2-V are arranged similarly to the curves $S-V$ and $L-V$ in the neighbourhood of the triple point $S-L-V$, it follows that in the case of two crystalline forms of a substance, the metastable form will, at a given temperature, have a higher vapour pressure than the stable form. The vapour pressure curve, for example, of rhombic sulphur must at temperatures above $95.5°$ (the transition point) lie above that for the stable form, monoclinic sulphur; and at temperatures below the transition point the vapour pressure curve for monoclinic sulphur must lie above that for rhombic sulphur (p. 66).

Quite generally, then, we can say that *in a one-component system the vapour pressure of a metastable phase is, at a given temperature, greater than that of the stable phase.*

Velocity of Transformation of Metastable Systems.   Although the presence of the more stable form of a substance may ensure that transformation of the metastable system takes place, the rate at which this transformation occurs may vary very greatly. In some cases, the change may take place so quickly as to appear almost instantaneous, while in other cases the change takes place so slowly as to require hundreds of years for its achievement.

In this connection, most attention has been paid to the study of the velocity of crystallisation of a supercooled liquid, the first experiments in this direction having been made by Gernez[51] on the velocity of crystallisation of phosphorus and sulphur. Since that time, the velocity of crystallisation of other supercooled liquids has been investigated, particularly by Tammann.[52]

On the basis of his experimental results, Tammann generalised the behaviour of (linear) crystallisation velocity in a manner which,

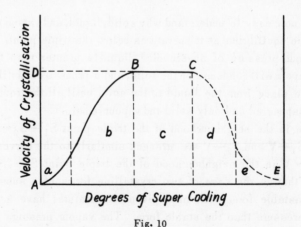

Fig. 10

on the whole, has resisted attack. According to him, the crystallisation velocity increases with the degree of supercooling in a manner approximately linear up to a maximum value which remains constant for a considerable range of supercooling, after which it decreases. This behaviour is illustrated in Fig. 10. Tammann saw the existence of a region of constant crystallisation velocity as a necessary consequence of his deduction that the temperature of the freezing point must exist at the crystallising boundary, at least over a considerable range of supercooling. This supposition was contested on theoretical grounds by Küster[53] and seems to have been disproved experimentally by Pollatschek.[54] The existence in fact of the region of constant crystallisation velocity has also been called in question and, indeed, if a constant temperature does not prevail at the crystallising boundary, there seems no reason why there should be such a region.

It has been shown frequently, although indeed it is obvious, that viscosity will oppose the propagation of a crystal boundary and that therefore, other things being equal, crystallisation velocity and viscosity are inversely related. As the degree of supercooling increases, so do both the tendency to crystallinity and the opposing viscosity. On the supposition that the tendency to crystallise increases in approximate proportion to the degree of supercooling but that the viscosity increases very rapidly after a certain degree of supercooling, as is known to be the case, it is easy to see how a maximum may occur on the curve expressing crystallisation velocity as a function of supercooling, but such a maximum value should immediately decrease as the viscosity increases still further. It must not be supposed that crystallisation velocity is determined solely by viscosity and that therefore, for example, two different substances possessing the same viscosity would necessarily have the same crystallisation velocity: in general they will not. A formula for the rate of crystallisation of an undercooled melt has been derived by Reinders.[55] Regarding crystallisation from vapour, many detailed studies of the rate of growth, once nuclei are formed, have revealed that this phenomenon is influenced by several factors,[56] viz. (a) temperature of formation, (b) vapour pressure of the gas at the temperature of growth, (c) presence of other gases, (d) orientation of the crystal with respect to the direction of flow of the vapour, (e) preferential directions of growth, (f) size of crystals.

Since the temperature at which the spontaneous formation of crystal nuclei has its maximum value is, in general, below that at which the velocity of crystallisation is a maximum, it is possible, by rapid cooling, to pass through the temperatures of maximum crystallisation velocity and maximum formation of nuclei, and to obtain the liquid at a temperature at which the velocity of crystallisation (and also of crystal nuclei formation) becomes negligible. Since the viscosity increases with fall of temperature, the liquid passes into a glassy mass, which will remain (practically) permanent even in contact with the crystalline solid.[57] Some substances can be supercooled to the glassy state more readily than others.

This simple view of the case has been contested by Parks and others.[58] Parks and his co-workers have studied the variation of a number of physical properties of various supercooled organic substances with respect to temperature, and find a marked discontinuity in the property-temperature curve at the temperature of vitreous formation. This would indicate that the vitreous state is a separate phase. Nevertheless, X-ray[59] and electron diffraction[60] methods have, in recent years, been applied to the investigation of the glasses, and this work has supported the older view that there is no structural difference between a glass and a supercooled liquid. All true glasses give broad diffraction-bands in their X-ray patterns, and are entirely similar to liquids in this respect. The liquid-glass transformation is not sharp, but inside a small temperature range the slope of various property-temperature curves changes markedly.[61]

In ordinary glass we have a familiar example of a liquid which has been cooled to a temperature at which crystallisation takes place with very great slowness. If, however, glass is heated, spontaneous formation of nuclei takes place and a temperature is reached, much below the melting-point of the glass, at which crystallisation occurs with appreciable velocity. We then observe the phenomenon of devitrification.[62]

When the velocity of crystallisation is studied at temperatures above the maximum point, it is found that the velocity is diminished by the addition of foreign substances. Bogojawlenski[63] has investigated the crystallisation velocities of a few mixtures and finds them, as might be expected, irregular. As one component crystallises, the concentration of the other changes. To obviate this difficulty a study of the crystallisation rates of eutectic mixtures has been made:[64] in this case a comparison, at equal degrees of supercooling, with the crystallisation velocities of the components is justifiable.

Marc[65] and Freundlich[66] have put forward the view that the velocity of crystallisation of supercooled liquids is influenced by adsorption phenomena, the dissolved substance being adsorbed on the surface of the crystals. In this connection, Freundlich and Oppenheimer[67] have shown that the crystallisation velocity of supercooled water is frequently, if not always, increased by colloidal substances the particles of which are non-spherical, whereas particles which are spherical, and also the truly dissolved substances, lower the velocity.

Whereas the transformation of a metastable, supercooled liquid into the stable solid phase takes place fairly rapidly if the degree of supercooling has not been too great, the corresponding transformation of metastable allotropic forms may take place only with great slowness. Thus, although calcite is the most stable form of calcium carbonate at the ordinary temperature,[68] the metastable modification, aragonite, nevertheless exists under the ordinary conditions in an apparently very stable state.

Ordinary white tin, also, although apparently possessing permanence, is in reality in a metastable state, under the ordinary conditions of temperature and pressure; and this great degree of permanence, and the apparent stability which makes possible the everyday use of this metal, are due to the sluggishness with which transformation into the stable grey form occurs (p. 69).

The behaviour found in the case of sulphur and of tin is met with also in the case of all transformations in the solid state, but the velocity of the change is less in some cases than in others, and appears to decrease with increase of the valency of the element.[69] To this fact van't Hoff attributes the great permanence of many really unstable (or metastable) carbon compounds.

The velocity of transformation can be accelerated by various means. One of the most important of these is the employment of a liquid which has a solvent action on the solid phases. Just as we have seen that at a given temperature the less stable form has the higher vapour pressure, but that at the transition point the vapour pressure of both forms becomes identical, so also it can be proved theoretically, and be shown experimentally, that at a given temperature the solubility of the less stable form is greater than that of the more stable, but that at the transition point the solubility of the two forms becomes identical.[70] If, then, the two solid phases are brought into contact with a solvent, the less stable phase will dissolve more abundantly than the more stable; the solution will therefore become supersaturated with respect to the latter, which will be deposited. A gradual change of the less stable form, therefore, takes place, through the medium of the solvent. In this way the more rapid conversion of white tin into grey in presence of a solution of tin ammonium chloride (p. 70) is to be explained. Although, as a rule, solvents accelerate the transformation of one solid phase into the other, they may also have a retarding influence on the velocity of transformation, as was found by Reinders in the case of mercuric iodide.[71]

The velocity of transformation, also, is variously affected by different solvents, and in some cases, at least, it appears to be slower the more viscous the solvent;[72] indeed, Kastle and Reed state that yellow crystals of mercuric iodide, which, ordinarily, change with considerable velocity into the red modification, have been preserved for more than a year under vaseline.

Change from the yellow to the red form of mercuric iodide at the ordinary temperature is retarded by the presence of mercuric chloride or bromide. Moreover, if mercuric iodide is heated to various temperatures above the melting-point, and then kept at the ordinary temperature, the velocity of change from yellow to red is all the greater the higher the temperature of heating.[73] It would appear that metastability is frequently if not always increased by the presence of impurities.[74]

Temperature, also, has a very considerable influence on the velocity of transformation. The higher the temperature, and the farther it is removed from the equilibrium point (transition point), the greater is the velocity of change. Above the transition point, these two factors act in the same direction, and the velocity of transformation will therefore go on increasing indefinitely the higher the temperature is raised. Below the transition point, however, the two factors act in opposite directions, and the more the temperature is lowered, the more is the effect of removal from the equilibrium point counteracted. A point will therefore be reached at which the velocity is a maximum. Reduction of the temperature below this point causes a rapid falling off in the velocity of change.[75] The point of maximum velocity, however, is not definite, but may be altered by various causes. Thus, Cohen found that in the case of tin, the point of maximum velocity was altered if the metal had already undergone transformation; and also by the presence of different liquids.[76]

Lastly, the presence of small quantities of different substances — catalytic agents or catalysts — has a great influence on the velocity of transformation. Thus, *e.g.*, the conversion of white to violet phosphorus is accelerated by the presence of iodine (p. 70).

The occurrence of allotropic forms and the persistence of the metastable state are facts of the highest practical and theoretical importance. In the case not only of tin, but also of a number of other metals, *e.g.* bismuth, cadmium, copper, silver, and zinc, allotropic modifications exist with transition points at temperatures above the ordinary; and, owing to the slowness of transformation, these metals exist, at the ordinary temperature, in a metastable state. On this fact depends the practical, everyday use of these metals.[77]

Recognition of the persistence of the metastable state is also, as Cohen more especially has emphasised, of the greatest importance in connection with the determination of the physical constants of the substances. Owing to the great slowness with which, in many cases, transformation of the metastable to the stable form takes place, great care must be exercised to ensure that one is dealing with a definite chemical individual and not with a mixture of allotropes. Many determinations, indeed, of the physical properties of substances, found in the literature, are of doubtful value owing to insufficient care having been taken to ensure that the material used was a single crystalline form and not a variable mixture of two allotropic forms.[78]

"Law" of Successive Reactions. In preparative chemistry it is very frequently observed that when a substance is formed in a reaction it appears first not in its most stable form but in a metastable form, which then, more or less rapidly, passes into the stable condition. This behaviour, which was called by Ostwald the law of successive reactions, is observed with especial ease and frequency in organic chemistry, where it is often found that when a substance is thrown out from solution it is first deposited as a liquid or as a metastable crystalline solid, which passes later into the form stable at the particular temperature.[79]

The prior formation of the less stable crystalline form can be well demonstrated by means of p-bromoacetanilide or by 2:4-dibromoacetanilide.[80] These compounds separate out from solution as needle-shaped crystals, forming a voluminous crystalline mass. When left in contact with the mother liquor, however, these crystals change, more or less rapidly, according to the solvent employed, into the more stable, compact crystalline form. The change in appearance is very marked, as is shown by the photographs (Fig. 11) of 2:4-dibromoacetanilide crystallised from alcoholic solution.[81]

This generalisation by Ostwald is not entitled to the name of a law, since many exceptions to it are known, but it sums up phenomena very frequently observed. Of the factors governing the appearance of a new phase the most important, according to Tammann,[82] is the readiness with which spontaneous formation of nuclei of the metastable and of the stable phases takes place in the supercooled system.

1   2

3   4

Fig. 11.—Crystallisation of 2 : 4-dibromoacetanilide.   Photographs taken at
intervals of two days.

[*To face page* 54.

NOTES

1. An exception must be made to this statement in the case of those substances which are capable of existing in the mesomorphic (liquid crystalline) state, if liquid crystals are considered to be liquids rather than crystals. Such substances can exist both as isotropic liquids and as anisotropic liquids. Thus the same component exists in two liquid phases and it may exist in more if, as is not infrequent, the substance forms more than one type of liquid crystal.

2. The term "solid" is not in itself sufficient to characterise a phase different from gas or liquid. An amorphous solid, glass, is merely a liquid cooled to such a low temperature that its viscosity becomes very great. The passage of an amorphous solid into liquid is a gradual and continuous one. In a crystalline solid, however, the atoms or molecules are arranged in a definite space lattice, and transition from a crystalline to a liquid phase is abrupt and definite.

3. See footnote 3, p. 19.

4. Although in the system liquid —vapour the liquid ceases to exist at the critical point, Tammann has found that the fusion curve (solid in contact with liquid) of phosphonium chloride can be followed up to temperatures above the critical point (*Arch. Néerland.*, 1901 [2], **6**, 244). See also Bridgman, *Physical Rev.*, 1914 [2], **3**, 126, 153.

5. Maass and Steacie, *Introduction to Physical Chemistry*, 2nd edit., p. 152, Wiley (1946).

6. The Le Chatelier principle applies only to changes in stable systems. It does not apply to transformations in metastable systems.

7. It can readily be proved, by means of the conception of thermodynamic potential, that the Clausius-Clapeyron equation is applicable to all p-t curves. (See Roozeboom, *Die Heterogenen Gleichgewichte*, I, 32).

8. Tammann, *Z. anorgan. Chem.*, 1904, **40**, 54; Johnston and Adams, *Amer, J. Sci.*, 1911 [4], **31**, 501.

9. This applies to the effect of "uniform pressure," or pressure acting equally on both phases. When the pressure acts only on one phase the effect is much greater. Thus, when ice only is subjected to pressure, the water being allowed to escape, the melting-point is lowered $0.09°$ per atmosphere. Non-uniform pressure *always lowers* the melting-point of a crystalline solid (Johnston and Adams, *Amer. J. Sci.*, 1911 [4], **31**, 501).

10. van't Hoff, *Studies on Chemical Dynamics,* p. 163.

11. Bridgman, *Z. anorgan. Chem.,* 1912, **77,** 377; *Physical Rev.,* 1914, **3,** 127; 1915, **6,** 1. See also Tammann, *Annalen d. Physik,* 1899 [3], **68,** 564; 1900 [4], **2,** 1, 424; *Z. physikal. Chem.,* 1910, **72,** 609; 1913, **84,** 257.

12. Barus, *Amer. J. Sci.,* 1892, **42,** 125; Mack, *Compt. rend.,* 1898, **127,** 361; Hulett, *Z. physikal. Chem.,* 1899, **38,** 629; Deffet, *Bull. Soc. chim. de Belg.,* 1935, **44,** 41. Johnston and Adams (*Amer. J. Sci.,* 1911 [4], **31,** 501) have found that the fusion curve for tin, bismuth, lead, and cadmium, is a straight line up to a pressure of 2000 atm.

13. Tammann, *Annalen d. Physik,* 1899 [3], **68,** 553, 629; 1900 [4], 1, 275; **2,** 1; **3,** 161. See also Tammann, *Kristallisieren und Schmelzen* (Leipzig, 1903), or *The States of Aggregation* (London, 1926); Block, *Z. physikal. Chem.,* 1913, **82,** 403; Bridgman, *Physical Rev.,* 1914 [2], **3,** 126, 153; 1915 [2], **6,** 1, 94; Timmermans, *Bull. Acad. roy. Belg.,* 1919, pp. 753, 767.

14. It has been shown, however, by Bridgman (*Physical Rev.,* 1914 [2], **3,** 126, 153; 1915 [2], **6,** 1, 94) that the curvature of the fusion curve above the pressure of 3000 kgm. per sq. cm. is much less than the curvature below this pressure.

15. The pressure of 1 atm. is equal to 1.0333 kgm. per sq. cm.: or the pressure of 1 kgm. per sq. cm. is equal to 0.968 atm.

16. Tammann, *Arch. Néerland.,* 1901 [2], **6,** 244; Bridgman, *Physical Rev.,* 1914 [2], **3,** 126, 153.

17. Waring, *Science,* 1943, **97,** 221.

18. A field is "enclosed" by two curves when these cut at an angle less than two right angles.

19. Roozeboom, *Das Heterogene Gleichgewicht,* I, p. 189.

20. Lowry, *Trans. Faraday Soc.,* 1916, **11,** 150.

21. Zawidski, *Z. physikal. Chem.,* 1904, **47,** 727; van Eyk, *ibid.,* 1905, **51,** 720; Janecke, *ibid.,* 1915, **90,** 280, 313; Cohen and Moesveld, *ibid.,* 1913, **85,** 419; 1920, **94,** 450; Cohen and Helderman, *ibid.,* 1914, **87,** 409; 1915, **89,** 493, 638, 728, 733, 742; Cohen and van den Bosch, *ibid.,* 1915, **89,** 757; Early and Lowry *J. Chem. Soc.,* 1919, **115,** 1387; Cohen and Kooy, *Z. physikal. Chem.,* 1924, **109,** 81; Bridgman, *J. Amer. Chem. Soc.,*

1914, **36**, 1344. For a study of mercuric iodide, see Smits and Bokhorst, *Z. physikal. Chem.*, 1914-15, **89**, 365, 374; Smits, *ibid.*, 1916-18, **92**, 345; Bridgman, *Proc. Amer. Acad. Arts Sci.*, 1916, **51**, 581; Losana, *Gazzetta*, 1926, **56**, 301.

22. Cohen and Kooy, *Z. physikal, Chem.*, 1924, **109**, 81. The heat of transformation is 4.99 cal. per gram (Cohen and Helderman, *Z. physikal. Chem.*, 1924, **113**, 145).

23. Bridgman, *Proc. Amer. Acad. Arts Sci.*, 1916, **51**, 581.

24. Lussana, *Nuovo Cim.*, 1895 [4], **1**, 105.

25. Bridgman, *Proc. Nat. Acad. Sci.*, 1915, **1**, 513; *Proc. Amer. Acad. Arts Sci.*, 1916, **51**, 581; Tammann, *Nachr. Ges. Wiss. Goettingen*, 1915, 59.

26. *Z. physikal. Chem.*, 1903, **46**, 818.

27. Bridgman, *Proc. Amer. Acad. Arts Sci.*, 1915, **51**, 55.

28. The two forms of iodine monochloride melt at $13.9°$ and $27.2°$, while those of benzophenone melt at $26°$ and $48°$. In the case of menthol four crystalline forms have been obtained melting at $31.5°$, $33.5°$, $35.5°$, and $42.5°$. Only the last form is stable (Wright, *J. Amer. Chem. Soc.*, 1917, **39**, 1515).

29. Roozeboom, *Das Heterogene Gleichgewicht*, I, p. 177.

30. *Ibid.*, p. 179. For discussions of the diamond problem and of the diagram of states of carbon, see Baur, Sichling, and Schenker, *Z. anorgan. Chem.*, 1915, **92**, 313; Lewis and Randall, *J. Amer. Chem. Soc.*, 1915, **37**, 462; Parsons, *Phil. Trans.*, 1919, A. **220**, 67; van Liempt, *Z. anorgan. Chem.*, 1921, **115**, 218; Tammann, *ibid.*, 1921, **115**, 145.

31. *Z. physikal. Chem.*, 1911, **76**, 421; 1913, **82**, 657; *Die Theorie der Allotropie* (Barth, 1921), translation by Smeath Thomas (Longmans); Terwen, *Z. physikal. Chem.*, 1916, **91**, 443.

32. See criticism, for example, by Tammann, *Z. physikal. Chem.*, 1913, **83**, 728; **84**, 753.

33. See Jänecke, *Z. physikal. Chem.*, 1915, **90**, 280, 313; Cohen, *Trans. Faraday Soc.*, 1915, **10**, 216.

34. Brauns, *Jahrb. Min. Beil.-Bd.*, 1900, **13**, 39.

35. The permanence or apparent permanence of a metastable system may be due to the fact that no nuclei of the stable phase are formed or

that their number is negligible, or to the fact that the velocity of transformation is very slow. Only in the former case is the system truly metastable (see also pp. 45 ff.) Cf. Othmer, *Z. anorgan. Chem.*, 1915, **91**, 219.

36. See Cohen and Moesveld, *Z. physikal. Chem.*, 1920, **94**, 450, 471; Cohen and Bruins, *ibid.*, 1920, **94**, 465.

37. In this connection, see Pawloff, *Z. physikal. Chem.*, 1908, **65**, 1, 545; Tammann, *ibid.*, 1909, **68**, 257; Berthoud, *J. chim. phys.*, 1910, **8**, 337.

38. Young and Sicklen, *J. Amer. Chem. Soc.*, 1913, **35**, 1067.

39. Pollatschek, *Z. physikal. Chem.*, 1929, **142**, 289.

40. Kondoguri, *Z. Physik.*, 1928, **47**, 589.

41. W. L. Webster, *Proc. Roy. Soc.*, 1933 [A], **140**, 653.

42. Bloch, Brings and Kuhn, *Z. physikal. Chem.*, 1931 [B], **12**, 415.

43. *J. Chem. Physics*, 1933, **1**, 68.

44. Miers, *Inst. Metals.* May Lecture, 1927.

45. *Trans. Faraday Soc.*, 1937, **33**, 299.

46. *Z. physikal. Chem.*, 1926, **119**, 295.

47. Hulett, *Z. physikal. Chem.*, 1901, **37**, 385; Bigelow and Trimble, *J. Phys. Chem.*, 1927, **31**, 1798; Dundon and Mack, *J. Amer. Chem. Soc.*, 1923, **45**, 2479; Dundon, *ibid.*, 1923, **45**, 2658.

48. Von Weimarn, *Kolloid-Z.*, 1909, **5**, 221; Campbell and Cook, *J. Amer. Chem. Soc.*, 1935, **57**, 387.

49. *Proc. Acad. Sci.*, Amsterdam, 1932, **35**, 441.

50. *Ibid.*, 1932, **35**, 798.

51. *Compt. rend.*, 1882, **95**, 1278; 1884, **97**, 1298, 1366, 1433.

52. *Z. physikal. Chem.*, **23-29**. See also Küster, *ibid.*, **25-28**; Müller, *ibid.*, 1914, **86**, 177.

53. Küster, *Z. physikal. Chem.*, 1898, **25**, 480.

54. Pollatschek, *Z. physikal. Chem.*, 1929, **142**, 289.

55. *Rec. trav. chim.*, 1932, **51**, 589.

56. Bernal and Wooster, *Annual Reports*, 1931, 265.

57. See Tammann (*Z. physikal. Chem.*, 1898, **25**, 472) for an investigation of the conversion of liquids into glasses by cooling. See, also, Tammann and Jellinghaus, *Annalen d. Physik*, 1929, [5], **2**, 264.

58. Parks, *Science*, 1926, **64**, 364; *J. Physikal Chem.*, 1927, **31**, 1843, *et seq.*; Jeffreys, *Proc. Camb. Phil. Soc.*, 1928, **24**, 19.

59. Warren, *Physical Rev.*, 1934 [ii], **45**, 657; Warren and Morningstar, *ibid.*, 1935 [ii], **47**, 808.

60. Schischakow, *Nature*, 1935, **136**, 514; 1936, **137**, 273.

61. Tammann and Elbrächter, *Z. anorgan. Chem.*, 1932, **207**, 268. See also, G. W. Morey, *Ind. Eng. Chem.*, 1933, **25**, 742.

62. W. Guertler, *Z. anorgan. Chem.*, 1904, **40**, 268; Tammann, *Z. Elektrochem.*, 1904, **10**, 532; *Z. anorgan. Chem.*, 1914, **87**, 248.

63. Bogojawlenski, *Z. physikal. Chem.*, 1898, **27**, 585.

64. Campbell and Pritchard, *Can. J. Res.*, 1947, B. **25**, 191.

65. *Z. physikal. Chem.*, 1908, **61**, 385; 1909, **67**, 470; **68**, 104; 1910, **73**, 685; **75**, 710.

66. *Ibid.*, 1910, **75**, 245.

67. *Ber.*, 1925, **58**, 143.

68. Foote, *Z. physikal. Chem.*, 1900, **33**, 740. See also Sosman, Hostetter, and Merwin, *J. Washington Acad. Sci.*, 1915, **5**, 563; Johnston, Merwin, and Williamson, *Amer. J. Sci.*, 1916, **41**, 473.

69. Van't Hoff, *Arch. Néerland.*, 1901, **6**, 471.

70. See, for example, the determinations of the solubility of rhombic and monoclinic sulphur, by J. N. Brönsted, *Z. physikal. Chem.*, 1906, **55**, 378; also solubilities of polymorphic phthalylhydrazides (Chattaway and Lambert, *J. Chem. Soc.*, 1915, **107**, 1773).

71. *Z. physikal. Chem.*, 1899, **32**, 506. See also Chattaway and Lambert, *J. Chem. Soc.*, 1915, **107**, 1766.

72. Kastle and Reed, *Amer. Chem. Jour.*, 1902, **27**, 209.

73. Losana, *Gazzetta*, 1926, **56**, 301.

74. Johnston, Merwin, and Williamson (*Amer. J. Sci.*, 1916 [4], **16**, 504) have pointed out that whereas natural calcite usually occurs in a very pure state, natural aragonite is contaminated by various impurities,

such as the carbonates of lead, strontium, etc.

75.   Lautz, Z. physikal. Chem., 1913, **84**, 611.   See also Bridgman, Proc. Amer. Acad. Arts Sci., 1916, **52**, 57;   Müller, Z. physikal. Chem., 1914, **86**, 177.

76.   Z. physikal. Chem., 1900, **35**, 581.

77.   See Cohen and Moesveld, Z. physikal. Chem. , 1913, **85**, 419; Cohen and Helderman, ibid., 1914, **87**, 409, 419, 426;   1915, **89**, 493, 638, 728, 742;   Cohen and Bosch, ibid., 1915, **89**, 757;   Heller, ibid., 1915, **89**, 761;   Cohen and Helderman, ibid., 1910, **74**, 202;   1915, **89**, 733;   Cohen, ibid., 1914, **87**, 431;   1915, **89**, 489;   Cohen and de Bruin, ibid., 1915, **89**, 748;   Cohen and Bruins, ibid., 1920, **94**, 443;   Cohen and Moesveld, ibid., 1920, **95**, 285.

78.   Cohen, Z. Elektrochem., 1925, **31**, 539;   Cohen and Kooy, Z. physikal. Chem., 1924, **109**, 81;   Cohen and Moesveld, ibid., p. 97;   Cohen, Helderman and Moesveld, ibid., p. 100;   Cohen and Helderman, ibid., 1924, **113**, 145;   Cohen and Moesveld, ibid., 1925, **115**, 151.   See also Cohen, Physico-chemical Metamorphosis and Problems in Piezochemistry (1926).

79.   Findlay, Introduction to Physical Chemistry, 1st edit., Longmans, Green and Co., London, 1933, p. 396.

80.   Chattaway and Lambert, J. Chem. Soc., 1915, **107**, 1766.

81.   For these photographs we are indebted to Dr. F. D. Chattaway. Transformation of the less stable needle-shaped crystals into the more stable compact crystals does not always take place spontaneously. Chattaway and Lambert state that needle-shaped crystals of 2 : 4-dibromo-acetanilide in contact with alcoholic solution were kept for two years in a sealed tube, without transformation to the compact crystals taking place.

82.   Tammann, States of Aggregation, p. 220, (1926).

CHAPTER IV

TYPICAL SYSTEMS

In the present chapter will be discussed the experimental investigation of a number of systems of one component, the behaviour of which will illustrate the general principles of the Phase Rule considered in the preceding chapter.

Water.

We have already, in the preceding chapter, referred in passing to the sublimation, vaporisation, and fusion curves of the substance water, the arrangement of which at the triple point S—L—V is represented diagrammatically in Fig. 12. The triple point, as we have seen, lies at a pressure of about 4.6 mm. of mercury and about 0.01°C. The curves BO, OA, and OC are the sublimation, vaporisation, and fusion curves respectively. The fusion curve slopes towards the pressure axis, indicating that the melting-point of ice is lowered by increase of pressure. The dotted curve OA' represents the metastable vaporisation curve for supercooled water. It is, of course, continuous with the curve OA. The critical point A lies at 374° and 218 atm.

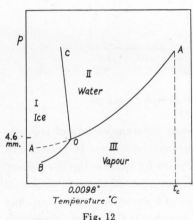

Fig. 12

Other Phases of the Substance Water. It was discovered by Tammann[1] that water can exist in solid forms other than that of ordinary ice; and the conditions under which these different solid phases can exist have been studied by him, and, more recently and fully, by P. W. Bridgman,[2] who has carried his investigations up to a pressure of about 50,000 atmospheres. A brief summary of the relationships as they are interpreted by Bridgman[3] is given here, the results being represented graphically in Fig. 13.

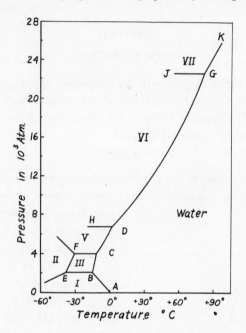

The System Water at High Pressures

Fig. 13

According to the Phase Rule, each different variety of ice constitutes a separate phase and, consequently, it must be possible to obtain not only the ordinary triple point for solid — liquid—vapour which has already been described, but also other triple points at which the other forms of ice exist. Of such forms Bridgman has distinguished no fewer than five, besides ordinary ice, these different forms being designated ice I (ordinary ice),[4] ice II, ice III, ice V, ice VI and ice VII. The existence of another form, ice IV, has been claimed by Tammann, but Bridgman has failed to find it.[5]

On investigating the equilibrium curve for ice I — liquid, it is found that at a certain temperature and pressure, a second solid phase, ice III, is formed, giving rise to the invariant system ice I—

ice III — liquid (Point B, Fig. 13).[6] Ice III behaves differently from ice I in that it expands on liquefying and, consequently, its melting point is raised by increase of pressure (curve BC). On following this curve to higher pressures and temperatures, another triple point (C) is reached at which ice V coexists with ice III and liquid. Similarly, one obtains the curves CD for ice V and liquid, DG for ice VI and liquid, D being the triple point for ice V — ice VI—liquid, and GK for ice VII and liquid, G being a triple point for ice VI — ice VII— liquid. The curve GK has been followed up to a pressure of about 50,000 atmospheres.

Besides the univariant curves for solid and liquid, one can also have univariant curves for two solid phases. Thus, BE represents the conditions of temperature and pressure for the coexistence of ice I and ice III, while CF, DH and GJ refer to the systems ice III— ice V, ice V—ice VI, and ice VI—ice VII, respectively.

The different areas in Fig. 13, bounded by the curves for the univariant systems, represent the conditions for the stable existence of single phases, as represented in the diagram. From this diagram it is seen that the region of stability of ice III is completely circumscribed.

In the following table are given the values of pressure and temperature corresponding with the various triple points as shown in Fig. 13.

Point.	System.	Temperature in °C.	Pressure. Kgm. per sq. cm.
B	Ice I—ice III—liquid	-22.0	2115
E	" I— " II—ice.III	-34.7	2170
C	" III— " V—liquid	-17.0	3530
F	" II— " III—ice V	-24.3	3510
D	" V— " VI—liquid	+0.16	6380
G	" VI— " VII—liquid	+81.6	22400

The metastable continuation of the curve BE for ice I—ice III can be followed for a considerable distance into the field for ice II. The values for the curve BE and its metastable prolongation are given in the following table: —

Temperature.	Pressure. Kgm. per sq. cm.	$\dfrac{dp}{dT}$.	$\triangle_v$	q. cals. per gm.
$-20°$	2103	-5.3	0.1777	$+5.6$
$-30°$	2156	-3.2	0.1919	3.5
$-40°$	2178	-0.6	0.1992	0.7
$-50°$	2160	2.0	0.2023	-2.1
$-60°$	2117	5.4	0.2049	-5.5

The curve, in its metastable portion, passes through a point of maximum pressure ($dp/dT = 0$) at $-43°$. At this temperature the heat of transformation of ice I into ice III becomes zero.

Other Phases of Deuterium Oxide. Bridgman[7] has also examined the system deuterium oxide, as far at least as deuterium ice VI and finds that the stable solid phases correspond to those of water, but the deuterium diagram is shifted to the right, that is, at equal pressures the deuterium solid phases occur at higher temperatures. The equilibrium diagram is reproduced in Fig. 14.

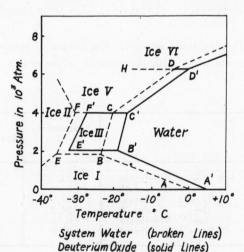

Fig. 14

System Water (broken Lines)
Deuterium Oxide (solid Lines)

Sulphur.

Sulphur exists in two well-known enantiotropic crystalline

forms —— rhombic and monoclinic. At the ordinary temperature, rhombic sulphur can exist unchanged, whereas, on being heated to temperatures somewhat below the melting-point, it passes into the monoclinic variety. On the other hand, at temperatures above 96°, monoclinic sulphur can remain unchanged, whereas at the ordinary temperature it passes slowly into the rhombic form.

If, now, we examine the case of sulphur with the help of the Phase Rule, we see that the following systems are theoretically possible:

I. *Bivariant Systems: One component in one phase.*

    (*a*) Rhombic sulphur.[8]

    (*b*) Monoclinic sulphur.

    (*c*) Sulphur vapour.

    (*d*) Liquid sulphur.

II. *Univariant Systems: One component in two phases.*

    (*a*) Rhombic sulphur and vapour.

    (*b*) Monoclinic sulphur and vapour.

    (*c*) Rhombic sulphur and liquid.

    (*d*) Monoclinic sulphur and liquid.

    (*e*) Rhombic and monoclinic sulphur.

    (*f*) Liquid and vapour.

III. *Invariant Systems: One component in three phases.*

    (*a*) Rhombic and monoclinic sulphur and vapour.

    (*b*) Rhombic sulphur, liquid and vapour.

    (*c*) Monoclinic sulphur, liquid and vapour.

    (*d*) Rhombic and monoclinic sulphur and liquid.

In Fig. 15 is represented the equilibrium diagram for these different systems of sulphur as determined by Tammann,[9] although, as more recent investigation has shown, the data on which the diagram was constructed are not quite accurate and take no consideration of the fact that sulphur exhibits dynamic allotropy and exists in different molecular species (p. 272). The diagram may, however, be taken as representing qualitatively the relations which exist. The more recent investigations of the melting-points of sulphur and of the equilibria which exist in molten sulphur will be discussed later (p. 271).

Point O (Fig. 15) is the triple point for rhombic sulphur — monoclinic sulphur — vapour, and is therefore the point of intersection of the three univariant curves, S_{rh}—V, S_{mon}—V, and S_{rh}—S_{mon}. At this triple point reversible transformation of rhombic and monoclinic sulphur can take place, these two forms of sulphur being enantiotropic. Under atmospheric pressure, the transition point lies at 95.5°.[10] Rhombic sulphur is metastable above, and monoclinic sulphur is metastable below the transition point. Both forms, however, can be obtained in the metastable state, and transformation to the stable form may take place with great slowness (p. 53). The vapour pressure of sulphur between the temperatures of 104° and

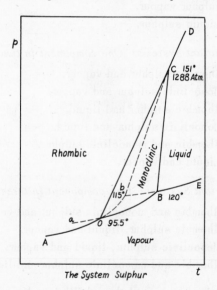

Fig. 15   The System Sulphur

543° has been determined by West and Menzies.[11] Some of the values obtained are given in the following table . (p. 67).

On plotting these numbers one obtains three curves of the type shown in Fig. 1 (p. 20), with points of intersection at about 92° (transition point) and 118° (melting-point). These curves are represented diagrammatically in Fig. 15 by AO, OB, BE.

Curve OC is the transition curve and represents the change of

VAPOUR PRESSURE OF SULPHUR

Temperature in °C.	Pressure in mm.	Temperature in °C.	Pressure in mm.
103.48	0.011	246.84	11.80
117.03	0.023	271.12	23.80
134.44	0.076	328.54	97.40
156.16	0.28	387.55	307.5
175.68	0.72	444.57	760.0
213.20	3.72	478.78	1225.8
219.94	4.56	487.23	1354.7
227.45	6.30	543.08	2689.2

the transition point with pressure. Since the passage of the rhombic into monoclinic sulphur is accompanied by an increase of volume ($\triangle v$ = 0.01395 c.c. per gram), it follows from the principle of Le Chatelier that the transition point is raised by increase of pressure. By means of this value of $\triangle v$ and the heat of transformation, 3.12 cal. per gram, the value of dT/dp can be calculated. Thus, for an increase of pressure of 1 atm. (1033.3 gm. per sq. cm.), we have

$$dT = \frac{368.5 \times 0.014 \times 1033}{3.12 \times 42,670} = 0.04°.$$

The transition point is raised 0.04° by an increase of pressure of 1 atm.[12]

At temperatures above 95.5°, monoclinic sulphur is the stable form. On being heated to 119.25° it melts.[13] This temperature may also be regarded as that of the triple point, S_{mon}—L—V (Point B, Fig. 15).

Since sulphur melts with increase of volume, the melting-point is raised by increase of pressure. The fusion curve BC, therefore, slopes to the right. The transition curve of rhombic and monoclinic sulphur, as we have seen, also slopes to the right, and more so than the fusion curve of monoclinic sulphur. There will, therefore, be a certain pressure and temperature at which the two curves will cut. This point lies at 151°, and a pressure of 1320 kilograms per sq. cm., or about 1288 atm. It, therefore, forms another triple point, at which rhombic and monoclinic sulphur are in equilibrium with liquid sulphur. It is represented in our diagram by the point C.

Beyond this point monoclinic sulphur ceases to exist in a stable condition. At temperatures and pressures above this triple point, rhombic sulphur will be the stable modification, and this fact is of mineralogical interest, because it explains the occurrence in nature of well-formed rhombic crystals. Under ordinary conditions, monoclinic sulphur separates out on cooling fused sulphur, but at temperatures above 151° and under pressures greater than 1288 atm., the rhombic form would be produced.

Metastable Systems. On account of the slowness with which transformation of one crystalline form into the other takes place, it has been found possible to heat rhombic sulphur up to its melting-point, 112.8°. At this temperature, both rhombic sulphur and the liquid are metastable, the vapour pressure being greater than that of solid monoclinic sulphur. This point is represented in Fig. 15 by point *b*. From the diagram it is seen that the melting-point of the metastable is lower than that of the stable form.

Not only has the metastable melting-point of rhombic sulphur been determined, but the metastable fusion curve, *b*C, has also been obtained. This curve must pass through the triple point for rhombic sulphur — monoclinic sulphur — liquid, and on passing this point it becomes a stable fusion curve. The continuation of this curve, therefore, above 151° forms the stable fusion curve of rhombic sulphur (curve CD).

Bivariant Systems. Just as in the case of the diagram of states of water, the areas in Fig. 15 represent the conditions for the stable existence of the single phases: rhombic sulphur in the area to the left of AOCD; monoclinic sulphur in the area OBC; liquid sulphur in the area EBCD; sulphur vapour below the curves AOBE. As can be seen from the diagram, the existence of monoclinic sulphur is limited on all sides, its area being bounded by the curves OB, OC, BC. At any point outside this area, monoclinic sulphur can exist only in a metastable condition.

Other crystalline forms of sulphur have been obtained, so that the existence of other systems of the one component sulphur besides those already described is possible. Of these forms one may mention the readily obtainable but not very familiar mother-of-pearl sulphur or S_{III}.

To obtain this modification, molten sulpnur, after being heated in a test-tube to above 150°, is cooled down to and maintained at a temperature of about 98° (*e.g.* in a water bath). On gently rubbing the inner walls of the tube with a glass rod, the sulphur crystallises in the nacreous form. [14] This form of sulphur is monotropic with respect to rhombic and monoclinic sulphur. At all temperatures up to its melting-point, 106.8°, mother-of-pearl sulphur is metastable.

Tin.

Another substance capable of existing in more than one crystalline form is the metal tin, and although the general behaviour, so far as studied, is analogous to that of sulphur, a short account of the two varieties of tin may be given here, not only on account of their metallurgical interest, but also on account of the importance which the phenomena possess for the employment of this metal in everyday life.

Transition Point. Just as in the case of sulphur, so also in the case of tin, there is a transition point above which the one form, ordinary white tin, and below which the other form, grey tin, is the stable variety. In the case of this metal, the transition point has been found by Cohen and van Lieshout[15] to be 13.2 ± 0.1°. Below this temperature grey tin is the stable form. But, as we have seen in the case of sulphur, the change of the metastable into the stable solid phase occurs with considerable slowness, and this behaviour is found also in the case of tin. Were it not so, we should not be able to use this metal for the many purposes to which it is applied in everyday life; for, during a considerable part of the year the mean temperature of a large part of Europe is below 13°. During that time, therefore, *white tin is, at the ordinary temperature, in a metastable condition.* The change, however, into the stable form at the ordinary temperature, although slow, nevertheless takes place, as is shown by the partial or entire conversion of articles of tin which have lain buried for several hundreds of years. Cases also are recorded of medals and other articles of tin, preserved in museums, which, even in a much shorter period, have suffered damage and disfigurement owing to the formation of wart-like patches

of grey tin; and tin organ pipes have become perforated and use-
less, even after the short space of seven years, owing to the spontaneous transformation of the less stable white into the more stable
grey tin.[16]

The transformation of white to grey tin is greatly retarded by
traces of bismuth, lead, antimony, cadmium, gold and silver, and is
accelerated by traces of aluminium, zinc, cobalt, manganese and
tellurium.[17]

The change of white tin into grey takes place also with increased
velocity in presence of a solution of tin ammonium chloride (pink
salt), which is able to dissolve small quantities of tin. In presence
of such a solution, also, it was found that the temperature at which
the velocity of transformation was greatest was raised to 0°. At
this temperature, white tin, in contact with a solution of tin ammonium chloride and the grey modification, undergoes transformation
to an appreciable extent in the course of a few days.

Besides grey tin and white tin, the crystalline form of which is
tetragonal, there exists a third or rhombic form which is stable
above 202.8°.[18] The brittleness which is developed in tin when
heated above about 200° is due to the change from the tetragonal
to the rhombic form.

Phosphorus.

Phosphorus has long been known to exist in two distinct crystalline forms, white phosphorus and violet phosphorus. When white
phosphorus is heated, transformation into the so-called red phosphorus takes place with appreciable velocity at temperatures above
260°, and the velocity of transformation increases as the temperature is raised. Even at lower temperatures the velocity of transformation is appreciable under the influence of light, or of catalysts
such as iodine and sodium. According to Ipatiev, Frost and
Vedinskii[19] there is no doubt that red phosphorus is actually a mixture of the two pure forms, the white and the ruby-violet, but the
most recent work[20] on the thermal analysis of red phosphorus indicates that red phosphorus, as ordinarily prepared, is a mixture of
four, and probably five, allotropic forms, of which, however, only

one is thermodynamically stable, that is, all transitions are mono-tropic. The stable form (presumably the ruby-violet of Ipatiev) is obtained by heating at 499° for seven hours or at 550° for fifteen minutes. Besides the ordinary white phosphorus which crystallises in the regular system, Bridgman [21] has discovered the existence of a second form of white phosphorus, possibly belonging to the hex-agonal system. These two forms of white phosphorus are enantio-tropic, with a transition point at -76.9° under atmospheric pressure.

From determinations of the vapour pressures of liquid white phosphorus and of solid violet phosphorus [22] it was found that the vapour pressure of the latter is considerably lower than that of the former at the same temperature, as is shown by the values given in the following tables:

VAPOUR PRESSURE OF LIQUID WHITE PHOSPHORUS.

Temperature.	Pressure. Atm.	Temperature.	Pressure Atm.	Temperature.	Pressure. Atm.
169°	0·04	229·8°	0·32	298·6°	1·38
181·3°	0·07	237·9°	0·42	331·8°	2·47
185·5°	0·09	252·0°	0·54	342·0°	2·95
206·9°	0·18	265·5°	0·74	355·7°	3·88
210·0°	0·20	280·5°	1·00	409·3°	7·36

VAPOUR PRESSURE OF VIOLET PHOSPHORUS.

Temperature.	Pressure. Atm.	Temperature.	Pressure. Atm.	Temperature.	Pressure. Atm.
308·5°	0·07	472·5°	3·88	581°	36·49
346°	0·13	486·5°	5·46	587·5°	41·77
379·5°	0·35	505°	8·67	588°	42·10
408·5°	0·79	515°	10·43	589·5°	43·1
433·5°	1·49	522°	11·61	(Triple point.)	
450·5°	2·30	561°	24·3		
463·5°	3·18	578°	34·35		

Throughout the whole range of temperature investigated, white phosphorus must be considered as the less stable (metastable) form, for although it can exist in contact with violet phosphorus for a long period, its vapour pressure is greater than that of the latter, and transformation of the white into the red or violet modification takes place spontaneously. The solubility of white phosphorus in different solvents, moreover, is greater[23] than that of violet phosphorus; and, as we shall find later, the solubility of the metastable form is always greater than that of the stable.

The vapour pressure of fused violet phosphorus has also been determined by Smits and Bokhorst[24] not only at temperatures above the triple point for solid — liquid — vapour, but also at temperatures considerably below this. The values found are contained in the following table:

VAPOUR PRESSURE OF LIQUID VIOLET PHOSPHORUS.

Temperature.	Pressure. Atm.	Temperature.	Pressure. Atm.
504°	23.2	602°	47.0
550°	33.0	621°	53.9
569°	37.6	634°	58.6
581°	41.1		

It will be observed that the measurements of vapour pressure of liquid violet phosphorus do not extend below 504° since it crystallises spontaneously below that temperature, nor those of liquid white phosphorus above 409.3° because the transformation of white to red becomes so rapid above this temperature that the pressure measured is that of the stable (solid) violet or rather of a red mixture containing violet. In other words, there exists a gap of about 100° in the measurements. Nevertheless it can be shown that these two sets of measurements belong to the same curve, if the results are plotted in the form of the equation, $\log p = A - B/T - C \log T$. This was done by Smits and Bokhorst and the fact that both sets of measurements lie on the same smooth curve is accepted as evidence that molten violet and molten white phosphorus give rise to identical liquids (at the same temperature). According to Macrae and Voorhis[25], who determined the vapour pressure of liquid phosphorus in the range 44.1° to 150° with great accuracy, the constants of the equation proposed by Smits and Bokhorst do not reproduce their measurements, but give values from 30 to 60% too low. They therefore propose the equation

$$\log_{10} p(\text{mm. Hg}) = 11.5694 - 2898.1/T - 1.2566 \log_{10} T$$

as representing with reasonable accuracy both their own results and those of Smits and Bokhorst. They agree, however, that the vapour pressure of liquid violet and liquid white phosphorus can be represented by a single smooth curve.

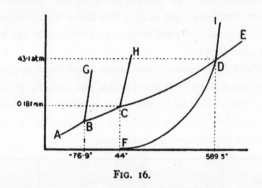

FIG. 16.

Taking into account the different facts set out above, we may represent the equilibrium conditions of the system phosphorus by the diagram, Fig. 16.

In this figure FD represents the conditions of equilibrium of the univariant system, violet phosphorus and vapour, which ends at D, the triple point for solid — liquid—vapour, or the melting-point of violet phosphorus under the pressure of its own vapour. This point, according to Smits and Bokhorst,[26] lies at 589.5° and a pressure of 43.1 atm. According to Marckwald and Helmholz,[26] the melting-point is 592.5° ± 0.5.

This triple point is the point of intersection of the three univariant systems solid—vapour (curve FD), liquid—vapour (curve DE), solid—liquid (curve DI). The values of the vapour pressures of solid and of liquid violet phosphorus are given in the tables on pp. 71 and 72. The curve DE will end abruptly at the critical point of liquid phosphorus. The critical temperature was found by W.A. Wahl[27] to lie at 695° C.; and from the course of the vapour-pressure curve, Smits and Bokhorst[28] have calculated that at this temperature the pressure (critical pressure) would be 82.2 atm. According to Marckwald and Helmholz, the critical temperature is 720.6° at which temperature the pressure would be 101.3 atms., according to the equation of Macrae and Voorhis.

It has been found possible to follow the vaporisation curve of (supercooled) liquid phosphorus downwards to more than 80° below the triple point.

The course of the curve DI has not yet been determined, but from oretical considerations (see p. 22), this curve must slope slightly to the right; that is, increase of pressure will raise the melting-point of violet phosphorus.

As has already been stated, two forms of white phosphorus are known which show a transition point under atmospheric pressure at -76.9°. This is represented by the point B in the equilibrium diagram. This transition point is raised by pressure, as is shown by the following data determined by Bridgman:

Pressure. Kgm. per sq. cm.	Temperature.	Pressure. Kgm. per sq. cm.	Temperature.
1	-76.9°	9,000	32.7°
6000	- 2.4°	11,000	54.4°
8000	+21.4°	12,000	64.4°

Increase of pressure by 1 atm. raises the transition point by about 0.012°. The transition curve, BG, therefore, slopes away from the pressure axis.

When white phosphorus is heated to 44.1°, it melts.[29] At this point, therefore, marked C in our diagram, we have another triple point, white phosphorus—liquid—vapour; the pressure at this point has been calculated to be 0.181 mm.[30] This point is the intersection of three curves, viz. the sublimation curve, vaporisation curve, and the fusion curve of white phosphorus. The fusion curve, CH, has been determined by Tammann[31] and by G. A. Hulett,[32] and it was found that increase of pressure by 1 atm.

raises the melting-point by 0.029°. Some of the values obtained are as follows:

Pressure in atm.	1	50	150	250	300
Melting-point	44.10°	45.50°	48.45°	51.33°	.52.80°

From these data it follows that the melting-point curve, CH, slopes more to the right than does the transition curve, BG. The sublimation curves, AB and BC, for the two crystalline forms of white phosphorus, have not been determined.

As can be seen from the tables of vapour pressures (pp. 71 and 72), the vapour pressure of molten white phosphorus has been determined up to 409°, and that of molten violet phosphorus (supercooled) down to a temperature of 504°, leaving a gap of about 100° in which vapour pressures could not be determined. From the course of the two vapour-pressure curves, however, it is certain that we are dealing with two parts of a continuous vapour-pressure curve;[33] and we must therefore conclude that molten white phosphorus is supercooled violet phosphorus. The vapour pressure curve CDE is therefore continuous.

When white phosphorus is heated at 200° under a pressure of 12,000 kgm. per sq. cm.,[34] or at room temperature under a pressure of 35,000 kgm. per sq. cm.,[35] transformation takes place into another allotropic modification known as black phosphorus. This forms a black crystalline solid, insoluble in carbon disulphide. It can be ignited with difficulty with a match, its ignition temperature in air being about 400°. It differs from the other forms of phosphorus in being a conductor of electricity. Its density is very high, being 2.6 — 2.7 as against 1.83 for white and 2.34 for red phosphorus. All three varieties when heated give a vapour composed of P_4 molecules, which condenses to white phosphorus. At lower temperatures (100° in a vacuum), the vapour of red phosphorus condenses unchanged. These facts seem to indicate that white phosphorus is composed of more or less loosely-bound P_4 molecules, from which the more complex structures of violet and black phosphorus are produced. Measurements of the viscosity of liquid (white) phosphorus indicate that association of the P_4 molecules sets in below 45°[36], and X-ray examination of the crystal structures of black and violet phosphorus shows them to be somewhat similar, the black phosphorus, however, possessing a more metallic structure.[37]

We have already seen in the case of water (p. 61) that the vapour pressure of supercooled water is greater than that of ice, and that therefore it is possible, theoretically at least, by a process of distillation, to transfer the water from one end of a closed tube to the other, and to condense it there as ice. On account of the very small difference between the vapour pressure of supercooled water and ice, this distillation process has not been experimentally realised. In the case of phosphorus, however, where the difference in the vapour pressures is comparatively great, it has been found possible to distil white phosphorus from one part of a closed tube to another, and to condense it there as red phosphorus; and since the vapour pressure of red phosphorus at 350° is less than the vapour pressure of white phosphorus at 200°, it is possible to carry out the distillation from a *colder* part of the tube to a *hotter*, by having white phosphorus at the former and red phosphorus at the latter. Such a process of distillation has been carried out by Troost and Hautefeuille between 324° and 350°.[38]

Liquid Crystals or Anisotropic Liquids.

Phenomena Observed. In 1888 it was discovered by Reinitzer that the two substances, cholesteryl acetate and cholesteryl benzoate, possess the peculiar property of melting sharply at a definite temperature to milky liquids; and that the latter, on being further heated, suddenly become clear, also at a definite temperature. Other substances, more especially p-azoxyanisole and p-azoxyphenetole, were, later, found to possess the same property of having apparently a double melting point. On cooling the clear liquids, the reverse series of changes occurred.

The turbid liquids which were thus obtained were found to possess not only the usual properties of liquids (such as the property of flowing and of assuming a perfectly spherical shape when suspended in a liquid of the same density), but also those properties which had hitherto been observed only in the case of solid crystalline substances, viz. the property of double refraction and of giving interference colours when examined by polarised light; the turbid liquids are *anisotropic*. To such liquids, the optical properties of which were discovered by O. Lehmann, the name *liquid crystals*, or crystalline liquids, was given. Since the term "crystal" implies the existence of a definite space lattice, which is not found in the case of "liquid crystals," it is perhaps better to use the term "anisotropic liquids," or mesomorphous state.

Equilibrium Relations in the Case of Liquid Crystals. Whatever the exact nature of the mesomorphous state may be, it is a well established fact that the transition from the mesomorphous to the amorphous liquid state takes place sharply at a definite temperature when the pressure is constant, and that the temperature of transition varies with the pressure. The equilibrium conditions, therefore, may be represented by a diagram similar to that employed in the case of enantiotropic substances, *e.g.* sulphur 'p. 66). These equilibria have been but little investigated in recent years; and determinations of the vapour pressure in the neighbourhood of the transition point, more especially, are lacking.

In Fig. 17 there is given a diagrammatic representation of the relationships found in the case of *p*-azoxyanisole.[39]

Although the vapour pressure of the substance, in the solid or

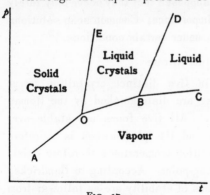

FIG. 17.

liquid state, has not been determined, it will be understood from what we have already learned, that the curves AO, OB, BC, representing the vapour pressure of solid crystals, liquid crystals, isotropic liquid, must have the relative positions shown in the diagram. Point O, the transition point of the solid into the liquid crystals, lies at 118.27°, and the change of the transition point with the pressure is + 0.032° for 1 atm. The transition curve OE slopes, therefore, slightly to the right. The point B, the melting-point of the liquid crystals, lies at 135.85°, and the melting-point is raised 0.0485° by increase of pressure of 1 atm. The curve BD, therefore, also slopes to the right, and more so than the transition curve. In this respect azoxyanisole is different from sulphur.

The areas bounded by the curves represent the conditions for the stable existence of the four single phases, solid crystals, liquid crystals, isotropic liquid, and vapour.

Some of the substances hitherto found to form liquid crystals are:[40]

Substance.	Transition point	Melting-point.
Cholesteryl benzoate	145.5°	178.5°
Azoxyanisole	118.3°	135.9°
Azoxyphenetole	134.5°	168.1°
Condensation product from benzaldehyde and benzidine .	234°	260°
Azine of p-oxyethylbenzaldehyde . . .	172°	196°
Condensation product from p-tolylaldehyde and benzidine	231°	
p-Methoxycinnamic acid	169°	185°

The question of the structure of liquid crystals is one of great complexity[41] but it must not be supposed that they occur only rarely or that they are of no practical importance. Common soap solutions exhibit the mesomorphous state, under certain conditions.[42]

Ammonium Nitrate

Ammonium nitrate exists in five distinct crystalline forms under ordinary pressure. These are distinguished by the Roman numerals I, II, III, IV and V. All five forms are stable over certain ranges of temperature and the phenomenon is therefore that of enantiotropy. Four transition temperatures therefore exist, form I being stable at the melting-point. According to Hendricks, Posnjak and Kracek,[43] the regions of stability are as follows: from the melting point (about 169°) to 125.2°, form I; from 125.2° to 84.2°, form II; from 84.2° to 32.3°, form III; from 32.3° to -18° form IV; from -18° downwards, form V. Bridgman[44] has investigated the effect of pressure on these transition points, that is, he has followed up the transition curves. Fig. 18 reproduces his results schematically. After the discussion of the water diagram, this diagram will be readily comprehensible.

It is interesting to notice that the transition can be greatly altered by admixture with isomorphous impurity, that is, with a substance which is capable of forming solid solutions with at least one of the crystalline modifications of ammonium nitrate. The effect was first noticed by Wallerant[45] and studied in detail by Campbell and Campbell[46]. The cause of the effect is discussed later. (See p. 170).

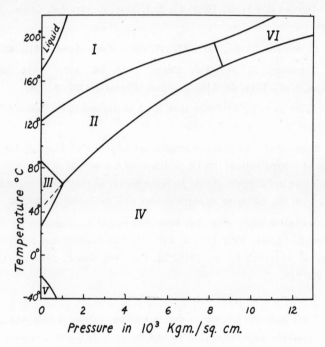

Regions of Existence of the NH_4NO_3
Modifications

Fig. 18

Extensive studies of allotropy under high pressure have been carried out by Bridgman.[47] He thus finds that the following elements possess more than one solid form: bismuth (4 forms), thallium

(3 forms), tellurium (3 forms), gallium (3 forms). The following elements appeared to exist in only one form under pressure: Li, K, Ca, Cd, Mg, Ba, In, C, Ge, Sn, Pb, P (the dense black form), As, Sb, S, Se. Of 90 inorganic compounds, 35 were shown to exhibit allotropy. It must not be supposed, however, that these modifications are only capable of existence under high pressure. On the contrary, Bridgman deduces from the form of the transition line that allotropy (under atmospheric pressure) must be a common phenomenon at absolute zero.

NOTES

1. *Annalen d. Physik*, 1900 [4], **2**, 1, 424; *Z. physikal. Chem.*, 1910, **72**, 609.

2. *Z. anorgan. Chem.*, 1912, **77**, 377; *Proc. Amer. Acad.*, 1912, **47**, 441.

3. Tammann, *Z. physikal. Chem.*, 1913, **84**, 257; 1914, **88**, 57; Bridgman, *ibid.*, 1914, **86**, 513; *J. Chem. Physics*, 1937, **5**, 964.

4. There is some evidence that ice I is dimorphic (Seljakow, *Compt. rend. Acad. Sci.* U. S. S. R., 1936, I, 293).

5. It is unfortunate that the numerology has been confused by the introduction of a hypothetical ice IV, which does not appear to have a real existence: the ice diagram should be renumbered, so that ice V becomes ice IV, etc., but the initiative appears to rest with Professor Bridgman.

6. A similar triple point has been determined by Tammann for phenol (*Annalen d. Physik*, 1902 [4], **9**, 249; "Kristallisieren und Schmelzen", p. 308; *Z. physikal. Chem.*, 1911, **75**, 75.) See also *Z. physikal. Chem.*, 1911, **75**, 733.

7. *J. Chem. Phys.*, 1935, **3**, 601.

8. X-ray analysis has shown that in rhombic sulphur a molecular grouping is definitely detectable (Warren and Burwell, *J. Chem. Physics*, 1935, **3**, 6), the configuration S_8 preserving its identity in the lattice. The S_8 molecule is found to be a puckered 8-atom ring.

9. *Annalen d. Physik*, 1899 [3], **68**, 663.

10. It has been shown that the transition temperature 95.5° refers to an equilibrium mixture of two molecular species, S_λ and S_μ (see p. 272). The transition point of rhombic sulphur, S_λ, free from S_μ, has been found by van

Klooster to be 95.3° (see Kruyt, Z. *physikal. Chem.*, 1912, **81**, 726).

11. *J. Physical Chem.*, 1929, **33**, 1880.

12. Tammann, *Annalen d. Physik*, 1899 [3], **68**, 629; Brönsted, Z. *physikal. Chem.*, 1906, **55**, 380.

13. Smith and Holmes, Z. *physikal. Chem.*, 1903, **42**, 469. See also p. 274.

14. Smith and Carson, Z. *physikal. Chem.*, 1911, **77**, 661.

15. Z. *physikal. Chem.*, 1935, A **173**, 32.

16. Z. *physikal. Chem.*, 1908, **63**, 625.

17. Cohen, Cohen-de Meester and van Lieshout, Z. *physikal. Chem.*, 1935-37, Vols. A **173**, **177**, **178**.

18. Smits and de Leeuw, *Proc. K. Akad. Wetensch. Amsterdam*, 1912, **15**, 676. See also Degens, Z. *anorgan. Chem.*, 1909, **63**, 207; Cohen, Z. *physikal. Chem.*, 1909, **68**, 214.

19. V. N. Ipatiev, A. Frost, and A. V. Vedinskii, *Bull. Soc. Chim.* 1931, **49**, 670.

20. Roth, DeWitt and Smith, J.A.C.S., 1947, **69**, 2881.

21. *J. Amer. Chem. Soc.*, 1914, **36**, 1344.

22. Smits and Bokhurst, *Proc. K. Akad. Wetensch. Amsterdam*, 1914, **16**, 1174; 1914-15, **17**, 678, 962, 973; 1916, **18**, 106; Z. *physikal. Chem.*, 1916, **91**, 249. Cf. also Jolibois, *Compt. rend.* 1909, **149**, 287; 1910, **151**, 382.

23. This is a familiar fact in the case of the solubility in carbon disulphide.

24. *Proc. K. Akad. Wetensch. Amsterdam*, 1914-15, **17**, 678, 962, 973. See also Z. *physikal. Chem.*, 1916, **91**, 249.

25. Macrae and Voorhis, *J. Amer. Chem. Soc.*, 1921, **43**, 547.

26. Smits and Bokhorst, Z. *physikal. Chem.*, 1916, **91**, 249; Marckwald and Helmholz, Z. *anorgan. Chem.*, 1922, **124**, 81. Various values have been obtained for the melting-point of red (violet) phosphorus, varying from 597° to 630° (Chapman, *J. Chem. Soc.*, 1899, **75**, 734; Stock and Gomolka, *Ber.*, 1909, **42**, 4510; Stock and Stamm, *ibid.*, 1913, **46**, 3497).

27. *Meddelanden fran Finska Kemist-Samfundet*, 1913, p. 3.

28. *Z. physikal. Chem.*, 1916, **91**, 249.

29. Smits and Bokhorst, *Z. physikal. Chem.*, 1914, **88**, 608. See also Smits and Leeuw, *ibid.*, 1911, **77**, 367; Boeseken, *Rec. trav. chim.*, 1907, **26**, 289; Macrae and Voorhis, *J. Amer. Chem. Soc.*, 1921, **43**, 547.

30. Macrae and Voorhis, *J. Amer. Chem. Soc.*, 1921, **43**, 547.

31. *Annalen d. Physik*, 1898 [3], **66**, 492.

32. *Z. physikal. Chem.*, 1899, **28**, 666.

33. Smits and Bokhorst, *Z. physikal. Chem.*, 1916, **91**, 249.

34. Bridgman, *J. Amer. Chem. Soc.*, 1914, **36**, 1344; 1916, **38**, 609. The existence of this form was predicted by Linck, *Z. anorgan. Chem.*, 1908, **56**, 393.

35. Bridgman, *Physical Rev.*, 1934, **45**, 844.

36. Dobinski, *Acad. Polonaise Sci. et Lettres*, Ser. A, 1934, p. 103; Campbell and Katz, *J. Amer. Chem. Soc.*, 1935, **57**, 2051.

37. Hultgren, Gingrich and Warren, *J. Chem. Physics*, 1935, **3**, 351; Bridgman, *Rev. Mod. Physics*, 1935, **7**, 20.

38. *Annales Chim. Phys.*, 1874 [5], **2**, 154.

39. Hulett, *Z. physikal. Chem.*, 1899, **28**, 629.

40. Schenck, *Kristallinische Flüssigkeiten und flüssige Kristalle*, p. 8 (Engelmann 1905); Vorländer, *Kristallinisch-flussige Substanzen* (Enke); also Vorländer. *Ber.* 1908, 41, 2033; Z. angew. Chem., 1922, **35**, 249.

41. For reports on symposia on the mesomorphous state, see *Z. Kryst.* 1931, **79**; *Trans. Faraday Soc.*, 1933, **29**, 881. It has been found that liquids may show varying degrees of complexity. Thus there are atomic liquids, such as liquid sodium, where the individual particle is the atom (Randall and Rooksby, *Nature*, 1932, **130**, 473); nematic liquids, where neighbouring molecules are oriented in parallel (Herrmann, Krummacher and May, *Z. Physik*, 1931, **73**, 419); and still more complex smectic liquids, where the molecules are arranged in regular planes which are free to move over one another (Herrmann, *T. Faraday Soc.*, 1933, **29**, 972).

42. Cf. for binary soap solutions, Doscher and Vold, *J. Phys. & Coll. Chem.*, **52**, 97, (1948), and for ternary solutions involving common salt, p. 383 of the present work.

43. *J. Amer. Chem. Soc.*, 1932, **54**, 2767.

44. *Proc. Amer. Acad.*, 1915-16, **51**, 605; *Proc. Nat. Acad. Washington,* 1915, **1**, 530; *Proc. Physical Soc. London*, 1928-29, **41**, 352.

45. *Bull. Soc. Franc. Minéralogie*, 1905, **28**.

46. *Can. J. Research*, 1946, B **24**, 93-108.

47. *Physical Rev.*, 1935, **48**, 893; *Proc. Nat. Acad. Sci.*, 1937, **23**, 202. See also, Bridgman, *The Physics of High Pressure.*

SECTION 3: TWO-COMPONENT SYSTEMS

CHAPTER V

In the preceding pages there has been studied the behaviour of systems consisting of only one component, or systems in which all the phases, whether solid, liquid, or vapour, have the same chemical composition (p. 11). In some cases, as, for example, in the case of phosphorus and sulphur, the component was an elementary substance; in other cases, however, *e.g.* water, the component was a compound. The systems which we now proceed to study are characterised by the fact that the different phases have no longer all the same chemical composition, and cannot, therefore, according to definition, be considered as one-component systems.

In most cases, little or no difficulty will be experienced in deciding as to the *number* of the components, if the rules given on pp. 10 and 11 are borne in mind. If the composition of all the phases, each regarded as a whole, is the same, the system is to be regarded as of the first order, or a one-component system; if the composition of the different phases varies, the system must contain more than one component. If, in order to *express* the composition of all the phases present when the system is in equilibrium, two of the constituents participating in the equilibrium are necessary and sufficient, the system is one of two components. Which two of the possible substances are to be regarded as components will, however, be to a certain extent a matter of arbitrary choice.

The principles affecting the choice of components will best be learned by a study of the examples to be discussed in the sequel.

Different Systems of Two Components.   Applying the Phase Rule

$$F = C - P + 2$$

84

to systems of two components or binary systems (C = 2), we see that in order that the system may be invariant, there must be four phases in equilibrium together. Two components in three phases constitute a univariant, two components in two phases a bivariant system. In the case of systems of one component, the highest degree of variance found was two (one component in one phase); but, as is evident from the formula, there is a higher degree of freedom possible in the case of two-component systems. Two components existing in only one phase constitute a trivariant system, or a system with three degrees of freedom. In addition to the pressure and temperature, therefore, a third variable factor must be chosen, and as such there is taken the *concentration of the components*. In systems of two components, therefore, not only may there be change of pressure and temperature, as in the case of one-component systems, but the concentration of the components in the different phases, or the composition of the phases, may also alter; a variation which does not occur with one-component systems.

Since a two-component system may undergo three possible independent variations, we should require for the graphic representation of all the possible conditions of equilibrium a system of three coordinates in space, three axes being chosen, say, at right angles to one another, and representing the three variables — total pressure, temperature, and concentration of components (Fig. 19). A curve

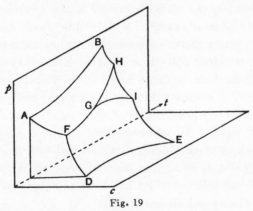

Fig. 19

(*e.g.* AB) in the plane containing the pressure and temperature

axes will then represent the relationship between pressure and temperature, the total concentration remaining unaltered (such a diagram is known as an isopleth or *p-t* diagram); one in the plane containing the pressure and concentration axes (*e.g.* AF or DF), representing the change of pressure with concentration, the temperature remaining 'constant (an isotherm or *p-c* diagram);[1] one in the plane containing the concentration and the temperature axes, the simultaneous change of these two factors at constant pressure being represented (an isobar or *t-c* diagram).[2] Any line (*e.g.* FG, or GH, or GI) situated in the space within the two planes, will represent the simultaneous variation of the three factors —pressure, temperature, concentration. Although we shall at a later point make some use of these solid figures, we shall for the most part consider, in any given case, the variation of only two of the variables pressure, temperature and concentration, and shall employ, therefore, the simpler plane diagram. It should, however, be borne in mind that no one plane diagram can give a complete representation of behaviour.

The number of different systems which can be formed from two components, as well as the number of the different phenomena which can there be observed, is much greater than in the case of one component. In the case of no two substances, however, have all the possible relationships been studied; so that for the purpose of gaining an insight into the varied behaviour of two-component systems, a number of different examples will be discussed, each of which will serve to give a picture of some of the relationships.

Although the strict classification of the different systems according to the Phase Rule would be based on the variability of the systems, the study of the many different phenomena, and the correlation of the comparatively large number of different systems, will probably be rendered easiest by grouping these different phenomena into classes, each of these classes being studied with the help of one or more typical examples. The order of treatment adopted here is, of course, quite arbitrary; but has been selected from considerations of simplicity and clearness.

Classification and Order of Treatment.

For the discussion of the equilibria occurring in two-component systems, the following classification of systems, which also gives the order in which they will be discussed, has been adopted:

A. Two Liquid Phases only.

B. Liquid and Vapour Phases only.
    I. Completely miscible liquids.
    II. Partially miscible liquids.
    III. Immiscible liquids.

C. Solid and Liquid Phases only.
    I. The components are completely miscible in the liquid state.
        (a) The only solid phases are the pure components.
        (b) Compounds are formed with a congruent melting-point.
        (c) Compounds are formed with an incongruent melting-point.
        (d) Solid solutions or mix-crystals are formed.
    II. The components are not completely miscible in the liquid state.

D. Solid and Gas Phases only.
    I. The two components are gases and give rise to a solid.
    II. The two components are volatile solids, which
        (a) do not form compounds,
        (b) do form compounds,
        (c) form solid solutions.
    III. Only one component is volatile.
        (a) Solid compounds can form.
        (b)   i. Solid solutions can form but not solid compounds.
              ii. Solid solutions as well as solid compounds can form.
              iii. Two series of solid solutions can form.

E. Combinations of the preceding.

F. Solid, liquid and gas phases coexist.

G. Dynamic allotropy and pseudobinary systems.

Solutions. In the case of the equilibria studied in the previous chapters, the different phases consisted of a single substance of definite composition or a definite chemical individual.

But this invariability of the composition is by no means imposed by the Phase Rule; on the contrary, it will be found that in the equilibria now to be studied the participation of phases of variable composition is in no way excluded. To such phases of variable composition there is applied the term *solution*. A solution, therefore, is defined as *a phase of variable composition*.

It will be understood from the definition just given that the term solution is not restricted to any particular physical state of substances, but includes within its range not only the liquid, but also the gaseous and solid states. We may therefore have solutions of gases in liquids, and of gases in solids; of liquids in liquids or in solids; of solids in liquids, or of solids in solids. Solutions of gases in gases are, of course, also possible; since, however, gas solutions never give rise to more than one phase, their treatment does not come within the scope of the Phase Rule, which deals with heterogeneous equilibria.

It should also be emphasised that the definition of solution given above neither creates nor recognises any distinction between solvent and dissolved substance (solute); and, indeed, a too persistent use of these terms and the attempt permanently to label the one or other of two components as the solvent or the solute, can only obscure the true relationships and aggravate the difficulty of their interpretation. In all cases it should be remembered that one is dealing with equilibria between two components (we confine our attention in the first instance to such), the solution being constituted of these components in variable and varying amounts. The change from the case where the one component is in great excess (ordinarily called the solvent) to that in which the other component predominates, may be quite gradual, so that it is difficult or impossible to say at what point the one component ceases to be the solvent and becomes the solute. The adoption of this stand-point need not, however, preclude one from employing the conventional terms solvent and solute in ordinary language, especially when reference is made only to some particular condition of equilibrium of the system, when the concentration of the two components in the solution is widely different.

NOTES

1. Referred to also as the p-x diagram, where x is the relative amount of one of the components.

2. Also called the t-x diagram.

CHAPTER VI

A. SYSTEMS CONSISTING OF TWO LIQUID PHASES ONLY

When mercury and water are brought together, the two liquids remain side by side without mixing. Strictly speaking, mercury undoubtedly dissolves to a certain extent in the water, and water no doubt dissolves, although to a less extent, in the mercury; the amount of substance passing into solution is, however, so minute, that it may, for all practical purposes, be left out of account, so long as the temperature does not rise much above the ordinary.[1] On the other hand, if alcohol and water be brought together, complete miscibility takes place, and one homogeneous solution is obtained. Whether water be added in increasing quantities to pure alcohol, or pure alcohol be added in increasing amount to water, at no point, at no degree of concentration, is a system obtained containing more than one liquid phase. At the ordinary temperature, water and alcohol can form only two phases, liquid and vapour. If, however, water be added to ether, or if ether be added to water, solution will not occur to an indefinite extent; but a point will be reached when the water or the ether will no longer dissolve more of the other component, and a further addition of water on the one hand, or ether on the other, will cause the formation of two liquid layers, one containing excess of water, the other excess of ether. We shall, therefore, expect to find all grades of miscibility, from almost perfect immiscibility to perfect miscibility, or miscibility in all proportions. In cases of complete immiscibility the components do not affect one another, and the system therefore remains unchanged. We shall concern ourselves first with the second and third cases, viz. with cases of complete and of partial miscibility. There is no essential difference between the two classes, for, as we see, the one passes into the other with change of temperature. The formal separation into two groups is based on the miscibility relations at ordinary temperatures.

Ideal Solutions and Raoult's Law. When we seek for the reason why some liquid pairs are miscible in all proportions (consolute), while others are only partially miscible or completely immiscible, we find a close connection with the applicability or non-applicability of Raoult's law. According to this law, the partial pressure of a liquid in a liquid mixture is connected with its vapour pressure in the pure state, at the same temperature, by the relation

$$p_A = N_A p_A^o ,$$

where p_A is the partial pressure of A, p_A^o its vapour pressure in the pure state, and N_A its mole fraction. If both constituents of a binary liquid mixture obey Raoult's law, the mixture is said to be ideal. If the actual partial pressure of one component is greater than that calculated from Raoult's law, that component is said to exhibit a positive deviation from Raoult's law. If one component of a binary mixture exhibits positive deviation from Raoult's law, then it is theoretically necessary that the other component must also exhibit positive deviation, so that the system as a whole may be said to deviate positively from Raoult's law. As will be seen when the vapour phase is considered (Chapter VII), either positive or negative deviations from Raoult's law tend to produce what may be called abnormalities on the vapour pressure and boiling point curves of liquid mixtures. When the positive deviations are very large, the phenomenon of partial miscibility occurs.

Partial or Limited Miscibility. In accordance with the Phase Rule, a pure liquid in contact with its vapour constitutes a univariant system. If, however, a small quantity of a second substance is added, which is capable of dissolving in the first, a bivariant system will be obtained; for there are now two components and, as before, only two phases—the homogeneous liquid solution and the vapour. At constant temperature, therefore, both the composition of the solution and the pressure of the vapour can undergo change; or, if the composition of the solution remains unchanged, the pressure and the temperature can alter. If the second (liquid) component is

added in increasing amount, the liquid will at first remain homogeneous, and its composition and pressure will undergo a continuous change; when, however, the concentration has reached a definite value, solution no longer takes place, and two liquid phases
are produced. Since there are now three phases present, two liquid phases and vapour, the system is univariant; at a given temperature, therefore, the concentration of the components in the two
liquid phases, as well as the vapour pressure, must have definite
values. Addition of one of the components, therefore, cannot alter
the concentrations or the pressure, but can only cause a change in
the relative amounts of the phases.

In actual practice it is often, though not always, convenient to
operate under constant (atmospheric, for instance) pressure. Under
these circumstances, it is said that the application of a pressure
greater than the vapour pressure causes the vapour phase to disappear, thus reducing the number of phases by one but, since the
use of a fixed arbitrarily chosen pressure has used up one degree
of freedom, the freedom of the system remains the same as if the
system were in equilibrium with its vapour. Obviously, however, if
the constant pressure is produced, as it usually is, by having an indifferent gas present, the vapour phase still exists under its own
partial pressure and, again, the same degree of freedom results since
the equilibrium (partial) pressure is now variable. Nevertheless,
there is a fundamental difference between the two cases in one of
which the vapour phase is actually caused to disappear (for instance
by means of a solid piston pressing on the liquid surface) and that
in which the total pressure is kept constant (for instance, by having
air present under the piston) but the partial pressure of the system
allowed to vary. A somewhat similar difference exists between the
cases of a pure liquid in contact only with its own vapour, and in
contact with its own vapour and an indifferent gas. In the latter
case, a well-known thermodynamic equation shows that the two
vapour pressures are not the same and may even differ considerably
if the pressure of the indifferent gas is very great. In the same way,
with mixtures of liquids the pressures (and compositions) are not
quite the same under constant total pressure as they would be under

variable equilibrium pressure, but as with the analogous pure liquid vapour pressure, the difference is quite negligible, unless either the constant external pressure or the vapour pressure is very great.

The two liquid phases can be regarded, the one as a solution of the component I. in component II., the other as a solution of component II. in component I. If the vapour phase be removed and the pressure on the two liquid phases be maintained constant (say, at atmospheric pressure), the system will still be univariant, and to each temperature there will correspond a definite concentration of the components in the two liquid phases; and addition of excess of one will merely alter the relative amounts of the two solutions. As the temperature changes, the composition of the two solutions will change, and there will therefore be obtained two solubility curves, one showing the solubility of component I. in component II., the other showing the solubility of component II. in component I. Since heat may be either evolved or absorbed when one liquid dissolves in another, the solubility may diminish or increase with rise of temperature (principle of Le Chatelier, p. 22). The two solutions which at a given temperature coexist in equilibrium are known as *conjugate solutions*.

Phenol and Water. When phenol is added to water at the ordinary temperature, solution takes place, and a homogeneous liquid is produced. When, however, the concentration of the phenol in the solution has risen to about 7 per cent., phenol ceases to be dissolved; and a further addition of it causes the formation of a second liquid phase, which consists of excess of phenol and a small quantity of water. In ordinary language it may be called a solution of water in phenol. If now the temperature is raised, this second liquid phase will disappear, and a further amount of phenol must be added in order to produce a separation of the liquid into two layers. In this way, by increasing the amount of phenol and noting the temperature at which the two layers disappear, the so-called solubility curve of phenol in water can be obtained.[2] The solubility increases with rise of temperature.

In a similar manner the solubility of water in liquid phenol can be determined, and in this case also, it is found, the solubility increases with rise of temperature.

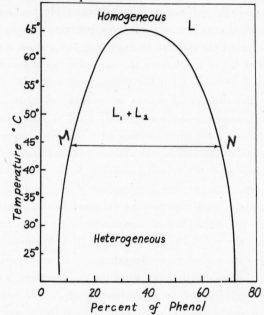

Fig. 20

Since, with rise of temperature, the concentration of water in the phenol layer, and, similarly, the concentration of phenol in the aqueous layer increase, the composition of the two solutions must become more and more nearly the same, and at a certain temperature the two solutions become identical. At this point, the two liquid solutions pass into one homogeneous solution. The temperature, however, at which two phases become identical is known as a critical temperature, and, accordingly, the temperature at which two conjugate solutions become identical is known as the *critical solution temperature*. The composition of the solution at this point may be called the *critical composition*. One may also speak of the con-solute concentration of the solution.

The mutual solubility of phenol and water has been determined by a number of investigators.[3] The values obtained by Campbell and Campbell, who determined by direct analysis the compositions of conjugate solutions, are given in the following table and represented diagrammatically in Fig. 20. The compositions of a pair of conjugate solutions have been joined by a line, known as a tie-line.

The use of such tie-lines to designate compositions of co-existing phases is common throughout Phase Rule work. The region in which only one liquid phase exists is designated "homogeneous", while the "heterogenous" region refers to the coexistence of two liquid phases.

Phenol and Water.

C_1 and C_2 are the percentage amounts of phenol by weight in the two layers, while the term "mean" gives the arithmetic mean of C_1 and C_2.

Temperature.	C_1	C_2	Mean.
2.6°	6.9	75,6	41.3
23.9°	7.8	71.2	39.5
29.6°	7.5	70.7	39.1
32.5°	8.0	69.0	38.5
38.8°	7.8	66.6	37.2
45.7°	9.7	64.4	37.1
50.0°	11.5	62.0	36.8
55.5°	12.0	60.0	36.0
59.8°	13.6	57.7	35.7
60.5°	14.0	55.5	34.8
61.8°	15.0	54.0	34.5
65.0°	18.5	50.0	34.3

On plotting these results, as shown in Fig. 20, the critical solution temperature is found to be 66.8°, but the critical concentration is not so easily found since the curve is very flat in the neighbourhood of the critical temperature. If, however, we plot the figures given under the heading "mean", that is the mean values of the compositions of the two conjugate solutions, a straight line is always obtained, which passes through the critical composition at the critical temperature. In this way the value 34.5 per cent phenol is obtained for the critical composition. This "law of the rectilinear diameter" as applied to partially miscible liquid pairs is obviously an analogue or extension of the corresponding law of Cailletet and Mathias on critical phenomena in the liquid-gas equilibrium. At any temperature below the critical solution temperature, two conjugate solutions containing water and phenol in different concentration can exist together; at all temperatures above the critical solution temperature, only homogeneous solutions of phenol and water can be obtained. Above the critical solution temperature, phenol and water are miscible in all proportions.

From Fig. 20 it is easy to predict the effect of bringing together water and phenol in any given quantities at any temperature. When phenol and water are brought together in amounts and at any temperature represented by a point in the area enclosed by the solubility curve, separation into two liquid layers will take place, whereas, when the total composition of the mixture and the temperature are represented by a point lying outside the solubility curve, only one homogeneous solution will be formed.

An important practical question is: given a mixture of fixed composition and temperature lying within the region of heterogeneity, what are the compositions of the conjugate liquids and how much of each is produced? The former question is easily answered: it is only necessary to draw the tie-line through the plotted point, parallel to the axis of composition and the ordinates corresponding to the points of intersection of the tie-line with the boundary curve give the compositions of the two layers. The latter question can be answered graphically by measuring the distances along the tie-line from the plotted point to the boundary curve. Then the relative proportions of the two solutions are inversely as these intercepts. It is probably more accurate, however, to do this arithmetically by application of the mixture rule. For example, suppose we have a mixture of phenol and water, whose total composition is 50.0 per cent phenol, at a temperature of 38.8°. Then the data of the table, or Fig. 20, indicate that the two liquids formed have the respective compositions 7.8 and 66.6 per cent phenol. Let x be the weight of aqueous layer in 100 grams of the mixture and therefore $100 - x$ the weight of phenolic layer. Then obviously

$$x(7.8/100) + (100 - x)(66.6/100) = 50$$

Whence x results as 28.3, that is, 100 grams of total mixture give rise to 28.3 grams of aqueous layer and 71.7 grams of phenolic layer, or 28.3 $\times$ 0.078 = 2.2 grams of phenol are present in the aqueous layer and 71.7 × 0.666 = 47.8 grams of phenol in the phenolic layer.

It should be noted that diagrams such as Fig. 20 do not give a complete representation of the behaviour of the system, since any liquid, if cooled sufficiently, will eventually solidify. Except where the region of partial miscibility is bounded by a closed curve, the curve of partial miscibility will eventually with falling temperature be intersected by curves representing the stable existence of solid phases. This is the case with phenol — water, where the partial miscibility curve is limited on both sides by the occurrence of solid phenol. At a still lower temperature, the eutectic temperature, ice also makes its appearance. In addition, in the truly (thermodynamically) stable system, a solid compound of phenol and water exists[4], although this compound never makes its appearance unless special precautions are taken. All this will be unintelligible to the reader until he has read the later sections, but the question is raised here because students, studying a partial miscibility curve in the laboratory, frequently ask "where the curve gets to", with falling temperature.

Methylethylketone and Water. In the case of phenol and water, the solubility of each component in the other increases continuously with the temperature. There are, however, cases where a maximum or minimum of solubility is found, *e.g.* methylethylketone and water. The curve which represents the equilibria between these two sub-

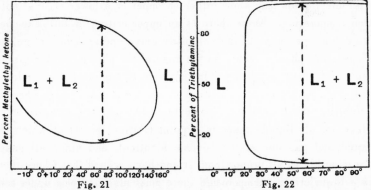

Fig. 21   Fig. 22

stances is given in Fig. 21, which shows clearly the occurrence of a minimum in the solubility of the ketone in water, and also a minimum (at about 10°) in the solubility of water in methylethylketone. Minima of solubility have also been found in other cases.

Triethylamine and Water. Although in most of the cases studied the solubility of one liquid in another increases with rise of temperature, this is not so in all cases. Thus, at temperatures below 18°, triethylamine and water mix together in all proportions; but, on raising the temperature, the homogeneous solution becomes turbid and separates into two layers. In this case, therefore, the critical solution temperature is found in the direction of lower temperature, not in the direction of higher.[5] This behaviour is clearly shown by the graphic representation in Fig. 22, and also by the numbers in the following table:

TRIETHYLAMINE AND WATER.

Temperature.	C_1 per cent.	C_2 per cent.
70°	1·6	—
50°	2·9	—
30°	5·6	96
25°	7·3	95·5
20°	15·5	73
± 18·5°	± 30	± 30

Completely Closed Solubility Curves. From the preceding discussion it will be clear that the solubility curve of two partially miscible liquids may show either an upper or a lower critical solution temperature. Where there is an upper critical solution temperature, the open ends of the solubility curve end at invariant points, where solid phases occur; in the case of the phenol—water system the solid phase is phenol. In the case of liquids having a lower critical temperature, the question arises: What will happen when the solubility determinations are extended to higher temperatures? Since for all liquids there is a point (critical point) at which the liquid and gaseous states become identical, and since all gases are miscible in all proportions, it has been argued that where there is a lower critical temperature there must also be some upper temtemperature at which the liquids will become completely miscible. Whether or not this argument is sound, the converse is not: there is no reason to assume that where an upper critical solution temperature exists there must also exist a lower one. Nevertheless, a number of systems are known in which the form of the concentration-temperature curve is that of a closed ring, that is, these systems have both upper and lower critical solution temperatures. Thus, nicotine and water are completely miscible at temperatures below 60.° and above 210° (Fig. 23),[6] and closed solubility curves are also given by the liquids, water— β-picoline, water—methyl piperidine, glycerol—guiacol, glycerol—benzylethylamine, etc.[7]

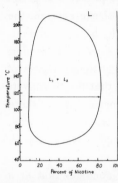

Fig. 23

The view that the general form of the concentration-temperature curve is that of a closed ring is supported by the fact that pairs of liquids which, under atmospheric pressure, give curves exhibiting only a lower or an upper critical solution temperature, give closed-ring solubility curves when the pressure is increased (p. 100). Thus, under a pressure of 150 atmospheres, methylethylketone and water give a closed-ring solubility curve with critical solution temperatures at -6° and 133°.[8]

With regard to the closed end of the curve, it may be said that it is continuous. The critical solution point is not the intersection of two curves, for such a break in the continuity of the curve could occur only if there were some discontinuity in one of the phases. No such discontinuity exists. The curve is, therefore, not to be considered as two solubility curves cutting at a point, but a curve of equilibrium between two phases which are undergoing continuous change.[9]

Influence of Pressure on the Critical Solution Temperature. If the pressure is kept constant and sufficiently large to prevent the formation of vapour, the system of two components existing in two (liquid) phases, has one degree of freedom, since one degree of freedom is used up in the assignment of an arbitrary fixed pressure. Hence composition becomes a function of temperature only and the behaviour of the system can be represented by a plane curve as has been done in the preceding sections. If, however, the condition of constant pressure is given up, then, provided the pressure is always great enough to prevent the formation of vapour, the system exhibits a variance of two, thus, for instance, composition becomes a function of both temperature and pressure. This means that if a third axis, of pressure, is added to the plane diagram, the equilibrium curve becomes an equilibrium surface on which tie-lines joining points of equal temperature and pressure will give the compositions of equilibrium solutions. The plane diagram is an isobaric section of such a model. Since the system is a condensed one, that is, it does not contain the gas phase, the Clapeyron equation shows that the effect of pressure is not great, unless the pressure is great.

At the critical solution temperature, in an isobaric section, the two liquid phases become identical and it might be thought that, since there is now only one liquid layer, the degree of freedom should increase, but this is fallacious. The additional degree of freedom is disposed of by the arbitrary condition that the two layers must have identical composition. The critical composition is therefore a function of both temperature and pressure or, in other words, both the critical temperature and the critical composition vary with pressure.

Another way of looking at the matter is to consider that at a temperature infinitesimally lower than the critical solution temperature two liquids exist, whose compositions are not identical. The arbitrary condition is then given up and the point, unlike any other point on the pressure—temperature—composition surface, corresponds to univariant behaviour.

The change of the critical solution temperature with the pressure depends, according to the principle of Le Chatelier and the equation of Clapeyron, on the change of volume which occurs when one of the components in the fused state is added to the nearly saturated solution. [10] It has been made the subject of experimental investigation by Kohnstamm and Timmermans, [11] and some of the results obtained are given in the following table (p. 101)::

From the following table it is clear that the lower critical solution temperature is raised, and the upper critical solution temperature is lowered, by increase of pressure. Under a pressure of 830

WATER AND *Sec.*-BUTYL ALCOHOL.

Pressure in kgm. per sq. cm.	Lower critical solution temperature.	$\frac{dt}{dp}$ per kgm.	Upper Critical solution temperature.	$\frac{dt}{dp}$ per kgm.
1	-12		$113 \cdot 8°$	$- 0 \cdot 071$
100	$5 \cdot 3°$	$> + 0 \cdot 1375$		
120			$105 \cdot 3°$	$- 0 \cdot 041$
200	$17 \cdot 8°$	$+ 0 \cdot 123$		
300	$24 \cdot 8°$	$+ 0 \cdot 070$		
500	$36 \cdot 7°$	$+ 0 \cdot 059$		
600	$42 \cdot 7°$	$+ 0 \cdot 060$	$85 \cdot 8°$	$- 0 \cdot 045$
700	$49 \cdot 6°$	$+ 0 \cdot 069$	$81 \cdot 3°$	$- 0 \cdot 078$
800	$58 \cdot 6°$	$+ 0 \cdot 090$	$73 \cdot 5°$	
830	$65°$		$65°$	

kgm. per sq. cm. the two critical solution points coincide. Under pressures higher than this, complete miscibility exists at all temperatures. A similar behaviour is found in the case of water and methylethylketone.

Whereas a lower critical solution temperature is always raised by increase of pressure, an upper critical solution temperature may be either raised or lowered. In the case of water and *sec.*-butyl alcohol, water and methylethylketone, water and isobutyric acid, the upper critical solution temperature is lowered by increase of pressure; in the case of water and phenol it is raised.

Influence of Foreign Substances on the Critical Solution Temperature. For a given pressure, the critical solution temperature is, as we have seen, a perfectly defined point. It is, however, altered to a very marked extent by the addition of a foreign substance (impurity), which dissolves either in one or in both of the partially miscible liquids. Although these systems are really three-component systems, and will be discussed more fully at a later point, the effect of small additions of a substance to a system of two liquid components is of such practical importance, that a brief discussion of the regularities observed may be given here.[13]

When the third substance *dissolves in only one of the two liquids,* the mutual solubility of the latter is diminished, and the temperature at which the system becomes homogeneous is raised in the case of liquids having an upper critical solution temperature, and lowered in the case of liquids having a lower critical solution temperature. The elevation (or the lowering) of temperature depends not only on the nature and amount of the added substance, but also on the composition of the liquid mixture. When the two liquids are present in the proportions of the critical composition, it is found that, for concentrations of the addendum (non-electrolyte) less than about 0.1 molar, the elevation (or depression) of the critical solution temperature is nearly proportional to the amount added. The elevation (or depression) of the critical solution temperature for small equi-molecular quantities of different substances is, however, not constant, but depends on the nature of the substance added.[14] In the following tables are given the values for the elevation of the critical solution temperature of phenol and water by naphthalene (soluble only in phenol) and by potassium chloride (soluble only in water). E represents the "molecular elevation" of the critical solution temperature:

WATER—PHENOL—NAPHTHALENE.				WATER—PHENOL—POTASSIUM CHLORIDE.			
Concentration of naphthalene.		Critical solution temperature.	E.	Concentration of potassium chloride.		Critical solution temperature.	E.
Molar.	Per cent.			Molar.	Per cent.		
—	—	65·3°	—	—	—	65·3°	—
0·0148	0·190	68·5°	216·2°	0·146	1·09	77·4°	83°
0·0343	0·440	72·6°	212·8°	0·292	2·18	87·3°	75°
0·059	0·76	77·6°	207·7°	0·410	3·06	94·0°	70°
0·081	1·04	82·0°	206·4°				
0·124	1·59	89·6°	196·1°				

According to Duckett and Patterson,[15] the elevation of the critical solution temperature of phenol and water by salts is the sum of two values, depending on the ions; and the anions and cations may be arranged, according to their influence, in a series which is almost identical with the Hofmeister series (for the coagulation of egg albumin).

Owing to the fact that the influence of the added substance on the saturation temperature of two liquids depends on the composition of the mixture, the solubility curve becomes distorted, and the maximum temperature of saturation is no longer shown by the system in which the two liquids are present in amounts corresponding with the critical composition (Fig. 24). This point will be further discussed in connection with three-component systems.

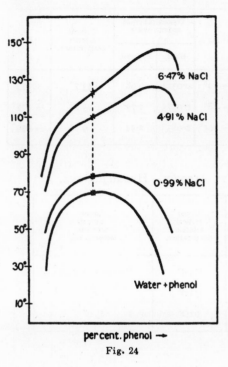

percent. phenol →

Fig. 24

When the third substance *dissolves in both the liquids*, the effect on the critical solution temperature will depend on the relative solubility of the added substance in the two liquids. If the solubility in the two liquids is very different, an upper critical solution temperature may still be raised, and a lower critical solution temperature may be depressed, although to a much less extent than when the added substance is, soluble in only one of the liquids. When, however, the solubility of the addendum in the two liquids is of the same order, the mutual solubility of the liquids will be increased. Consequently, an upper critical solution temperature will be lowered, and a lower critical solution temperature will be raised, as is shown by the numbers in the following tables (p. 104).

The very large effect produced by sodium oleate has been applied industrially to the production, at the ordinary temperature, of a highly concentrated solution of tar-acids (phenol and cresols), commonly known as lysol.

WATER—PHENOL—SUCCINIC ACID.

Concentration of succinic acid.		Critical solution temperature.	E.
Moles.	Per cent.		
0·190	2·25	51·6°	− 72°
0·321	3·81	40·3°	− 78°
0·685	8·09	− 8·0°	− 105°

WATER—PHENOL—SODIUM OLEATE.

Concentration of sodium oleate.		Critical solution temperature.	E.
Moles.	Per cent.		
0·0324	0·98	43·7°	− 673°
0·0575	1·75	25·8°	− 687°
0·083	2·51	9·2°	− 679°

WATER—*Sec.*-BUTYL ALCOHOL—HYDROQUINONE.

Concentration of hydroquinone.		Upper critical solution temperature.	Lower critical solution temperature.
Moles.	Per cent.		
0	0	113·5°	Below eutectic
0·639	7·03	71·0°	16·5°
0·747	8·21	62·2°	25·0°

NOTES

1. That mercury does dissolve in water can be argued from analogy, say, with mercury and bromonaphthalene. At the ordinary temperature these two liquids appear to be quite insoluble the one in the other, but at a temperature of 280° the mercury dissolves in appreciable quantity; for on heating a tube containing bromonaphthalene over mercury the latter sublimes *through* the liquid bromonaphthalene and condenses on the upper surface of the tube.

2. See Findlay, *Practical Physical Chemistry* (Longmans). On cooling the homogeneous solution, a turbidity generally makes its appearance quite sharply at the temperature at which the line representing the composition of the solution cuts the solubility curve. Supersaturation may,

however, take place, and has been observed in the case of nitrobenzene and water, and carbon disulphide and water (Davis, *J. Amer. Chem. Soc.*, 1916, **38**, 1166). See also Flaschner, *Z. physikal. Chem.*, 1908, **62**, 493; Gürtler, *Z. anorgan. Chem.*, 1904, **40**, 225.

3. Timmermans, *Z. physikal. Chem.*, 1907, **58**, 184; *J. Chim. Phys.*, 1923, **20**, 491; Hill and Malisoff, *J. Amer. Chem. Soc.*, 1926, **48**, 918; Campbell and Campbell, *J. Amer. Chem. Soc.*, 1937, **59**, 2481.

4. Rhodes and Markley, *J. Physical Chem.*, 1921, **25**, 530.

5. A similar behaviour is found in the case of diethylamine and water (R. T. Lattey, *Phil. Mag.*, 1905 [6], **10**, 397). See also Rothmund, *Z. physikal. Chem.*, 1898, **26**, 433; Flaschner, *ibid.*, 1908, **62**, 493.

6. Hudson, *Z. physikal. Chem.*, 1904, **47**, 113.

7. Flaschner, *J. Chem. Soc.*, 1909, **95**, 668; Flaschner and McEwen, *ibid.*, 1908, **93**, 1000; McEwen, *ibid.*, 1923, **123**, 2284; Parvatiker and McEwen, *ibid.*, 1924, **125**, 1484; Cox and Cretcher, *J. Amer. Chem. Soc.*, 1926, **48**, 451; Cox, Nelson and Cretcher, *ibid.*, 1927, **49**, 1080.

8. Kohnstamm and Timmermans, *Proc. K. Akad. Wetensch. Amsterdam*, 1913, **15**, 1021.

9. For a discussion of the equilibria in the case of partially miscible liquids, see Büchner, *Z. physikal. Chem.*, 1906, **56**, 257.

10. See Timmermans, *Bull. Soc. Chim. Belg.*, 1909, **23**, 433; *Acad. R. Belg., Classes des Sci.*, 1919, p. 753.

11. Kohnstamm and Timmermans, *Proc. K. Akad., Wetensch. Amsterdam*, 1913, **15**, 1021; Timmermans, *Arch. Néerland.*, 1922 [3], **6**, 127; *Jour. Chim. Phys.*, 1922, 20, 491.

12. Under atmospheric pressure, water and *sec.*-butyl alcohol are only partially miscible at all temperatures down to the freezing-point of the solution, namely, – 8.45°. A lower critical solution temperature makes its appearance only when the pressure is increased.

13. See Timmermans, *Z. physikal. Chem.*, 1907, **58**, 129; Schükareff, *ibid.*, 1910, **71**, 90.

14. Timmermans, *Z. physikal. Chem.*, 1907, **58**, 129; Drucker, *Rec. trav. chim.*, 1923, **42**, 552; Boutari and Nabot, *Compt. rend.*, 1923, **176**, 1618; Bailey, *J. Chem. Soc.*, 1923, **123**, 2579; Wagner, *Z. physikal.*

Chem., 1928, **132**, 273; Dolique, *Compt. rend.*, 1932, **194**, 289.

15. *J. Physical Chem.*, 1925, **29**, 294. See also Patterson and Duckett, *J. Chem. Soc.*, 1925, **127**, 624; Carrington, Hickson and Patterson, *ibid.*, 1925, **127**, 2544; Howard and Patterson, *ibid.*, 1926, pp. 2787, 2791; Cernatescu and Papafil, *Z. physikal. Chem.*, 1927, **125**, 331; Cernatescu, *ibid.*, 1928; **133**, 31.

CHAPTER VII

B. SYSTEMS CONSISTING OF LIQUID AND VAPOUR PHASES ONLY

Henry's Law. When a gas dissolves in a liquid, a two component system is existing in two phases and it is therefore bivariant. If the temperature is fixed, the system becomes isothermally univariant, that is, the composition of the solution or solubility still varies with the pressure: this is a well known experimental fact. The direction of variation can be predicted from the principle of Le Chatelier. Since the act of solution of a gas in a liquid is necessarily accompanied by a diminution of volume, the effect of pressure will always be to increase the solubility of a gas in a liquid. The quantitative variation is covered by Henry's Law. This law states that the mass of gas dissolved by a fixed volume of liquid at a fixed temperature is proportional to the pressure or, in symbols,

$$m = kp$$

where m is the mass of gas in grams dissolved by the fixed volume of liquid, p is the pressure, and k a constant characteristic of a given gas and a given solvent at a given temperature, and known as the Henry's law constant. The constant k must be determined experimentally. Since the volume of a gas is approximately inversely proportional to the pressure, Henry's law may be stated in the form: The volume of a gas, measured under the experimental conditions, dissolved by a given mass (or volume) of liquid is independent of the pressure. The following table (p. 108) for carbon dioxide in water at $25°$ illustrates the law.[1] The constancy of the ratio V_2/P shows that Henry's law is valid.

The solubility of a gas in a liquid is expressed either in terms of the solubility coefficient (S), *i.e.* the volume of gas, measured under the conditions of the experiment, absorbed by one volume of the liquid (see second column), or of the absorption coefficient[2] (α), *i.e.*

Pressure in Milli-metres of Mercury. (P)	Volume of Gas, measured under the Experimental Conditions, Dissolved by 1 Volume of Water (V_1).	Volume of Gas, measured at S.T.P., Dissolved by 1 Volume of Water (V_2).	V_2/P $\times 10^4$
271	0.825	0.270	9.95
495	0.825	0.492	9.93
755	0.826	0.751	9.95
927	0.826	0.922	9.96
1211	0.825	1.205	9.95
1350	0.824	1.343	9.95

the volume of gas reduced to S.T.P., dissolved by one volume of liquid under a pressure of one atmosphere. The two coefficients are related through the expression

$$S = \alpha T/273$$

where T is the absolute temperature. For gases which obey Henry's law, the value both of the solubility coefficient and of the absorption coefficient is independent of the pressure. Strictly speaking, Henry's law is an ideal gas law and therefore only applicable without error to actual gases at very low pressures. At high pressures the law becomes less exact, as shown by the variation of the proportionality constant. As with other ideal gas laws, the higher the temperature and the lower the pressure the more exactly the law is obeyed.

Henry's law holds fairly accurately for slightly soluble gases but marked deviations are found with the very soluble gases, *e.g.* ammonia, hydrogen chloride, etc., in water. Under constant pressure the solubility of a gas will vary with the temperature and usually in the sense that the solubility diminishes with rise of temperature. There are, however, numerous exceptions to this, particularly when the solvent is not water.

It is often stated that the cause of pronounced deviation from Henry's law is to be sought in chemical combination of the solute gas with the solvent. This is not true, since it is easy to show that the occurrence of compound formation will have no influence upon Henry's law, as far as constancy of the ratio of concentrations of the gas in the two phases is concerned.[3] On the other hand, if the solute (the gas) has a different molecular weight in the two phases, *i.e.* if it associates or dissociates in one phase but not in the other, obedience to Henry's law cannot be expected. In fact, Henry's law is a special case of the distribution law, according to which, at constant temperature, there is a constant ratio of distribution between two phases in equilibrium, for each molecular species, independent of the presence of other types of molecule, whether they are in chemical equilibrium with the former or not.[4]

Ideal Solutions. When considering the behaviour of actual gas we use the behaviour of an ideal gas, a theoretical abstraction, as a standard of reference, since the properties of an ideal gas can be predicted with certainty. Similarly, when dealing with solutions, we imagine an ideal solution whose properties are additively composed of those of its components. When two liquids are mixed to give an ideal solution, there is no heat exchange with the surroundings, nor will any heat exchange result from the dilution of the solution with either component. The total volume will be equal to the sum of the volumes of the components in the free state, that is the partial molar volumes of the components in solution are equal to their molar volumes in the free state. In short, any physical property of such a solution can be calculated by the mixture rule, *i.e.* from the molar composition and the magnitudes of the property for the components in the free state. Finally, ideal solutions must obey Raoult's law of vapour pressures exactly throughout the complete range of concentrations over which they can be considered as ideal. As will be seen, the deviation of actual solutions from these conditions varies from almost complete compliance to extreme deviation when the two liquids form two layers.

Raoult's Law. This law permits the calculation, for ideal solutions, of the partial pressure of any component in terms of its vapour pressure in the pure state at the same temperature. As already seen (p. 91) it states that the partial vapour pressure of a constituent of a solution is proportional to the mole fraction of that constituent. In symbols

$$p_A = N_A p_A^\circ,$$

where p_A and N_A are the partial pressure and mole fraction, respectively, of component A in the solution, and p_A° is the vapour pressure of pure A, all at the same temperature. It can be readily shown that Henry's law in the form given above may be written as $p_{solute} = KN_{solute}$ where K is now a different proportionality constant from k; it is, in fact, the value of p_{solute} when $N_{solute} = 1$, *i.e.*, it is the vapour pressure of the pure liquid solute which we may call p_{solute}°. Therefore $p_{solute} = p_{solute}^\circ N_{solute}$ — an equation identical in form to Raoult's law. In an ideal solution, that is, whenever Raoult's law holds, it can be shown by thermodynamics[5] that this form of Henry's law will also hold.

I. Completely Miscible Liquid Pairs.

Ideal solutions are defined, among other criteria, as solutions which obey Raoult's law exactly. For such an ideal liquid pair, the partial pressure of either component (at constant temperature) can therefore be calculated exactly from Raoult's law, knowing its vapour pressure in the pure state and the composition of the solution. If the total pressure is not very high, Dalton's law will be obeyed and the total pressure will be equal to the sum of the partial pressures. If for a given temperature the partial pressure is plotted against mole fraction, it is evident from the form of Raoult's law that the graph will be a straight line running from the vapour pressure of the pure component at mole fraction unity of that component to zero at mole fraction zero. The same will be true of the partial pressure of the second component, the straight line graph running from zero to the vapour pressure of the pure component. If the sum of the ordinates for given compositions, that is the total pressure, is plotted against mole fraction on the same graph, this total pressure will also be represented by a straight line joining the vapour pressures of the two pure components. This behaviour is illustrated in Fig. 25 which gives the partial and total vapour pressures against molar composition (mole fraction or mole per cent).

Graphs such as those of Fig. 25 may be called liquid composition curves, since they give the composition of liquid correspond-

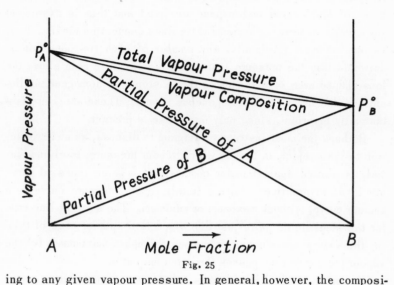

Fig. 25

ing to any given vapour pressure. In general, however, the composition of the vapour given off will be different from that of the parent liquid, indeed, the form of Raoult's law shows that this must be so unless the two liquids happen to have the same vapour pressure. Raoult's law also shows that while the ratio of concentrations in the liquid phase is N_1/N_2, where N_1 and N_2 are the respective mole fractions, the ratio in the vapour phase is N_1p_1/N_2p_2 (interpreting partial pressure as proportional to number of molecules in terms of Avogadro's theorem.); that is, the vapour is always richer than the liquid in the more volatile component. In order, therefore, to represent completely the state of affairs, the vapour pressure diagram must also show, in addition to the liquid curves, curves of vapour composition which will not in general be coincident with the liquid curves except for points representing the pure liquids and certain other points in special cases. In Fig. 25, the vapour composition curve is seen to lie just below the total vapour pressure line. In this way, a lens-shaped area is formed corresponding to the coexistence of liquid and vapour. A two-component system existing in two phases possesses two degrees of freedom, but since the temperature is fixed, the area is isothermally univariant: pressure is a function of composition only. For a given pressure, the compositions of both liquid and vapour are fixed and this is expressed graphically by drawing horizontal tie-lines connecting the liquid and vapour curves. Obviously, any number of such tie-lines can be drawn, within the pressure limits of the area. The area above the lens-shaped area corresponds to the existence of homogeneous liquid and that below it to homogeneous vapour. These areas are isothermally bivariant, since only one phase is present.

Perhaps the most instructive diagram to discuss, as an introduction to the subject, is that in which vapour pressure, total and partial, is plotted against molar composition. Three types of curve are found in practice: (a) the (total) vapour pressure curve is a smooth curve, without maximum or minimum. The straight line type for the ideal liquid pairs just discussed is a special case of this; (b) the vapour pressure curve passes through a maximum; (c) the vapour pressure curve passes through a minimum.

Examples of ideal liquid pairs, whose vapour pressure is represented by the straight line relation, are not uncommon. The liquid pair ethylene bromide—propylene bromide give such a curve. In general substances tend to give ideal solutions, that is to obey Raoult's law, the more they resemble one another chemically. The total vapour pressure P of such mixtures will, of course, always be reproduced by the formula

$$P = N_A p_A^o + (1 - N_A) \cdot p_B^o,$$

where p_A^o and p_B^o are the vapour pressures of the two liquids respectively, and N_A is the mole fraction of component A.

Raoult's law would be expected to hold when the molecules of one component have no effect on the forces existing between the molecules of the other, and conversely. This condition is expressed analytically by Galitzine and D. Berthelot in the form of the equation

$$a_{12} = \sqrt{a_1 a_2}$$

where a_{12} represents the van der Waals' force of attraction between molecules of different kinds, and a_1 and a_2 the forces between molecules of the same kind. If the two components are chemically different, the attraction between different types of molecule will not comply with the above relationship and Raoult's law will not be obeyed. If the attraction between one type of molecule is much stronger than that between another type, i.e. if $a_1 >>> a_2$ or conversely, the tendency will be for the former to force the latter out of the liquid phase into that of the vapour, that is the vapour pressure will be greater than that calculated from Raoult's law. This is known as a positive deviation from Raoult's law. It can be shown that if one component of a binary mixture exhibits positive deviation, the other must do so also and the mixture as a whole exhibits positive deviation. Hence the total vapour pressure will always be greater than that calculated and the curve expressing total vapour pressure as a function of composition will lie above the ideal straight line joining the vapour pressures of the two pure components. Such a curve may or may not exhibit a maximum, depending on the difference in vapour pressure of the pure components and the extent of the positive deviation. The case of positive deviation without maximum is common and is exemplified by the system: cyclohexane—carbon tetrachloride[6] at 40° (Fig. 26). In Fig. 26, the

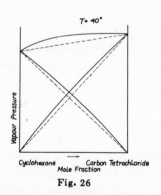

$T = 40°$

Vapour Pressure

Cyclohexane — Carbon Tetrachloride
Mole Fraction

Fig. 26

straight lines (broken) represent ideal behaviour. The vapour composition is not shown.

If the positive deviation is great, and particularly if the difference in vapour pressures of the pure components is not great, a maximum may be produced on the vapour pressure curve, as for example, with the system acetone — carbon disulphide at 35.17° (Fig. 27).[7] According to the theorem of Gibbs-Konovalov, if, at constant temperature, a certain composition of liquid mixture has a maximum

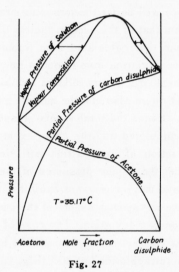

Fig. 27

or minimum vapour pressure, the equilibrium vapour evolved by this liquid must have the same composition as the liquid, that is, the curves of liquid and vapour composition must touch tangentially at the point of maximum or minimum pressure. (See p. 147 under "Indifferent Point"). In these types, two lens-shaped areas of univariant behaviour, crossed by tie-lines, are formed; the interpretation is the same as in the simple case dealt with previously.

If the molecules of the two constituents attract one another strongly, i.e. if $a_1a_2 >>> a_1$ or a_2, and particularly if a compound is formed to some extent in the liquid, the partial pressure of each component, and therefore the total vapour pressure of the mixture, will be less than that calculated from Raoult's law: this constitutes negative deviation from ideal behaviour. If the effect is extreme, a minimum may be produced on the curve of total pressure.

In accordance with the theorem of Gibbs-Konovalov, liquid and vapour curves touch tangentially at such a point of minimum vapour
pressure. Fig. 28 shows this behaviour for the system acetone—
chloroform at 35.17°.[7]

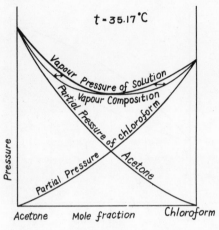

Fig. 28

Isothermal Distillation. If the temperature of a liquid mixture
is kept constant and the vapour progressively removed, the composition of the liquid will in general alter as the process goes on.
This procedure is known as isothermal distillation and, though not
very common in practice, it can readily be carried out, particularly
if the vapour pressure is high. As the process continues under constant temperature, the total vapour pressure must necessarily fall.
This is contrasted with ordinary distillation in which the pressure
remains (approximately) constant and the temperature rises during
distillation. It is perhaps rather easier from the theoretical point
of view to consider isothermal distillation before proceeding to
isobaric distillation.

We consider first a liquid mixture of the type of Fig. 29, of
which Fig. 26 (p. 113) is an actual example, that is, there is neither maximum nor minimum on the vapour pressure curve. A mixture of the composition a (Fig. 29) will have a total pressure of P_1.

This pressure is produced in a closed space by the liquid generating a vapour of composition b, the composition of the liquid remaining essentially unchanged if the vapour space is small and the volume of the liquid large. It will be noted that the vapour b is much richer

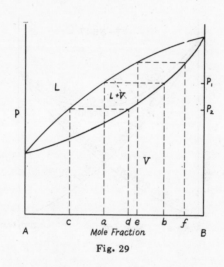

Fig. 29

in the more volatile component B than the parent liquid. If now the pressure is reduced below P_1, the liquid will continue to give off vapour and, since this vapour is richer in the more volatile component, the residual liquid will become richer in the less volatile A, and its composition will move along the curve of vapour pressure towards pure A with falling vapour pressure. Suppose distillation is continued until the residual liquid has the composition c: it will then be giving off an equilibrium vapour of composition d, the total vapour pressure having fallen to P_2. If the vapour removed has been condensed to a liquid, the liquid distillate will obviously have a composition somewhere between b and d, say e. If now, e is submitted to isothermal distillation in the above manner it will at first give rise to a vapour having the composition f, still richer in the more volatile component. Obviously, continued fractionation of the distillate in this manner will lead eventually to a distillate of pure B. Continued removal of the vapour from the residual liquid would also lead to a residue of pure A, but the amount so obtained would be very small. In actual practice, residues from volatile distillates are mixed with distillates from fractions of lower vapour pressure and again submitted to fractionation. In this way, complete separation of the mixture into its two components is theoretically possible.

If there is a maximum on the vapour pressure curve, as in Fig. 27, complete separation is no longer possible. If a vertical is drawn through the maximum, the diagram is divided into two portions each of which is a replica of the preceding. In each portion of the diagram, therefore, separation is possible, by fractional distillation, into the mixture having the composition of the maximum as final distillate, and a residue of the component in excess, either acetone or carbon disulphide in the case of Fig. 27. The solution at this maximum is known as the azeotropic or constant boiling mixture.[15] The reason for this is obvious: as the distillates approach in composition that of the azeotropic mixture the composition of the vapour approximates more and more to that of the liquid until eventually these compositions must become identical when the azeotropic composition is reached. The azeotropic mixture is not a chemical individual, but from the point of view of distillation it behaves as if it were, since the composition does not change on boiling. It should be noted that while, at constant temperature, the azeotropic mixture does not change its composition on distillation, at some other constant temperature the azeotropic composition will in general be different. As will be seen shortly, at constant pressure, the azeotropic mixture boils at a constant temperature without change of composition, but the azeotropic composition is different under different pressures.[8]

Similarly, a mixture showing an azeotropic minimum on the vapour pressure curve cannot be separated into its pure components by distillation, but only into the azeotropic mixture and the other component. In this case, however, since the azeotropic mixture has the lowest vapour pressure, it will be obtained as the eventual residue, the result of continued fractionation of the distillate being the pure component in excess.

Isobaric Distillation — Boiling-Point Curves. If the pressure is maintained constant, say at atmospheric pressure, the temperature at which the vapour pressure of the system is equal to the superincumbent pressure, *i.e.* the boiling-point of the solution, will vary with the composition. The curve which represents this variation is called the boiling-point curve.

It is obvious that to represent completely the behaviour of a binary system with respect to temperature, pressure and composition, three axes of reference are necessary, giving rise to a solid model. If composition is represented along a horizontal axis, and temperature along a second horizontal axis at right angles to the first, while pressure is measured along a vertical axis, the solid model will be a double envelope the two surfaces of which meet along their edges in lines lying in each of the two faces of the model that are in the plane of the temperature and pressure axes. These edges are the vapour pressure curves of the pure liquids. The solid model is thus divided into three volumes, one included between the double envelope, and one lying above it and one below. Any point in the volume above the double envelope represents homogeneous liquid, in the volume below it homogeneous vapour, while a point within the double envelope corresponds to the coexistence of liquid and vapour. The compositions of equilibrium liquid and vapour are joined by tie-lines in a plane parallel to the base of the model (t,x plane). Vertical sections parallel to the plane containing the axes of composition and pressure will represent isothermal sections; they will be the pressure-composition diagrams which have just been discussed. Horizontal sections, parallel to the axes of composition and temperature, will be isobaric sections and will contain the boiling-point curves about to be discussed. For the sake of completeness, vertical sections parallel to the axes of temperature and pressure represent the pressure-temperature relations of mixtures of fixed composition, isopleths, but such diagrams are of little importance in this connection.

It is easy to see, from the above description of the solid model, that the isobaric section is, qualitatively though not quantitatively, a mirror image of the isothermal section. Thus, if the isothermal section is represented by a simple double curve, without maximum or minimum, the boiling-point curve will also be a simple double curve, except that the high vapour pressure end is now the low boiling-point end, and conversely, so that the double curve now slopes in the opposite direction, and the vapour composition curve is always nearer to the lower boiling-point side than the liquid composition curve. A fact sometimes overlooked is that, even if the isothermal vapour pressure curve is ideal, that is, a straight line joining the vapour pressures of the components, the boiling-point curve cannot be a straight line but is convex to the axis of composition: this is because vapour pressure, for a pure component or mixture of fixed composition is not a straight line function of the temperature but increases logarithmically, more or less in accordance with the Clapeyron equation.

Under the conditions laid down in the preceding paragraph, the boiling-points of all mixtures will be intermediate between the boiling-points of the pure components, as in the case of mixtures of chlorobenzene and bromobenzene.[9] By a treatment similar to that in which the isothermal diagram was discussed, it can be shown that such a mixture can be separated by repeated fractional distillation into the two pure components.

If the mixture shows either an azeotropic maximum or minimum on the isothermal diagram, the liquid and vapour surfaces of the solid model will touch not merely at their edges but also along a space curve which represents the behaviour of the azeotropic mixture with respect to temperature, pressure and concentration. Obviously, then, an azeotropic maximum on the isothermal system produces an azeotropic minimum on the isobaric system and conversely, though the corresponding maxima and minima will not lie at the same composition. Just as in isothermal distillation, separation into the two pure components is not possible by isobaric distillation, but separation into the azeotropic mixture and the component in excess is possible. The system water— *n*-propyl alcohol is a good example of a system with an azeotropic minimum on the boiling-point curve (Fig. 30).[10] The relative position of liquid and vapour curves is such that the vapour is richer than the liquid, at

the same temperature, in the lower boiling constituent which in this
case is always the azeotropic mixture. The azeotropic mixture it-

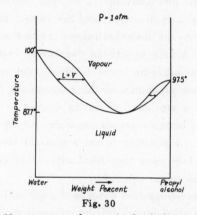

Fig. 30

self contains 71.69 per cent of propyl alcohol by weight and boils
at 87.72° under atmospheric pressure, against boiling-points of
100° and 97.5° for water and propyl alcohol respectively. Solutions containing less than 71.69 per cent of the alcohol give off a
vapour richer in alcohol than the liquid, whereas solutions containing more than 71.69 per cent of the alcohol give off a vapour richer
in water than the liquid. If a mixture of the first category is distilled, the final residue will be practically pure water and the refractionated distillate the azeotropic mixture; a mixture of the
second category gives rise to the same distillate with a residue of
pure propyl alcohol. The azeotropic mixture will boil unchanged in
composition at constant temperature so long as the pressure remains
unchanged, but the composition of the constant boiling mixture
varies with pressure. This means that such a mixture can only be
separated by fractional distillation into a residue of the pure component in excess of the azeotropic composition and a fractionated
distillate of the azeotropic composition. This is the case with the
industrially very important substance ethyl alcohol. The azeotropic
distillate contains about 92 per cent by weight of alcohol and this
is the strongest alcohol which can be obtained by distillation.

Mixtures of acetone and chloroform, water and hydrogen chloride, water and nitric acid, etc., give boiling-point curves which show a maximum. The azeotropic mixture of water and nitric acid contains 68.2 per cent of acid and boils under atmospheric pressure at 121.7°.[11] When a more dilute solution is distilled, the distillate will be relatively rich in water and the residue will become richer in acid with progressive distillation, the temperature rising the while, as it always must in isobaric distillation. A residue of azeotropic composition will eventually be obtained. If a more concentrated acid is distilled, the distillate will be relatively rich in acid, the residue will become more dilute, the boiling-point rising as before, and again a residue of the constant boiling mixture is obtained. Either pure water or pure nitric acid can be obtained by refractionation of the distillate.

If a mixture shows azeotropic behaviour, either maximum or minimum, it cannot, in accordance with what has been said, be separated completely by fractional distillation into its components, but only into one component and the azeotropic mixture. Alteration of pressure, however, alters the azeotropic composition. It is conceivable that in some cases alteration of pressure might even cause the disappearance of the azeotropic character, giving rise to the type of curve for which the boiling-points lie entirely between those of the components. In any case, alteration of pressure (increase or decrease) may alter the azeotropic composition to a more favourable ratio, *i.e.* to one containing more of a given component.

Industrial Fractional Distillation. The process of fractional distillation, as outlined in the preceding sections, can be represented by some such diagram as Fig. 31. The interpretation of this diagram is that, in the first stage, distillation is carried out until half of the total liquid has distilled. In the second stage, the distillate is removed and in turn distilled until one half has distilled: at the same time the original residue is distilled in the same manner. Thus, at the end of the second stage, there are two distillates and two residues. Distillate D_2' is mixed with residue R_2'' and so on. As the process is repeated, the outermost members approximate more and more the two pure components, on the assumption, of course, that the two pure components can be obtained by fractional dis-

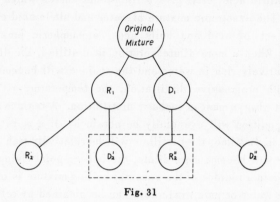

Fig. 31

tillation, *i.e.*, that the vapour pressure or boiling-point diagram is of the type which presents neither maximum nor minimum. Such a process, though occasionally resorted to in the laboratory, is very laborious and therefore time-consuming and expensive. Hence, in industry, and for that matter in the laboratory also, the operation is carried out continuously by means of a fractionating column, shown in Fig. 32.[12] In this diagram A is a heated still, D is the column consisting of a series of plates, and F the condenser. The previously heated mixture to be distilled is admitted about the middle of the column through the pipe E onto one of the plates and overflows down the pipe (2) to the plate below. On this lower plate the liquid comes in contact with vapour moving upward from the still through the "bubble caps" (3) and (4). These caps are so designed that the vapour must bubble through the layer of liquid on each plate before it can escape. In doing so, part of the less volatile constituent is condensed out of the vapour, and part of the more volatile constituent is vapourised out of the liquid. The vapour moving onto the next higher plate through (3) and (4) is richer in the more volatile constituent than the vapour which approached the plate from below, while the liquid overflowing to the next lower plate through (1) is richer in the less volatile constituent than the liquid which reached the plate from above. The net result of the interaction between the vapour and the liquid at the plate is, therefore, a redistribution in favour of the more volatile constituent in the vapour and the less volatile constituent in the liquid, *i.e.* each plate acts like a miniature still.

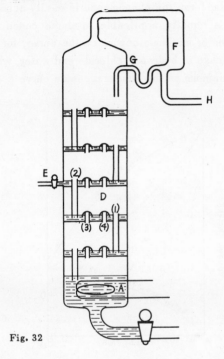

Fig. 32

Since this process repeats itself at each plate, it is possible with a sufficient number of plates to separate the mixture into two end fractions, a residue of the less volatile component running into A, where it can be drawn off, and a vapour passing from the top of the column containing essentially the more volatile constituent. This vapour is fed into a condenser F, where it is liquefied. Part of this liquid is drawn off through H, while part, the reflux, is returned to the column through G in order to maintain the stock of essentially pure distillate on the plates.

Fuming Liquids. It is a common laboratory observation that certain liquids fume when exposed to the (moist) atmosphere: they

do not fume in an anhydrous atmosphere. It is also observed that
dilute aqueous solutions do not fume.. Assuming for the sake of
simplicity that the isothermal diagram (Fig. 33), expressing the
vapour pressures of mixtures of the substance A and water, is of
the simple lenticular form, the phenomenon is easily accounted for.
The explanation is equally applicable to those cases where an
azeotropic maximum or minimum occurs cn the curve, for instance,
in the well known case of hydrogen chloride and water, where there
is an azeotropic minimum on the vapour pressure curve.

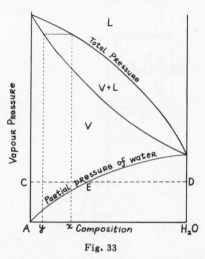

Fig. 33

In Fig. 33, let x represent a mixture rich in the more volatile
component A. This liquid gives off a vapour y, containing very
little water. The partial pressure of water in this mixture, as can
be seen from the diagram, is below that of water vapour in the atmosphere. Water therefore condenses into the mixture with formation of a liquid drop. This behaviour will be shown by all solutions
which give rise to vapour in which the partial pressure of water is
less than that of water in the atmosphere CD. The weakest solution which will show this behaviour is represented by the point of
intersection E of the curve giving partial pressure of water in the
vapour with the horizontal straight line representing the (constant

for given conditions) pressure of aqueous vapour in the atmosphere: solutions weaker than this will not fume.

II. Two Partially Miscible Liquids in Equilibrium with Vapour.

When two liquid layers are formed an extra phase is formed, so that the system now consists of two liquid phases (L_1, L_2) and a vapour phase (V). Such a system is isothermally invariant and we deduce that at constant temperature the total vapour pressure is constant as long as two liquid phases are present. Hence, if vapour pressure is plotted against total composition, at constant temperature, the curve will exhibit a horizontal portion for the region over which two liquid layers exist. This horizontal, representing the constant vapour pressure of the two liquid layers, may lie either above the higher vapour pressure of the two components, or between the two. It is not possible for the total vapour pressure of a system of two layers to be less than that of the less volatile component.

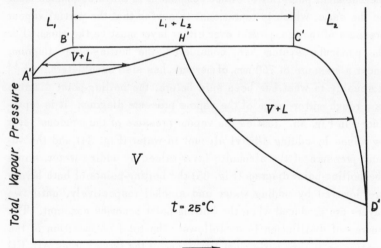

Fig. 34   Wt. Percent N-Butyl Alcohol

The former case is represented in Fig. 34, which expresses total vapour pressure and vapour composition in the system water— n-butyl alcohol,[13] at 25°. The horizontal B'H'C' represents the constant vapour pressure prevailing when two liquid layers are present at the constant temperature of 25°. The curves A'H' and

D'H' represent the composition of vapour given off, in the former case by homogeneous solutions in water and in the latter by homogeneous solutions in butyl alcohol. The two curves meet at H', on the horizontal B'H'C', indicating, not merely that both layers have the same vapour pressure, but that both liquid layers give off an identical vapour. This means that the partial pressure of each component given off from each layer is the same, and this must obviously be so if the two layers are in equilibrium, since, if the vapours given off were different in composition, even if the total pressure were the same, the partial pressures of the two components in the two vapours would not be the same, and a process of distillation would result from one layer to the other, with resultant change of composition, in other words the two layers could not be in equilibrium. Another way of expressing this is to say that if the two liquid layers are in equilibrium with one another and with vapour, the chemical potential of either component in all three phases must be the same, which is tantamount to saying that the partial vapour pressure of that component over either layer must be the same. For the particular system here considered, the boiling-point diagram, under a pressure of 760 mm. of mercury, has also been determined. [14] Agreeably to what has been said before, the boiling-point diagram is a rough mirror-image of the vapour pressure diagram: it is reproduced in Fig. 35. Just as the vapour pressure of the aqueous layer is raised by adding n-butyl alcohol to water (Fig. 34) and the vapour pressure of the alcoholic layer raised by adding water, so on the boiling-point diagram (Fig. 35) the boiling-points of both layers are lowered by adding water and alcohol respectively, until two layers are produced when the boiling-point becomes constant. The course of distillation is as follows: the total composition of the mixture as it first boils must lie on one of the three curves AB, CD or BC. In the former cases the mixture is homogeneous, in the latter heterogeneous. If the composition of the mixture lies on curve AB, say at F, it will give off the vapour G, much richer in alcohol than the original mixture. This first distillate, incidentally, lies within the mixture gap, though the parent mixture does not, and hence will separate into layers on condensation. Since the parent mixture is

impoverished in respect of alcohol its composition will move, with
continued distillation, along the curve BA towards A, so that the

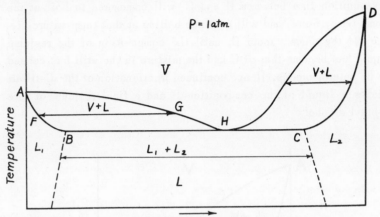

Fig. 35

final residue will be pure water. As the residue approaches pure
water the equilibrium vapour will pass out of the miscibility gap.
The net results of fractionation will be a final residue of pure
water and a refractionated distillate (two-layer mixture) of total
composition H, which however can be separated by gravity into two
mixtures of composition corresponding to B and C, or whatever
values B and C have at room temperature. Obviously a homogenous
mixture on the curve CD behaves in the same way, the residue being
pure butyl alcohol and the distillate of total composition H. Mixtures lying within the miscibility gap must be classified into those
lying to the left and those to the right of the point H, that is, between H and B and between H and C.

A mixture whose composition lies between B and H will commence to boil at the temperature corresponding to the horizontal
BHC, giving off vapour of constant composition H. Since this
vapour is richer in alcohol than the original mixture, the composition of the residual mixture must move along HB towards B. When
the point B is reached the liquid in the still becomes homogeneous.
If the distillate collected up to this point is removed it will have
the composition H. If the residue in the still is boiled further,

the course of distillation follows the path already described, pure water being eventually left in the still. Similarly, a mixture whose composition lies between H and C will commence to boil at the same temperature, and will continue boiling at that temperature giving off the same vapour H, until the composition of the residual liquid has become that of C and the mixture in the still has ceased to be heterogeneous. Hence continued fractionation of the distillate yields a liquid of the composition H and a final residue of pure n-butyl alcohol.

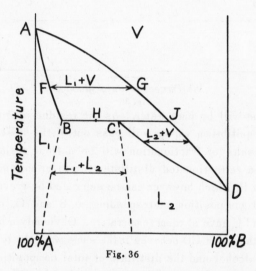

Fig. 36

In the preceding example the composition of the vapour given off by a two-layer liquid lies itself in the mixture gap. The case where this is not so, *i.e.* the vapour evolved forms a homogeneous liquid on condensation, is known and illustrated in Fig. 36. After the detailed discussion of the preceding case, the behaviour here will be fairly obvious. If the liquid F is distilled the boiling point will rise to that of pure A. If the mean composition of the distillate is taken to be H, somewhere between B and C, the distillate will separate into two layers on condensation. If the liquefied distillate is now distilled it will boil at constant temperature, as long as two layers are present, giving a distillate of constant composition J, while the quantity of layer of composition C decreases continuously. If the distillate of constant composition J is removed at this point and submitted to fractional distillation it will give a refractionated distillate of pure B. Hence, in this case, separation into the two pure components is possible, despite the existence of the miscibility gap.

III. Two Immiscible Liquids—Distillation with Steam.

As with partially miscible liquids, two immiscible liquids in equilibrium with vapour form an isothermally invariant system. The vapour pressure of such a system is a function of temperature only, no matter what the composition of the system. Moreover, since the liquids are mutually insoluble, they have no effect on one another's vapour pressure, that is the partial pressure of each component in the mixture is the same as its vapour pressure in the pure state.

Just as with the partially miscible liquids, a distillate of constant composition will be obtained, under constant pressure or temperature, with the difference, however, that while the constancy ceases as soon as the partially miscible system ceases to show two layers, it persists in the other system until one or other component is entirely exhausted, simply because two layers will always form if both liquids are present. It is apparent, therefore, that the mole or volume ratio of the two liquids in the vapour being produced will be the ratio of their vapour pressures in the pure state at the temperature of distillation. The ratio by weight of the two substances in the distillate will be obtained by multiplying this ratio by the ratio of their respective molecular weights.

The above theoretical treatment is exemplified by the common laboratory process of distillation with steam, frequently resorted to as an alternative to distillation under reduced pressure, for substances which decompose when boiled under a pressure of one atmosphere. For example, it is found experimentally that a mixture of water and nitrobenzene (immiscible) boils about 99° under standard atmospheric pressure, in other words when nitrobenzene is distilled with steam the temperature of the chamber through which the steam is passing is about 99°. At this temperature the vapour pressure of water is 733 mm. and therefore, by Dalton's law, that of nitrobenzene is 760 - 733 = 27 mm. Hence the volume ratio of distillation is 27:733 = 1:27. If the molecular weights of nitrobenzene and water were similar, it would not be worth the expense of steam-raising for so small a yield of nitrobenzene. The weight ratio, however, is much more favourable, viz. 18 × 733/123 × 27, where 18 and 123 are the molecular weights of water and nitrobenzene respectively. This ratio works out to 1:3.98, *i.e.* the distillate contains about 20 per cent nitrobenzene. The example shows that the low molecular weight of water, compared with the relatively high molecular weight of most organic substances, is a factor in the commercial success of steam distillation. A still larger yield can be obtained by distilling with superheated steam, since the relative rise in the vapour pressure of the organic substance with rising temperature is greater than the relative rise in the vapour pressure of water. The rise in temperature produced by using a closed system may, however, have a deleterious effect on the purity of the substance distilled.

In theory at least, the calculation detailed in the preceding paragraph can be reversed and the molecular weight of the substance being steam distilled calculated from the weight ratio of water and substance in the distillate. Thus terpinene was found to distil with steam at a temperature of 95 °C under a pressure of 744 mm. At this temperature the vapour pressure of water is 634 mm. That of terpinene is therefore 744 - 634 = 110 mm. The distillate is found experimentally to contain 55 per cent by weight of terpinene. Hence

$$55/45 = 110 \times M/634 \times 18$$

and M = 127, as against a formula molecular weight of 136. The method might be used to find the order of magnitude of a molecular weight.

Comparison of Types. Five types of system, involving equilibrium of liquid and vapour, have been discussed in this chapter, viz. complete immiscibility, partial miscibility, complete miscibility with maximum on the vapour pressure curve, complete miscibility without either maximum or minimum on the vapour pressure curve, complete miscibility with minimum on the vapour pressure curve. These types can be discriminated in terms of ideality as represented by adherence more or less complete to Raoult's law. (1) Extreme positive deviation from Raoult's law leads to complete immiscibility. The total vapour pressure is then represented by the sum of the vapour pressures of the two liquids in the pure state (curve ee of Fig. 37 where ab and cd represent the vapour pres-

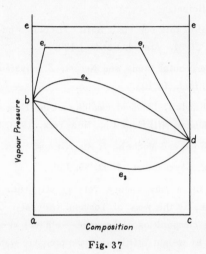

Fig. 37

sures of the pure liquids). Positive deviation not so extreme leads to partial miscibility. The horizontal straight line ee changes to the curve be_1e_1d. Since the partial pressure of each component in the miscibility gap must be less than the vapour pressure of that substance in the pure state, e_1e_1 must lie below ee, but it will usually lie above bd. With positive deviation still present, but insufficient to cause the formation of two layers, a maximum is produced on the vapour pressure curve (curve be_2d). Perfect agreement with Raoult's law, that is, ideal behaviour, yields the straight line bd. Negative deviation from Raoult's law leads, if marked, to the occurrence of a minimum on the vapour pressure curve (curve be_3d).

The occurrence of a minimum, for instance in the case of formic acid and water, suggests chemical action—formation of a hydrate, for instance. The azeotropic mixtures themselves are of course not chemical compounds, since their composition varies with pressure, but equilibria in which hydrates do take part may occur.

NOTES

1. A. Findlay and B. Shen, *J. Chem. Soc.*, 1912, **101**, 1459.

2. The absorption coefficient, as here defined, is sometimes called the solubility coefficient.

3. For the proof of this see van't Hoff: "Lectures on Physical Chemistry", Part II, pp. 30-31. Arnold, London, 1899.

4. For an experimental study see Nernst, *Z. physikal. Chem.*, 1891, **8**, 110; *cf.* Aulich, *ibid.*, **8**, 105.

5. Lewis and Randall, Thermodynamics and the Free Energy of Chemical Substances, McGraw-Hill Book Co., New York, 1923, Chapter 20.

6. Scatchard, Wood and Mochels, *J. Amer. Chem. Soc.*, 1939, **61**, 3208.

7. Zawidsky, *Z. phys. Chem.*, 1900, **35**, 129.

8. The composition may change very greatly with pressure, as is shown, for example, by the work of Tomassi (*Roczniki Chem.*, 1947, **21**, 108), in which the composition of benzene —ethanol azeotropes changed from 32.0 to 90.4% by weight EtOH, when the pressure was changed from 1 to 55 kg./cm^2.

9. Young, *Trans. Chem. Soc.*, 1902, **81**, 768.

10. Young and Fortey, *J. Chem. Soc.*, 1902, **81**, 717.

11. Creighton and Githens, *J. Franklin Inst.*, 1915, **179**, 161.

12. *Cf.* Prutton & Maron: "Fundamental Principles of Physical Chemistry," Macmillan, New York, 1947, p. 167.

13. Butler, *J. Chem. Soc.*, 1933, 674.

14. Stockhardt and Hull, *Ind. Eng. Chem.*, 1931, **23**, 1438.

15. For a reference table of systems with and without azeotropes see Horsley, Anal. Chem., 1947. **19**, 508; 1949, **21**, 831.

C. SYSTEMS CONSISTING OF SOLID AND LIQUID PHASES ONLY

It is now proposed to consider the behaviour of two-component systems in which equilibrium exists between a solid and a liquid phase only. Such systems are among the most important in the whole range of heterogeneous equilibria. The interest and importance of the investigation of such systems lie in the determination not only of the conditions for the stable existence of the participating substances, but also of the conditions under which chemical combination (if any) takes place between the two components. From such investigations, also, one may ascertain the nature of the compounds formed and the range of their existence. In all such investigations the Phase Rule becomes of conspicuous value on account of the fact that its principles afford, as it were, a touchstone by which the character of the system can be determined, and that from the form of the equilibrium curves obtained, conclusions can be drawn as to the nature of the interaction between the two components. Except where otherwise stated these systems will be considered as existing under a constant pressure (say atmospheric) greater than the vapour pressure of the system, so that there is no vapour phase. Fixing the pressure, of course, exhausts one degree of freedom.

I. The Components are Completely Miscible in the Liquid State.

(a) The only Solid Phases are the Pure Components.

Since the two components in the liquid state are miscible in all proportions, only one liquid phase will exist, namely, a homogeneous mixture or solution of the two components. Since, also, only the pure components can occur as solid (crystalline) phases, the only systems possible are S_1—L, S_2—L, and S_1—S_2—L, where S_1 and S_2 represent the crystalline components, and L the liquid solution.

A system which consists of only two phases, S_1—L or S_2—L will be bivariant, and two of the variables, pressure, temperature and composition, must be given definite values before the system is entirely defined. If the pressure is given a definite value, say atmospheric pressure, then the system will become univariant, or the composition will vary with the temperature; or, if the temperature is fixed, the composition will vary with the pressure. On the other hand, the system S_1—S_2—L is univariant, and if the pressure is fixed, the system will be entirely defined. Under a given pressure, the system S_1—S_2—L can exist only at a single definite temperature, and the composition of the liquid phase will also be definite. Such a system is isobarically invariant. If the condition of constant pressure is given up and the pressure reduced to the vapour pressure of the system, the vapour phase will also make its appearance. A two-component system is then existing in four phases and it is therefore completely invariant, temperature, composition and pressure being all determined. If, now, the pressure is increased but still considered a variable, the vapour phase will disappear, and the system develops one degree of freedom, that is, temperature and composition will vary with pressure. This means that the composition of the liquid phase and the temperature of equilibrium are not quite the same in the absence of vapour as they are in its presence and the difference will in general be greater the greater the pressure. In condensed systems, however, the effect of pressure on temperature and composition is slight and therefore, to all intents and purposes, the temperature and composition under a relatively small constant pressure (say one atmosphere) will be indistinguishable from temperature and composition in the presence of vapour. If the equilibria be represented in a temperature-concentration or temperature-composition diagram, the systems S_1—L and S_2—L will be represented by curves, and the system S_1—S_2—L by a point, We thus obtain an equilibrium diagram such as that shown in Fig. 38. In this diagram, which represents the simplest possible equilibrium diagram for a two-component system in which solid solutions

are not formed, the points A and B represent the melting-points of
the pure components. Since the freezing-point of a liquid is lowered
by dissolving another substance in it, it follows that if a quantity
of the component B be dissolved in molten (or liquid) A, the temperature at which solid A will be in equilibrium with the solution will
be below the freezing-point of pure A; and the greater the concentration of B in the liquid, the lower will be the temperature at which
A can exist in equilibrium with it. The curves AC and BC are frequently called freezing-point curves. They can, however, be equally
well described as solubility curves, as becomes immediately obvious if one of the components is water. Thus, if in Fig. 38 A were

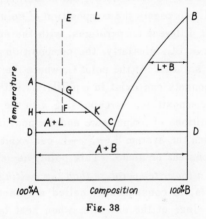

Fig. 38

water and B a substance solid at room temperature, the reader immediately recognises the curve BC as the solubility curve of B in
water. Curve AC, sometimes known as the ice curve, may equally
well be designated the solubility curve of ice in liquid B. This
conception leads to the conclusion that, in the absence of other
complications, the solubility must become infinite at the melting-
point of the solute.

For small additions of B, the lowering of the freezing-point of A
can be calculated by the simple van't Hoff formula which may be
written in the form, $dT/dx_a = RT^2/L_a$, where x_a is the molar fraction of the component A (the component crystallising as solid
phase); T is its melting-point on the absolute scale; R, the gas

constant (expressed in heat units); and L_a, the latent heat of fusion of A per gram-molecule.   For wider temperature ranges one may use the integrated expression

$$\log_{10} x_a = \frac{-L_a}{2.303 \times 1.99}\left(\frac{1}{T} - \frac{1}{T_0}\right)$$

where T is the equilibrium temperature and T_0 is the melting-point of pure A, on the absolute scale.[1] These expressions, however, hold strictly only in the case of "ideal" solutions. The above equation, while it gives the freezing-point of any solution of known composition, can also be used to find the composition corresponding to any assigned temperature, in other words, the solubility.

The curve AC represents the composition of solutions which are in equilibrium, at different temperatures, with the solid component A;   and the curve BC, similarly, the composition of solutions in equilibrium with solid B. At the point C, where the two curves cut, both solid components can exist in equilibrium with a liquid solution of definite composition, corresponding with the point C. Point C gives the conditions of temperature and composition of the liquid phase under which the system S_1—S_2—L can exist in stable equilibrium under constant pressure. This point, as is clear from the diagram, lies *at a lower temperature than the melting-point of either component*. It is, in consequence, called a eutectic point. The reaction taking place at the eutectic, when heat is added, known as a phase reaction, is A + B → L - ΔH where ΔH is the increase in heat content, or the "heat of the reaction". Actually, the true eutectic involves the presence of the vapour phase and it is truly invariant, while the eutectic as described above is really univariant;   for instance, the composition will vary with changing pressure.[2] Thermodynamically speaking, the eutectic is a mixture of two phases, not a separate phase, and must always be so considered when calculating degree of freedom, but the term "eutectic structure" is often used when the microscopic structure of a solidified system is being studied. This is because the eutectic crystallisation is of a very intimate nature, the crystals of both phases being generated simultaneously. The microscopic characteristic of a eutectic is therefore that of a very fine-grained closely-knit structure, which can be readily discriminated from the relatively large crystals of the primary formation. This is of considerable importance in geology and metallurgy since it is often possible for a skilled microscopist to say, from an examination of the solidified mass, what phase separated first, that is, prior to eutectic crystallisation.

At all temperatures lying above the curves AC, BC, the system can exist only as a homogeneous, liquid solution, and at all temperatures below the eutectic horizontal, DD', only the solid components or mixtures of the solid components can exist as stable systems. When the temperature and composition are represented by a point in the area ACD, solid component A can exist along with liquid solutions. Similarly, points in the area BCD' give the conditions of temperature and composition for the coexistence of solid B and solution.

If a liquid solution E, having a composition lying to the left of the eutectic point C, be cooled down, following an isopleth, the solid component A will commence to crystallise out (supersaturation supposed excluded) when the temperature reaches the point G on the curve AC corresponding with the initial composition of the solution. If the temperature be allowed to fall still further, more and more of the component A will crystallise out, and the composition of the liquid solution will alter in the direction of C. When the composition of the point C is reached, solid B, also, can begin to crystallise out. If one continues to withdraw heat from the system, solid A and solid B will separate out together, while *the temperature remains constant*. Since the composition of the solution must also remain constant (point C represents an invariant system when the pressure is constant), it follows that *the components A and B must crystallise out from the eutectic solution in constant proportions*. Although, therefore, the solution having the composition of the eutectic point freezes at constant temperature, the solid which separates out is not a compound but a *mixture (or conglomerate) of two solid phases*.

On the other hand, if a liquid mixture having a composition represented by a point lying to the right of the eutectic point C be cooled down, the solid component B will separate out, and the composition of the solution will change in the direction of C. When this point is reached, solid A also will crystallise out, and the temperature and composition of the solution will now remain constant while the solid components A and B crystallise out as a eutectic conglomerate.

On cooling down a liquid mixture which has the composition represented by the eutectic point C, no solid will crystallise out until the temperature of the eutectic point is reached. At this temperature the eutectic mixture will separate out.

A question of some practical importance is the following: if the temperature of the mixture E has fallen to that of the horizontal HK, what is the composition of the liquid in equilibrium with solid A, and what proportions of the original mixture exist as solution and as solid A? The point K, where the horizontal through the plotted conditions meets the equilibrium curve AC, gives the composition of the liquid phase. The amount of solution is to the amount of separated A, as FH is to FK, where F represents the temperature of the problem on the vertical EGF. Since the total weight must be equal to the sum of the weights of solution and separated A, the problem is easily solved by this graphical method.

Although a eutectic mixture is not a chemical compound, attempts have been made to establish general rules regarding the composition of eutectics. Thus Plato[3] found a connection between the composition of the eutectic and the molecular (or atomic) weights of the components; and, more recently, Stockdale put forward a series of empirical rules which are claimed to give more accurate results than the majority of such rules.[4] The general validity of these rules, which would make it possible to predict the composition of a eutectic without experimental study of the system, has still to be established.

An equilibrium diagram belonging to the class of systems just discussed is given by the system potassium chloride—silver chloride (Fig. 39). The solid phase in equilibrium with solution represented by the left-hand branch of the curve is potassium chloride (m.p.

790°); that in equilibrium with the solutions represented by the

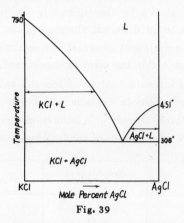

Fig. 39

right-hand branch, is silver chloride (m.p. 451°). At the eutectic point (306°), these two solid phases can coexist with the liquid phase. This equilibrium curve, therefore, shows that potassium chloride and silver chloride do not combine with each other in the solid state.

Equilibrium diagrams such as the above are found frequently in the studies of metallurgy and geology. For instance, alloys of bismuth and cadmium[5] belong to this type, as does the system diopside—anorthite.[6]

Freezing Mixtures. In the case of systems in which water is one of the components, the eutectic point long ago received the name *cryohydric point,* a term which arose from a study of the freezing of salt solutions. On cooling a solution of common salt in water to a temperature of —3°, Guthrie observed that the hydrate NaCl, $2H_2O$ separated out. This salt continued to be deposited until at a temperature —22° opaque crystals made their appearance, and the liquid passed into the solid state without change of temperature. A similar behaviour was found by Guthrie in the case of a large number of other salts, a temperature below that of the melting-point of ice being reached at which, on continued withdrawal of heat, the solution solidified at a constant temperature. When the system had attained this minimum temperature, it was found that the composition of the solid depositing and the liquid phases was the same, and is shown by the figures in the table below which give the composition of different samples of the solid phases deposited from the solution at constant temperature. The system is obviously invariant within the error of experiment.

Conversely, an intimate mixture of ice and salt containing 23.6 per cent, of sodium chloride melts at a definite and constant temperature, and exhibits, therefore, a behaviour supposed to be characteristic of a pure chemical compound. This, then, combined with

No.	Temperature of solidification.	NaCl per cent.
1	− 21° to − 22°	23·72
2	− 22°	23·66
3	− 22°	23·73
4	− 23°	23·82
5	− 23°	23·34
6	− 23°	23·35
	Mean . . .	23·6

the fact that the solid which was deposited was crystalline, and that the same constant temperature was attained, no matter with what proportions of water and salt one started, led Guthrie to the belief that the solid which thus separated at constant temperature were definite chemical compounds, to which he gave the general name *cryohydrate*. A large number of such eutectics were prepared and analysed by Guthrie, and a few of these are given in the following table, (p. 141), together with the temperature of the eutectic point. [7]

The chemical individuality of these cryohydrates was, however, called in question by Pfaundler, and disproved by Offer, who showed that in spite of the constancy of the melting-point, the cryohydrates had the properties, not of definite chemical compounds, but of mixtures; the arguments given being that the heat of solution and the specific volume are the same for the cryohydrate as for a mixture of

Eutectics involving Ice.

Salt	Eutectic Temperature	Percentage of anhydrous salt in the eutectic
Sodium bromide	$-28.0°$	40.3
Sodium chloride	$-21.1°$	23.3
Potassium iodide	$-23.0°$	52.3
Sodium nitrate	$-15.4°$	44.8
Ammonium sulphate	$-18.3°$	39.8
Ammonium chloride	$-15.4°$	19.7
Sodium iodide	$-31.5°$	39.0
Potassium bromide	$-12.6°$	31.3
Potassium chloride	$-10.7°$	19.7
Magnesium sulphate	$- 3.9°$	16.5
Potassium nitrate	$- 3.0°$	11.20
Sodium sulphate	$- 1.1°$	3.84

ice and salt of the same composition; and it was further shown that the cryohydrate had not a definite crystalline form, but separated out as an opaque mass containing the two components in close juxtaposition. The heterogeneous nature of eutectics can also be shown by a microscopical examination. Further evidence is to be found in the fact that, in the absence of vapour, the eutectic composition changes with pressure.

At the eutectic point, therefore, we are not dealing with a single solid phase, but with two solid phases, ice and salt; and, as we have already learned, the constancy of temperature and composition at the eutectic point is due to the fact that we are dealing with an invariant system. The eutectic point is thus clearly seen to be the point of intersection of the solubility curve of the salt and the freezing-point curve of water.

Not only will the composition of a univariant system undergo change when the temperature is varied, but, conversely, if the *composition* of the system is caused to change, corresponding changes of temperature must ensue. Thus, if ice is added to the univariant system salt—solution—vapour, the ice must melt and the temperature fall; and if sufficient ice is added, the temperature of the eutectic point must be at length reached, for it is only at this temperature that the four phases ice—salt—solution—vapour can coexist. On the other hand, if salt is added to the system ice—solution—vapour, the concentration of the solution will increase, ice must melt, and the temperature must thereby fall; and this process also will go on until the eutectic point is reached. In both cases ice melts and there is a change in the composition of the solution; in the former case, salt will be deposited[8] because the solubility diminishes as the temperature falls; in the latter, salt will pass into solution. This process may be accompanied either by evolution or, more generally, by absorption of heat; in the former case the effect of the melting of ice will be partially counteracted; in the latter case it will be augmented.

These principles are made use of in the preparation of *freezing mixtures*. The lowest temperature which can be reached (under atmospheric pressure) by means of these, is the eutectic point. This temperature-minimum is, however, not always attained in the preparation of a freezing mixture, and that for various reasons. The chief of these are radiation and the heat absorbed in cooling the solution produced. The lower the temperature falls, the more rapid does the radiation become; and the rate at which the temperature sinks decreases as the amount of solution increases. Both these factors counteract the effect of the latent heat of fusion and the heat of solution so that a point is reached (which may lie considerably above the eutectic point) at which the two opposing influences balance. The absorption of heat by the solution can be diminished by allowing the solution to drain off as fast as it is produced; and the effect of radiation can be paritally annulled by increasing the rate of cooling. This can be done by the more intimate mixing of the components. Since, under atmospheric pressure, the temperature of the eutectic point is constant, the eutectics are very valuable for the production of baths of constant low temperature.

Method of Mixed Melting-Points. A common practice in organic chemistry for the confirmation of the identity of a substance, is to mix the substance with a pure sample of the substance with which it is suspected to be identical, and determine the melting-point.

If the melting-point of the mixture is the same as that of the substance by itself, the probability that the two substances are identical is very great. The explanation for this results immediately from a consideration of Fig. 38. If the two substances are not identical, the second substance is a foreign substance with respect to the first and will therefore depress its melting-point. The melting-point is here considered to be the highest temperature at which solid persists and is thus identical with the freezing point defined as the highest temperature at which solid appears: obviously a mixture neither freezes nor melts completely at one temperature. A limitation on the above method should be noticed. If the second substance is isomorphous with the first, it is possible that the melting-point may be raised. It could not remain the same, except in the extremely unlikely case of an isomorphous substance having the same melting point. Perhaps the best criterion of all is the fact that mixtures do not melt sharply but over a range of temperature.

Allotropy of Components. The curves AC and BC, shown in Fig. 38, represent diagrammatically the equilibrium relations which obtain when the pure components crystallise out from the fused or liquid mixture. We have seen, for example, that the solid phase in equilibrium with solutions of composition represented by points on the curve BC is the component B. So long as this solid phase undergoes no change, the curve BC must be a continuous curve, as shown in Fig. 38. If, however, the solid component can exist in enantiotropic, allotropic forms, the equilibrium curve will show a "break" at the transition point of the crystalline forms, for, at the transition point, there will coexist two solid phases (allotropic forms) and a liquid phase. At constant pressure, therefore, the system will be invariant. Below the transition point the one crystalline form, and above the transition point the other crystalline form, will exist in equilibrium with solution. At the transition point these two equilibrium curves will cut. We shall consider this in more detail (p. 242).

Purification by Partial Liquefaction. Considering once again Fig. 38, if a solidified mixture of the composition C, that is, the eutectic composition, is heated, it melts completely at the constant temperature of the horizontal DD' (the eutectic temperature). If any other solidified mixture, *e.g.* E, is heated, partial melting will occur at the eutectic temperature and, in the case of mixture E lying to the left of the eutectic composition, the temperature will remain constant at the eutectic temperature until all of component B has melted out of the mixture. A will of course melt at the same time in the proportion called for by the eutectic composition. If, however, the temperature is maintained at the eutectic temperature, after melting is complete the excess of A over the eutectic composition will remain unmelted as a pure solid and it can be removed by filtration or decantation. If the original mixture contains more B than corresponds to the eutectic composition, the result of this process will be a liquid of the same eutectic composition, and excess of pure solid B. The proportions of eutectic liquid and solid A or B can be calculated by simple arithmetic as already shown. This process of purification by partial liquefaction is occasionally resorted to in metallurgy.

(b) Compounds are Formed with a Congruent Melting-point.

When two components can form a stable compound possessing a *congruent melting-point, i.e.* capable of existing as a solid compound, in equilibrium with a liquid of the same composition, a third equilibrium curve (compound in equilibrium with liquid solution) must be added to the two curves discussed in the preceding section. Moreover, since the compound has a definite congruent melting-point, and since this melting-point will be lowered by dissolving in the liquid either of the pure components, it follows that the melting-point of the compound must be a maximum point on the equilibrium curve. Such a maximum is known as a "dystectic". The equilibrium diagram, therefore, takes the general form shown in Fig. 40. A, B, and D are the congruent melting-points of component A, component B, and of the compound A_xB_y respectively. Curve AC gives the composition of liquid mixtures (solutions) of A and B in equilibrium at different temperatures with the component A as solid phase; curve BE gives the composition of solutions in equilibrium with component B as solid phase; and curve CDE gives the composition of solutions in equilibrium with the compound as solid phase. C and E are eutectic points at which eutectic conglomerates of A and A_xB_y and of B and A_xB_y respectively can coexist in contact with solutions of

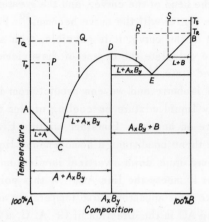

Fig. 40

definite composition. The curve for the compound may occupy a
large or a small part of the diagram, and the melting-point, D, of the
compound may lie either higher or lower than that of either of the
components, or it may have an intermediate position. If more than
one compound with congruent melting-point can be formed, a series
of curves similar to CDE will be obtained—one for each compound.
In each case the maximum point on the curve gives the composition
of the compound and its melting-point.

With regard to the form of the curve CDE, it might be thought that
since D is the melting-point of a pure substance, and since this
melting-point (equilibrium point) will be lowered by addition of a
second substance to the liquid phase, the two branches of the curve
should not pass continuously one into the other, but *intersect* at the
point D. This would be the case if the compound were *completely
undissociated* into its components, even in the vapour phase, *e.g.*
the compound of pyridine and methyl iodide.[9] When, however, dissociation of the compound into the components takes place in the
liquid phase, we are dealing throughout with mixtures of molecules
in the liquid phase and the composition of this mixture varies continuously with the temperature. ' So long, therefore, as the solid
phase remains unchanged, the equilibrium curve must be continuous,

and the crest of the curve, CDE, will be rounded. The less the degree of dissociation of the compound in the liquid phase, the sharper will be the bend of the curve; and the greater the degree of dissociation, the flatter will the curve become.[10] From the extent of the flattening of the curve, it is possible, with some degree of approximation, to calculate the degree of dissociation of the compound in the fused state.[11]

Figure 40 is isobaric and we can predict from it the isobaric behaviour of any liquid mixture on cooling or, for that matter, of any solid mixture on heating. Consider mixture P at temperature T_P. It is under these conditions a homogeneous liquid. On cooling, the temperature drops down a vertical isopleth until the vertical through the point P meets the line AC. At this point, crystals of solid A first make their appearance and temperature and composition now change along AC in the direction of C. At C, a eutectic point, solid compound A_xB_y makes its appearance, and solidification goes to completion at constant temperature and composition. The final solid mass is a heterogeneous mixture of pure A and compound A_xB_y. A mixture of composition Q, cooled from the temperature T_Q will first deposit crystals of the compound A_xB_y at the temperature at which the vertical through Q meets the curve DC. Composition and temperature then change in the direction of the eutectic C with progressive separation of A_xB_y. At C, solid A makes its appearance and solidification goes to completion at constant temperature and with constant composition. Mixture R on cooling yields first compound A_xB_y followed at the temperature of the eutectic E by solid B: solidification to a heterogeneous mixture of A_xB_y and B. Mixture S yields first solid B, then the eutectic mixture of B and A_xB_y.

The phase reaction occuring at eutectics has already been discussed. At the maximum, D (Fig. 40), corresponding to the melting-point of the pure compound A_xB_y, the phase reaction on adding heat is:

$$A_xB_y \rightarrow L - \Delta H$$

The Indifferent Point. A two-component system consisting of only two phases, a solid and a liquid, possesses, according to the

Phase Rule, a variance of two. We have, however, just learned that a compound with a congruent melting-point may be formed in a two-component system, and that this melting-point varies only with the pressure. In other words, at the congruent melting-point of a compound of two components, the two-phase system, solid—liquid, is not bivariant, but univariant. *The variance of the system has therefore been diminished.*

A point such as that to which reference has just been made, which represents the special behaviour of a system of two (or more) components in which two phases become identical in composition, is known as an *indifferent point;* and it has been shown that, under a given pressure, the temperature at the indifferent point is the *maximum* or *minimum* temperature possible at the particular pressure [12] (*cf.* critical solution temperature). At such a point a system loses one (or more) degrees of freedom, or behaves like a system of a lower order.

An example of a system which forms compounds with congruent melting-points is that of water and ferric chloride which forms four stable compounds (hydrates), namely, $FeCl_3 \cdot 6H_2O$, $FeCl_3 \cdot 3\frac{1}{2}H_2O$, $FeCl_3 \cdot 2\frac{1}{2}H_2O$, and $FeCl_3 \cdot 2H_2O$. The equilibrium diagram is shown, in part, in Fig. 41. The points C, E, G, and J are

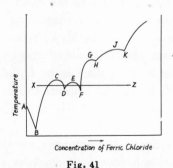

Fig. 41

the melting-points of the hydrates with $6H_2O$, $3\frac{1}{2}H_2O$, $2\frac{1}{2}H_2O$ and $2H_2O$ respectively; and the points D, F, H, and K are eutectic points at which the solid phases $6H_2O$ and $3\frac{1}{2}H_2O$, $3\frac{1}{2}H_2O$ and

$2\frac{1}{2}H_2O$, $2\frac{1}{2}H_2O$ and $2H_2O$, $2H_2O$ and anhydrous salt respectively coexist with solution.

After the detailed description, in connection with Fig. 40, of what happens on cooling any solution, the reader will have no difficulty in deciding what phases will separate on cooling any solution of ferric chloride in water. There remains the interesting question of what happens when a solution of ferric chloride in water is evaporated at constant temperature. Consider the point X Fig. 41, representing a solution rich in water and at a temperature lying between those of the eutectic F and the dystectic E. As water is removed by evaporation at constant temperature, the solution becomes richer in ferric chloride its composition moving along the isothermal XZ. When the composition reaches the curve BC, the solid compound $FeCl_3 \cdot 6H_2O$ begins to separate, the quantity of liquid solution becoming less until, when the residual mass has the exact composition of the hexahydrate, all will be solid. Further removal of water vapour will result in partial liquefaction until the total composition, moving along XZ, has reached the curve CD when all has again become liquid. The system now remains liquid until the composition reaches the curve DE, when separation of the $3\frac{1}{2}$ hydrate commences. This continues, as before, to complete solidification followed by partial liquefaction and then complete liquefaction as the line XZ passes through the curve EF. Solidification again commences when the point moving along XZ intersects the curve FG, with deposition of the $2\frac{1}{2}$ hydrate. Solidification becomes finally complete when the residual composition is that of the $2\frac{1}{2}$ hydrate and from here on there is no further liquefaction, although the solid $2\frac{1}{2}$ hydrate is converted to solid dihydrate and eventually to anhydrous ferric chloride as water is progressively removed.

Inevaporable Solutions. If a saturated solution in contact with two hydrates, or with a hydrate and anhydrous salt is heated, the temperature and composition of the solution will, of course, remain unchanged so long as the two solid phases are present, for such a system is invariant. In addition to this, however, the *quantity* of the solution will also remain unchanged, the water which evaporates being supplied by the higher hydrate. The same phenomenon is also observed in the case of eutectic points when ice is a solid phase; so long as the latter is present, evaporation will be accompanied by fusion of the ice, and the quantity of solution will remain constant. Such solutions are called *inevaporable*.

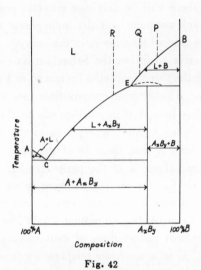

Fig. 42

(c) Compounds are Formed with an Incongruent Melting-point.

When a compound is formed which undergoes decomposition with formation of another solid phase at a temperature below the congruent melting-point of the compound, the equilibrium diagram assumes the general form shown in Fig. 42. This corresponds to the case where a compound can exist only in contact with solutions containing excess of one of the components. The metastable continuation of the equilibrium curve for the compound is indicated by the dotted line,[13] the summit of which would be the congruent melting-point of the compound. Before this temperature is reached, however, the solid compound ceases to be stable, and undergoes decomposition into another solid phase[14] and liquid at the point E. Since the composition of the liquid formed is not the same as that of the compound, this point is spoken of as an *incongruent melting-point, or peritectic point*. This point, therefore, represents the limit of the existence of the compound A_xB_y under the particular constant pressure which is assumed. If a series of compounds can be formed none of which possesses a congruent melting-point, then a series of curves will be obtained none of which exhibits a temperature maximum, and there will be only one eutectic point. The limits of existence of each compound (or the incongruent melting-point) will in each case be marked by a break in the curve.

It is instructive to follow the behaviour on cooling (at constant pressure) along the three isopleths indicated in Fig. 42 as P, Q and R respectively. These three compositions are so chosen that the first (P) contains less A than corresponds to the compound A_xB_y; the second (Q) more A than corresponds to the composition of the compound, but less A than there is at the peritectic point E; the third more A than there is at the peritectic but less A than there is at the eutectic C. On cooling P, there is no change in concentration of the melt until the isopleth meets the curve BE, when pure solid B begins to separate, the mother liquid becoming richer in A, and temperature and composition of melt moving along BE in the direction of E. E is a maximum temperature (under the given constant pressure) for the stable existence of compound A_xB_y. It is therefore a true transition point and is often spoken of as such. When temperature and composition of melt have reached the point E, the separated solid B reacts (provided it has not been previously removed) with the melt to form the compound. As, however, there is insufficient A in the melt to react with all the B present to form compound, solidification goes to completion, resulting in the formation of a heterogeneous solid mixture of B and A_xB_y. The behaviour along Q is similar until the point E is reached. As, however, there is now more than sufficient A in the original mixture to convert all the separated B into compound after the solid phase has been entirely converted to A_xB_y, liquid is still left at the point E. Therefore, after a halt of constant temperature at E, solidification continues along the curve EC, with separation of compound, until the eutectic C is reached, when the simultaneous separation of solid

A and compound begins and the system solidifies completely at this temperature. Whether in actual practice eutectic solidification would be observed is somewhat doubtful, since the mixture contains so small an excess of A over that required for the formation of the compound. On cooling the third mixture R, no transition temperature is observed, since the isopleth does not meet the curve BE The first solid phase to deposit is the compound, when the isopleth meets the curve EC. Eutectic solidification follows as before.

At the peritectic point the phase reaction on addition of heat to the system is: $S_1 \rightleftharpoons S_2 + L - \Delta H$, (pressure constant). This will be seen by following in the direction of higher temperature any isopleth at a composition between that of E and pure B. The nature of the phase reaction emphasises the fact that the peritectic point is a transition point, that is, a temperature above which the compound is incapable of stable existence.

An example of the type just discussed is found in the system sodium-potassium. [15] These two elements combine to form the incongruently melting compound Na_2K. Referring to Fig. 42 point A corresponds to the melting-point of potassium ($62°$), B to that of sodium ($97.5°$), and E to the incongruent melting-point of Na_2K, $7°C$. Here the composition of E is not greatly different from that of Na_2K. The solubility curve of the compound is, at the same time, nearly horizontal at its upper end, so that if the compound melted congruently, its melting-point would not be much higher than the actual incongruent melting-point.

Sodium Sulphate and Water. Another example of incongruent melting, which possesses several features of interest, and to which we shall also refer later (p. 239) in another connection, is the system sodium sulphate-water. At the ordinary temperatures, sodium sulphate crystallises from water with ten molecules of water of crystallisation, forming Glauber's salt. On determining the solubility of this salt in water, it is found that the solubility increases as the temperature rises, the values of the

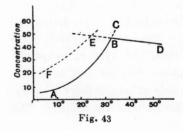

Fig. 43

solubility being represented graphically by the curve AC (Fig. 43),

On continuing the investigation at higher temperatures, it was found that the solubility no longer increases, but *decreases with rise of temperature.* At the same time, it was observed that the solid phase is now different from that in contact with the solution at temperatures below about 33°; for whereas in the latter case the solid phase is sodium sulphate decahydrate, at temperatures above 33° the solid phase is the anhydrous salt. The course of the solubility curve of anhydrous sodium sulphate is shown by BD.

As is evident from the figure, the solubility curve which is obtained when anhydrous sodium sulphate is present as the solid phase, cuts the curve representing the solubility of the decahydrate, at a temperature of about 32.4° (see below).

If a solution of sodium sulphate which has been saturated at a temperature of about 34° be cooled down to a temperature below 17° while care is taken that the solution is protected against access of particles of Glauber's salt, crystals of a second hydrate of sodium sulphate, having the composition $Na_2SO_4, 7H_2O$, separate out. On determining the composition of the solutions in equilibrium with this hydrate at different temperatures, the curve FE (Fig. 43) was obtained.

Since, as has already been stated, each solid substance has its own solubility curve, there are three separate curves to be considered in the case of sodium sulphate and water. Where two curves cut, the solution must be saturated with respect to two solid phases; at the point B, therefore, the point of intersection of the solubility curve of anhydrous sodium sulphate with that of the decahydrate, the solution must be saturated with respect to these two solid substances. But a system of two components existing in three phases, anhydrous salt —hydrated salt— solution, is invariant, if the pressure be constant. This is the case when solubilities are determined in open vessels; the pressure is then equal to atmospheric pressure. Under these circumstances, then, the system, anhydrous sodium sulphate — decahydrate — solution, will possess no degree of freedom, and can exist, therefore, only at one definite temperature and when the solution has a certain definite composition. The temperature of this point is 32.383°, or, in round figures, 32.4°,[16] and the solution contains 33.20 per cent. of anhydrous salt. This temperature is not quite the same as that of the quadruple point anhydrous salt —►hydrated salt —solution—vapour, because the latter is the temperature at which the system is under the pressure of its own vapour (see p.233). Since, however, the influence of pressure on the solubility is comparatively slight, the positions of the two points will not be greatly different. The quadruple point lies at 32.6° and 30.8 mm. of mercury.

The curve showing the change of the incongruent melting-point with pressure has been determined by Tammann,[17] and has been found to pass through a point of maximum temperature.

Suspended Transformation. Although it is possible for the anhydrous salt to make its appearance at the temperature of the quadruple point B (Fig. 43) it will not necessarily do so; and it is therefore possible to follow the solubility curve of sodium sulphate decahydrate to a higher temperature. Since, however, the solubility of the decahydrate at temperatures above the quadruple point is greater than that of the anhydrous salt, the solution which is *saturated* with respect to the former will be *supersaturated* with respect to the latter. On bringing a small quantity of the anhydrous salt in contact with the solution, therefore, anhydrous salt will be deposited; and all the hydrated salt present will ultimately undergo conversion into the anhydrous salt, through the medium of the solution. In this case, as in all cases, the solid phase, which is the most stable at the temperature of the experiment, has at that temperature the least solubility.

Similarly, the solubility curve of anhydrous sodium sulphate has been followed to temperatures below 32.4°. Below this temperature, the solubility of this salt is greater than that of the decahydrate, and the saturated solution of the anhydrous salt will therefore be supersaturated for the decahydrate, and will deposit this salt if a "nucleus" is added to the solution. From this we see that at temperatures above 32.4° the anhydrous salt is the stable form, while the decahydrate is unstable (or metastable); at temperatures below 32.4° the decahydrate is stable. This temperature, therefore, is the *transition temperature* for decahydrate and anhydrous salt.

From Fig. 43 we see further that the solubility curve of the anhydrous salt (which at all temperatures below 32.4° is metastable) is cut by the solubility curve of the heptahydrate; and this point of intersection (at a temperature of $24.2°$) must be the *transition point* for heptahydrate and anhydrous salt. Since at all temperatures the solubility of the heptahydrate is greater than that of the decahydrate, the former hydrate must be metastable with respect to the latter; so that throughout its whole course the solubility curve of the heptahydrate represents only metastable equilibria. Sodium sulphate, therefore, forms only one stable hydrate, the decahydrate.

The solubility relations of sodium sulphate illustrate very clearly the importance of the solid phase for the definition of saturation and supersaturation. Since the solubility curve of the anhydrous salt has been followed backwards to a temperature of about 18°, it is readily seen, that at a temperature of, say, 20°, three different *saturated* solutions of sodium sulphate are possible, according as the anhydrous salt, the heptahydrate or the decahydrate, is present as the solid phase. Two of these solutions, however, would be metastable and *supersaturated with respect to the decahydrate*.

Further, the behaviour of sodium sulphate and water furnishes a very good example of the fact that a "break" in the solubility curve occurs when, and only when, the solid phase undergoes change. So long as the decahydrate, for example, remains unaltered in contact with the solution, the solubility curve is continuous; but when the anhydrous salt appears in the solid phase, a distinct change in the direction of the solubility curve is observed.

Dehydration by Means of Anhydrous Sodium Sulphate. The change in the relative stability of sodium sulphate decahydrate and anhydrous salt in presence of water at a temperature of 32.4° explains why the latter salt cannot be employed for dehydration purposes at temperatures above the transition point. The dehydrating action of the anhydrous salt depends on the formation of the decahydrate; but since at temperatures above 32.4° the latter is unstable, and cannot be formed in presence of the anhydrous salt, this salt cannot of course, effect a dehydration above that temperature.

Since at the incongruent melting-point (transition point) of Glauber's salt, there are three phases in equilibrium, the system will, under constant pressure (say atmospheric) be invariant. The temperature, therefore, will be perfectly definite. On this account the proposal has been made to adopt this as a fixed point in thermometry.[18] The temperature is, as we have seen, affected only comparatively slightly by change of pressure.

Other Systems. In the case of sodium sulphate there is only one stable hydrate. Other salts are known which exhibit a similar behaviour; and we shall therefore expect that the solubility relationships will be represented by a diagram similar to that for sodium sulphate. A considerable number of such cases have, indeed, been found, and in some cases there is more than one metastable hydrate. This is found, for example, in the case of nickel iodate,[19] the solubility curves for which are given in Fig. 44. As can be seen from

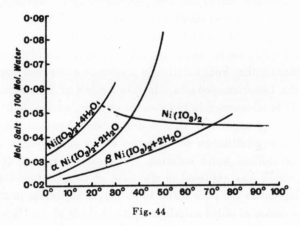

Fig. 44

the figure, suspended transformation occurs, the solubility curves having in some cases been followed to a considerable distance beyond the transition point. One of the most brilliant examples, however, of suspended transformation in the case of salt hydrates, and the sluggish transition from the less stable to the more stable form, is found in the case of the hydrates of calcium chromate.[20]

In the preceding cases, the solubility curve of the hydrated salt cuts the solubility curve of the anhydrous salt. It can, however, happen that the solubility curve of one hydrate cuts the solubility curve, not of the anhydrous salt, but of a lower hydrate; in this case there will be more than one stable hydrate, each having a stable solubility curve; and these curves will intersect at the temperature of the transition point. Various examples of this behaviour are known.

(d) Solid Solutions or "Mix-Crystals" are Formed.

The introduction by van't Hoff of the term "solid solution" resulted from the discovery of a number of deviations from the Raoult-van't Hoff law for the depression of the freezing-point by dissolved substances. In all cases, the depression was too small; in some instances, indeed, the freezing-point was raised. To explain these irregularities, van't Hoff assumed that the dissolved substance crystallised out along with the solid solvent; and he showed how this would account for the deviations from the law of the depression of the freezing-point, which had been developed on the assumption that only the pure solvent crystallises out from the solution.

Crystalline solid solutions can be formed either by sublimation[21] or from a liquid phase; and in the latter case the solid solution can be deposited either from solution in a common solvent or from a mixture of the fused components. In this method of formation, which alone will be discussed in the present chapter, we are dealing with the fusion curves of two substances, where, however, the liquid solution is in equilibrium not with one of the pure components, but with a crystalline solid solution. The simple scheme (Fig. 38, p. 135) which was obtained in the case of two components which crystallise out in the pure state, is no longer sufficient in the case of the formation of solid solutions. With the help of the Phase Rule, however, the different possible systems can be classified; and examples of the different cases predicted by the Phase Rule have also been obtained by experiment.

Just as two liquids may show partial miscibility so also may two solids. If the components are completely miscible in the solid state an unbroken series of solid solutions is formed; if partial miscibility, a broken series.

For the purpose of representing the relationships found here we shall again employ a temperature-concentration diagram (under constant pressure), in which the ordinates represent the temperature and the abscissae the concentration of the components. Since there are two solutions, the liquid and the solid, and since the concentration of the components in these two phases is not, in general, the same, two curves will be required, one relating to the liquid phase, the other relating to the solid. The temperature at which solid begins to be deposited from the liquid solution will be called the freezing-point of the solution, and the temperature at which the solid solution just begins to liquefy will be called the melting-point of the solid solution. The temperature-concentration curve for the liquid phase will therefore be the freezing-point curve; that for the solid solution, the melting-point curve. The latter may be represented by a dotted line. These curves are also very generally referred to as the "liquidus" and the "solidus" curve respectively.

(i) *The Two Components can form an Unbroken Series of Solid Solutions.*

Since a solid solution constitutes only one phase it is evident that if the two components are miscible with each other in all proportions in the solid state, there can never be more than one solid phase present, viz. a solid solution of varying composition. If the components are completely miscible in the solid state they will also be completely miscible in the liquid state, and there can therefore be only one liquid phase. The system cannot become invariant, (except in special cases) because there cannot be more than two phases present (under a constant pressure greater than the vapour pressure), viz. solid solution and liquid solution. Since the system is one of two components existing in two phases and one of the variables has been fixed, the system is isobarically univariant and the equilibrium curve is continuous. Of these systems three types are found:

(a) The freezing-points of all mixtures lie between the freezing-points of the pure components (Type I).

(b) The freezing-point curve passes through a maximum (Type II).

(c) The freezing-point curve passes through a minimum (Type III).

(a) The freezing-points of all mixtures lie between the freezing-points of the pure components (Curve I., Fig. 45). This type of curve is represented by the solid solutions of silver chloride and sodium chloride. The addition of sodium chloride to silver chloride raises the freezing point of the latter. The freezing-point curve is concave to the axis of concentration and joins the melting-points of the two components. The freezing-point curve thus lies above the straight line joining the freezing-points of the pure components. This is the usual form of the curve, although it sometimes lies below the straight line. The melting-point curve like the freezing-point curve, must also be continuous, and the melting-points of the different solid solutions will lie between the melting-points of the pure components. This is represented by the dotted line in Fig. 45, I. The relative position of the two curves, which can be deduced with the help of thermodynamics and also by experimental determination, is found in all cases to be in accordance with the following rule: At any given temperature, *the concentration of that component by the addition of which the freezing-point is depressed, is greater in the liquid than in the solid phase;* or, conversely, *the concentration of that component by the addition of which the freezing-point is raised, is greater in the solid than in the liquid phase.* An illustration of this rule is afforded by the two substances silver chloride and sodium chloride, just mentioned. The addition of silver chloride lowers the melting-point of sodium chloride. In accordance with the rule, therefore, the concentration of the silver chloride in the liquid phase must be greater than in the solid phase; and this was found experimentally.

From this it will also be clear that on cooling a fused mixture of two substances capable of forming solid solutions, the temperature of solidification will not remain constant during the separation of the solid; nor, on the other hand, will the temperature of liquefaction of the solid solution be constant. Thus, for example, if a liquid solution of two components, A and B, having the composition represented by the point x (Fig. 46), is allowed to cool, the system will pass along the line xx' . At the temperature of the point a, a solid solution will be deposited, the composition of which will be that represented by *b*. As the temperature continues to fall, more and more solid will be deposited; and since the solid phase is relatively rich in the component B, the liquid will become relatively poorer in this. The composition of the liquid solution will therefore pass along the curve *ad*, the composition of the solid solution at the same time passing along the curve *bc*; at the point *c* the liquid will solidify completely.[22]

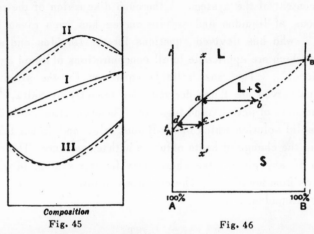

Fig. 45   Fig. 46

Conversely, if a solid solution of the composition and at the temperature *x'* is heated, liquefaction will begin at the temperature *c*, yielding a liquid of the composition *d*. On continuing to add heat, the temperature of the mass will rise, more of the solid will melt, the composition of the two phases will change as represented by the curves *da* and *cb*. When the temperature has risen to *a*, complete liquefaction will have occurred. The process of solidification or of liquefaction is therefore extended over a temperature interval *ac*.

Even when the freezing-point curve is a straight line joining the melting-points of the pure components, the melting-point curve will not necessarily coincide with the freezing-point curve, although it may approach very near to it; complete coincidence can take place only when the melting-points of the two components are identical. An example of this will be given later (p. 192).

Examples of this type are common in metallurgy and geology, *e.g.* the systems bismuth — antimony, copper — nickel and, in the field of geology, anorthite—albite.

A problem of great theoretical and practical interest is that of calculating the compositions of equilibrium liquid and solid solutions at any temperature. Since any phase transformation involves changes in the heat content, the composition and the volume, it should be possible thermodynamically to derive a relation between composition of the liquid and solid phases in equilibrium and the heat content of the system. A thorough discussion of the relative positions of liquidus and solidus curves has been given by van Laar,[23] who has devised equations for the liquidus and solidus curves which are applicable to all concentrations of liquid and solid solutions.   The most reliable equations for the solidus and liquidus curves are those derived more recently by Seltz,[24] using the concepts of activity and fugacity. These equations were derived for a solid solution which obeys Raoult's law and do not take into account the change of heats of fusion with temperature. Their application to any given case shows how far the system in question deviates from ideality.[25] The equations follow:

(a) Liquidus:

$$x_b^l = \frac{1 - K_a \cdot e^{L_a/RT_x}}{K_b \cdot e^{L_b/RT_x} - K_a \cdot e^{L_a/RT_x}}$$

or

$$x_b^l = \frac{1 - e^{(L_a/R)(1/T_x - 1/T_a)}}{e^{(L_b/R)(1/T_x - 1/T_b)} - e^{(L_a/R)(1/T_x - 1/T_a)}}$$

where $K_a = \dfrac{1}{e^{L_a/RT_a}}$ and $K_b = \dfrac{1}{e^{L_b/RT_b}}$

(b) Solidus:

$$x_b^s = x_b^l \cdot K_b \cdot e^{L_b/RT_x}$$

The symbols are:

R = Gas Constant.

L = Latent heat of fusion of solid per mole.

x = Concentration expressed as mole fraction.

T_x = Absolute freezing temperature of the solution.

T_a, T_b = Absolute freezing temperatures of pure components A and B respectively.

The subscripts a and b refer to components A and B, the superscripts l and s to the liquid and solid phases respectively.

(b) ***The freezing-point curve passes through a maximum*** (Curve II., Fig. 45). This curve exhibits the greatest degree of contrast

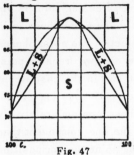

Fig. 47

with the freezing-point curve which is obtained when the pure components crystallise out. For since the curve passes through a maximum, it is evident that the freezing-point of each of the components must be *raised* by the addition of the other component.

Very few cases belonging to this type are known. The best example is found in the freezing-point curve of mixtures of *d*- and *l*-carvoxime[26] ($C_{10}H_{14}N \cdot OH$). The freezing-points and melting-points of the different mixtures of *d*- and *l*-carvoxime are represented graphically in Figure 47. In this figure, the melting-point curve, *i.e.* the temperature-concentration curve for the solid solutions, is represented by the lower curve. Since the addition of the lævo-form to the dextro-form raises the melting-point of the latter, the concentration of the lævo-form (on the right-hand branch of the curve) must, in accordance with the rule given, be greater in the solid phase than in the liquid. Similarly, since addition of the dextro-form raises the melting-point of the lævo-form, the solid phase (on the left-hand branch of the curve) must be richer in dextro- than in lævo-carvoxime. At the maximum point, the melting-point and freezing-point curves touch; at this point, therefore, the composition of the solid and liquid phases must be identical. It is evident, therefore, that at the maximum point the liquid will solidify, and the solid will liquefy completely without change of temperature; and, accordingly, a solid solution of the composition represented by the maximum point will exhibit a definite melting-point, and will in this respect behave like a simple substance.

Doubt has from time to time been cast upon the existence of this type of equilibrium curve, namely on the occurrence of a maximum. [27] Certainly, examples of the type are rare, though a number are quoted by Timmermans. [28] It seems, however, that the type is theoretically sound, despite its relatively infrequent occurrence.

(c) The freezing-point curve passes through a minimum. (Curve III., Fig. 45). In this case, as in the case of those systems where the pure components are deposited, a minimum freezing-point is obtained. Unlike the latter case, however, only one solid phase is in equilibrium with liquid phase: at a binary eutectic, two solid phases are present. In the latter case also, there are two freezing-point curves which intersect at the eutectic point, but in the case where mix-crystals are formed there is only one continuous curve. On one side of the minimum point the liquid phase contains relatively more, on the other side relatively less, of the one component than does the solid phase; while at the minimum point the composition of the two phases is the same. At this point, therefore, complete solidification and complete liquefaction will occur without change of temperature, and the solid solution will accordingly exhibit a definite melting-point.

As an example of this there may be taken the solid solutions of gehlenite and akermanite. [29] Gehlenite melts at 1592°, and akermanite at 1459°. The solid solution of constant melting-point (minimum point) contains about 74 per cent akermanite, the melting-point being 1388°C, Fig. 48 is a diagrammatic representation of this system.

The system KNO_3—$NaNO_3$, similarly, forms a continuous series of solid solutions with a minimum point at 225.7°, the composition being 55 per cent. KNO_3. [30]

Fractional Crystallisation of Solid Solutions. With the help of the diagrams already given it will be possible to predict what will be the result of the fractional crystallisation of a fused mixture of two substances which can form solid solutions. Suppose, for example, a fused mixture of the composition x (Fig. 49) is cooled down; then, as we have already seen, when the temperature has fallen to a, a solid solution of composition b is deposited. If the temperature is allowed to fall to x', and the solid then separated from the

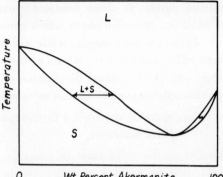

Fig. 48

liquid, all the solid solution so obtained will have the composition
represented by e. If, now, the solid solution e is completely fused
and the fused mass allowed to cool, separation of solid will occur
when the temperature has fallen to the point f. The solid solution
which is deposited has now the composition represented by g,
i.e. it is richer in B than the original solid solution. By repeating
this process, the composition of the successive crops of solid solu-

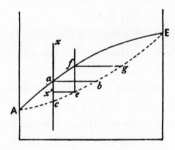

tions which are obtained approximates more and more to that of the
pure component B, while, on the
other hand, the composition of the
liquid phase produced tends to that
of pure A. By a systematic and
methodical repetition of the process
of fractional crystallisation, therefore, a *practically* complete separation of the components can be

Fig. 49

effected; a perfect separation is theoretically impossible. The
similarity of this process to that of fractional distillation (Fig.
29, p.116) will be obvious.

From this it will be readily understood that in the case of substances the freezing-point of which passes through a maximum,
fractional crystallisation will ultimately lead to a solid solution
having the composition of the maximum point, while the liquid phase
will more and more assume the composition of either pure A or pure

B, according as the initial composition was on the A side or the B side of the maximum point. In those cases, however, where the curves exhibit a minimum, the solid phase which separates out will ultimately be one of the pure components, while a liquid phase will finally be obtained which has the composition of the minimum point. Again, the analogy with the fractional distillation of binary liquid mixtures having azeotropic maxima or minima is complete.

(ii) *The Two Components do not Form a Continuous Series of Solid Solutions.*

Partial miscibility in the solid state is possible, just as it is in the liquid state, that is, solid A may dissolve in solid B, and solid B in solid A, up to a limit of saturation only, the temperature and pressure being constant. The equilibrium diagram is then identical with that of a partially miscible liquid pair: in both cases a critical solution temperature exists, which may or may not be realizable. Since solid solubility, like liquid solubility, usually increases with rising temperature, the critical solution temperature is usually approached with rising temperature, but a lower critical temperature is sometimes met, as in the case of solid solutions of ammonium chloride and manganous chloride dihydrate.[31]

If, at constant pressure, such a curve of partial miscibility in the solid state exists and lies completely below a liquid — solid equilibrium curve of any of the types of Fig. 45 then, on cooling the completely solidified system, the solid phase which was at first homogeneous will break up into two solid phases and become heterogeneous: this phenomenon is called ex-solution. The condition is represented in Fig. 50, where a liquid-solid equilibrium of Type I is assumed, though the form of this curve has no bearing on the matter so long as there is complete miscibility in the solid state at temperatures at which liquid can exist. S_1 and S_2 in the figure represent the two immiscible series of solids.

If a liquid of composition P is allowed to cool, it will commence to crystallise at temperature T_1 and, with sufficiently slow cooling, will eventually form a homogeneous solid of composition P at temperature T_2. From there down to temperature T_3, where the isopleth through P enters the region of partial (solid) miscibility, the solid remains homogeneous. At temperature T_3 an infinitely small amount of a new solid phase having the composition B begins to separate. As the temperature falls still lower, increasingly greater amounts of this phase separate, the composition varying, however, along the curve OC and that of the residual solid phase along OD. Then, at some lower temperature, say T_4, assuming that cooling has been slow enough for thermodynamic equilibrium to be established, the solid will consist of a heterogeneous mixture of two crystal forms having the compositions E and F and the amounts of which can be calculated from the inverse ratio of the intercepts XG and XH.

It is conceivable that at some pressure other than that of Fig.

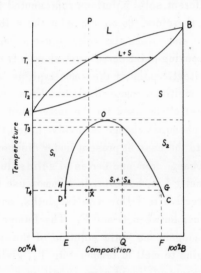

Fig. 50

50, the partial miscibility curve may approach and intersect the curve of liquid—solid equilibrium, giving rise to a liquidus curve with a break. This means, in effect, that the two components do not form a continuous series of solid solutions at temperatures at which liquid can exist. Two types of curve then arise, depending on whether the curve of partial miscibility in the solid state intersects an equilibrium diagram of type I or type III (Fig. 45): intersection with type II is impossible. We shall now consider these two types.

(a) *The freezing-point curve exhibits a transition point* (Fig. 51).

As is evident from the figure, addition of B raises the melting-point of A, and, in accordance with the rule previously given, the concentration of B in the solid solution will be greater than in the liquid solution. This is represented in the Figure by the dotted curve AD. On the other hand, addition of A lowers the melting-point of B, and the two curves BC and BE are obtained for the liquid and solid phases respectively. At the temperature of the line CDE the liquid solution of the composition represented by C is in equilibrium with the two different solid solutions represented by D and E. At this temperature, therefore, the *t-c* curve for the solid phase exhibits a discontinuity; and, since the solid phase undergoes change at this point, the freezing-point curve must show a break (p. 143). Such a break is a peritectic point of the same type as is observed with an incongruently melting compound. It has been suggested that the the term "meritectic" be used for the latter kind of discontinuity, that is, where a chemical change is involved, and that "peritectic" be applied only to the case at present under discussion, that is, the break is due to change from one series of solid solutions to another. The term "peritectic" is, however, in common use for both phenomena. It is instructive to follow two isopleths, one lying between C and D, the other between D and E. The former (composition P) is initially a homogeneous solid solution of the series S_1. As it is heated, it begins to melt at temperature T_1, giving rise to an infinitely small amount of liquid of composition F. As melting proceeds the temperature rises to that of the peritectic horizontal, the liquid composition changing to C and that of the solid to D. At this point there is still solid unmelted and the phase reaction $S_1 \rightarrow L + S_2$ takes place, that is, the solid D is converted completely to solid E, and more liquid of composition C. The temperature remains constant since three phases are present and the pressure is constant. When the last trace of D has disappeared, temperature rises along CB to T_2 when the last trace of solid, having the composition G, melts. Mixture Q is, at low temperature, a heterogeneous mixture of solid solutions S_1 and S_2. In this case, on heating,

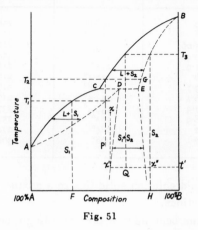

Fig. 51

no melting occurs until the peritectic temperature is reached, but the two solid solutions alter their compositions along their respective solid solubility lines. When the peritectic temperature is reached, the equilibrium solids have the compositions D and E respectively. Melting now takes place, at constant temperature, with production of liquid C, the phase reaction again being $S_1 \rightarrow L + S_2$. When the solid of composition $D(S_1)$ has completely melted, the system is now isobarically univariant one phase having disappeared. With further rise of temperature, the liquid changes in composition along CB up to the temperature T_3, when the last trace of solid having the composition H, melts.

Curves of the form given in Fig. 51 have been found experimentally in the case of silver nitrate and sodium nitrate.[32] The following table (p. 168) contains the numerical data, which are also represented graphically in Fig. 52.

The temperature of the transition point is $217.5°$; at this point the liquid contains 19.5, and the two conjugate solid solutions 26 and 38 molecules of sodium nitrate per cent. respectively.

(b) The freezing-point curve exhibits a eutectic point (Fig. 53).

In this case the freezing-point of each of the components is lowered by the addition of the other, until at last a point is reached

Molecules NaNO₂ per cent.	Freezing-point.	Melting-point.
0	208·6°	208·6°
8	211·4°	210°
15·06	215°	212°
19·46	217·2°	214·8°
21·9	222°	215°
26	228·4°	216·5°
29·7	234·8°	217·5°
36·2	244·4°	217·5°
47·3	259·4°	237·6°
58·9	272°	257°
72	284°	274°
100	308°	308°

at which the liquid solution solidifies to a mixture or conglomerate of two solid solutions.

After what has been said of the preceding type of diagram, the

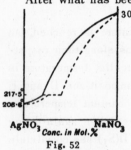

Fig. 52

isobaric behaviour along an isopleth can be disposed of shortly. An entirely solid mixture of composition P is heterogeneous, consisting of a mixture of solids, S_1 and S_2. The composition of the mixture is chosen to the left of the vertical through the eutectic composition. On heating, melting commences at the eutectic temperature, the phase reaction being, $S_1 + S_2 \rightarrow L$. Since the original mixture contains an excess of S_1 over the eutectic composition, S_2 disappears before S_1, and the system $S_1 + L$ is left. On further heating, the liquid composition follows the path CA, melting being complete at temperature T_1. Similarly ,the mixture Q melts at the eutectic temperature to give, eventually, $S_2 + L$ after which the liquid composition moves along the curve CB until melting is complete at temperature T_2.

At the eutectic point the liquid solution is in equilibrium with two different solid solutions, the composition of which is represented by D and E respectively. If, therefore, a fused mixture containing the two components A and B in the proportions represented by C is cooled down, it will, when the temperature has reached the point C, solidify completely to a *conglomerate* of two solid solutions, D and E.

Examples of this class are numerous, *e.g.* potassium nitrate

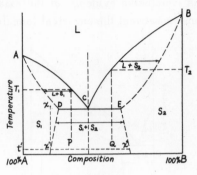

Fig. 53

thallous nitrate, naphthalene —— monochloracetic acid, mercuric iodide ——silver iodide, silver chloride——cuprous chloride, lead—antimony, silver—copper, lead—tin, cadmium—zinc, etc.

(c) A sixth type of solid solution is said to exist.[33]

According to this, solid B is not soluble in solid A until a certain minimum concentration of B is reached. Quantities of B larger than this critical minimum concentration dissolve to to give a homogeneous solid solution until a critical maximum concentration of B is reached beyond which it is no longer dissolved. In some cases one of these two critical concentrations corresponds to the composition of a known chemical compound, but in none is this true for both critical concentrations. A freezing-point diagram suggested by the case in which neither critical concentration corresponds to that of a compound is shown in Fig. 54, in which S denotes the solid solution and the other symbols have their usual meaning.

Several experimental examples of the occurrence of this type are quoted by Ricci, but, if it is real, it is difficult to see how it can be explained in terms of lattice behaviour. If the lattice of A will tolerate the entrance of B at all, why does it refuse to do so until the concentration of B in the liquid phase has attained a certain value? On the other hand, if it is claimed that a type of lattice different from those of either A or B exists in the region of solid solubility, then this new lattice would be considered, at least in metallography, as conclusive evidence of the existence of a compound, however unsymmetrical the empirical formula might be.

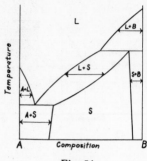

Fig. 54

Changes in Solid Solutions with the Temperature.   Referring again to Figs. 51 and 53, suppose that a solid solution of the composition x is cooled down. It will remain unchanged until, when the temperature has fallen to t', the homogeneous solid solution breaks up into a conglomerate of two solid solutions the composition of which is represented by x' and x'' respectively. From this, then, it can be seen that in the case of substances which form two solid solutions, the solid solutions which are deposited from the liquid fused mass need not remain unchanged in the solid state, but may at some lower temperature lose their homogeneity. This fact is of considerable importance for the formation of alloys and the mechanism of the process is at present being actively investigated by the method of X-ray analysis.[34]

When allotropic transformation takes place in completely solid systems which form solid solutions, the transition temperatures of the pure phases are altered and solid solubility curves are generated which may give rise to a eutectoid. For instance, the transition temperature for NH_4NO_3 IV $\rightleftharpoons$ NH_4NO_3 III lies at 32.3° C (*cf.* p. 78). By addition of potassium nitrate, in the form of solid solution in ammonium nitrate, this transition temperature is lowered, so that NH_4NO_3 III becomes the form stable at room temperature.[35]

In other cases, the transition temperature is raised: it depends on whether the added substance is more or less soluble in the form disappearing than in the form appearing. In the system NH_4NO_3—KNO_3, potassium nitrate is more soluble in NH_4NO_3 III than it is in NH_4NO_3 IV; hence the transition point is lowered. When transition temperatures are altered in this way by formation of solid solution with a foreign body, there will always be two solid solubility

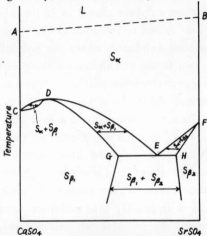

Fig. 55   CaSO₄   SrSO₄

curves expressing the solubility of the added substance in the two allotropic modifications. Such curves of solid solubility may intersect other curves of solid solubility, giving rise to eutectoid points, at which (in binary system) three solid phases are in equilibrium. The term "eutectoid" is identical in meaning with "eutectic", except that the change in the last syllable indicates that the system is entirely solid. In a binary system under constant pressure, invariance will be produced whenever three solid phases are in equilibrium: this invariant point will be a eutectoid if it is also a minimum temperature for the existence of the phase of intermediate composition. These points are well illustrated by a study of the system calcium sulphate—strontium sulphate,[36] (Fig. 55). A is the melting point of pure calcium sulphate (1450°), B that of pure strontium sulphate (1605°). Both substances are completely isomorphous in the high temperature (α) form. Hence the continuous curve AB (drawn dotted because it was not determined experimentally) is the freezing point curve (liquidus) for mixtures of calcium and strontium sulphates. If AB is the liquidus it must, of course, be accompanied by a solidus about which nothing is known. The area ABFEDC represents the region of stable existence of homogeneous mix-crystals of the α-series of calcium and strontium sulphates. C is the transition point (1193°) at which $\alpha CaSO_4$ passes into $\beta CaSO_4$. Since strontium sulphate is at first more soluble in the β form of calcium sulphate than it is in the α form, the transition point is at first raised to the point D (11° above the transition point of pure calcium sulphate), where the solubility of strontium sulphate in the two forms of calcium sulphate becomes the same (about 20 mole per cent strontium sulphate). From here on, strontium sulphate is more soluble in the α form of calcium sulphate than it is in the β form. Hence the transition temperature is now depressed to the point E (1006°), when the β form of calcium sulphate is saturated with strontium sulphate (the point G represents this saturation capacity). Point F is the $\alpha \rightarrow \beta$ transition point of pure strontium sulphate. Since calcium sulphate is always more soluble in $\alpha Sr SO_4$ than it is in $\beta Sr SO_4$ this transition temperature is continuously depressed by addition of calcium sulphate until the eutectoid temperature E is reached, when $\beta Sr SO_4$ is saturated with calcium sulphate (point H). On the eutectoid horizontal GEH the three phases G, E and H coexist; these phases are: saturated solution of strontium sulphate in calcium sulphate of β series (β_1), saturated solution of calcium sulphate in strontium sulphate of β-series (β_2) and equilibrium solid solution of the α-series of composition E. The phase reaction on heating any mixture in the gap GH is $\beta_1 + \beta_2 \rightarrow \alpha$. Such eutectoids are common in the more complicated systems: for instance, there is a well-known one in the iron—carbon system (*v. infra*).

II. The Components are not Completely Miscible in the Liquid State.

When one passes to the consideration of the equilibrium relations which exist in the case of two components which are not completely miscible in the liquid state, the additional complexity is introduced that at a certain value of the temperature and composition two liquid phases are formed. Since, at this point, there now coexist three phases, solid and two liquids, the system is invariant, at constant pressure. Not only the temperature, therefore, but also the compositions of the two liquid phases must have definite values. If the solid phase is allowed to be absent, then the system becomes univariant, and the composition of the two liquid phases will alter with the temperature. Into the ordinary equilibrium diagram there will be introduced a curve for the relation between the temperature and the composition of the two liquid phases.

To illustrate the behaviour of such a system, we may consider the complete equilibrium diagram for the system water—phenol, which was fully studied by Campbell.[37]

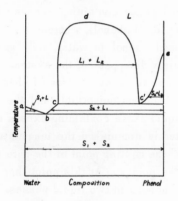

Fig. 56

If to the system ice—water at 0° phenol is added, the temperature will fall; and continued addition of phenol will lead at last to the eutectic point b (Fig. 56), at which solid phenol, ice and solution can coexist. The temperature of the eutectic point is -1.3°, and the composition of the solution is 5.8 per cent phenol. From a to b the solid phase in contact with the solution is ice. If the temperature be now raised so as to cause the disappearance of the ice, and the addition of phenol be continued, the concentration of the phenol in the solution will increase as represented by the curve bc. The solid phase in equilibrium with the solutions represented by the curve bc is phenol. At the point c, (1.3°), when the concentration of the phenol in the solution has increased to 6.8 per cent, the phenol melts and two liquid phases are formed; the concentration of the phenol in these two phases is given by the points c and c · As there are now three phases present, viz. solid phenol, solution of fused phenol in water and solution of water in fused phenol, the system is invariant, at constant pressure. Since at this point the concentration, temperature, and pressure are completely defined, addition or withdrawal of heat can only cause a change in the relative amounts of the phases, but no variation of the concentrations of the respective phases. As a matter of fact, continued addition of phenol and addition of heat will cause an increase in the amount of the liquid phase containing excess of phenol (*i.e.* the solution of water in fused phenol), whereas the other liquid phase, the solution of fused phenol in water, will gradually disappear. When it has completely disappeared, the system will be represented by the point c , where the concentration of phenol is now 76.0 per cent, and it again becomes univariant, and the two phases being solid phenol and liquid phase containing excess of phenol. As the amount of the water is diminished the temperature of equilibrium rises, until at 42.5° the melting point of the pure phenol is reached.

Return now to the point c. At this point there exists the invariant system, solid phenol and two liquid phases. If heat be added, and the total composition kept between c and c′, the solid phenol will disappear, and there will be left the univariant system consisting of two liquid phases. Such a system will exhibit relationships similar to those already studied in a previous chapter.

At all temperatures and concentrations lying above the curve abcdce there can be only one liquid phase. At all temperatures between 1.3° and 66.8°, mixtures having a total composition represented by a point within the area cdc′ will separate into two liquid phases. As the temperature rises, the mutual solubility of the two fused components becomes greater and, when the curve cdc′ is crossed, homogeneity results. One mixture, namely that having the critical composition, will remain heterogeneous until the critical solution temperature (66.8°) is reached.

In this discussion of the system phenol—water, it should be pointed out that it is claimed that a solid compound of phenol and water, a hydrate, exists and that, therefore, the diagram as given here represents a metastable system.[38] Even if this is true it does not in the least diminish the validity of the diagram as a representation of the general behaviour. In any case, this hydrate never comes into existence under ordinary conditions.

"Melting Under the Solvent." It is a common observation in the practice of organic chemistry that when a solid substance is heated with a solvent, with the object, say, of recrystallising the solid, it appears to melt at a temperature much below the normal melting-point. The phenomenon is illustrated by the behaviour of benzoic acid heated with water, the equilibrium diagram for which system is reproduced in Fig. 57. After what has been said about the behaviour of the system phenol—water, the explanation is almost self-evident. Addition of water to benzoic acid lowers its melting point from about 120 to 95°. Further addition of water, at constant temperature, causes the formation of two liquid layers, a saturated solution of water in benzoic acid and of benzoic acid in water. At the invariant point, the concentrations of the two layers are about 5 and 75 per cent benzoic acid, respectively: the critical solution

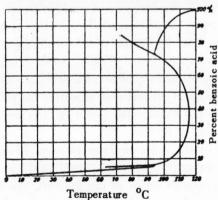

Temperature °C

Fig. 57

temperature is about 115°. Hence, if benzoic acid is mixed with water in any proportions lying between 10 and 70 per cent benzoic acid and the solution heated say, to 100° it will separate into two liquid layers, that layer, however, which appears to be molten benzoic acid being actually a solution of water in benzoic acid.

Suspended Transformation. Just as suspended transformation is rarely met with in the passage from the solid to the liquid state, so also it is found that in the case of the melting of substances under the solvent suspended fusion does not occur, but that when the temperature of the invariant point is reached at which, therefore, the formation of two liquid layers is possible, these two liquid layers, as a matter of fact, make their appearance. Suspended transformation can, however, take place from the side of the liquid phase, just as water or other liquid can be cooled below the normal freezing-point without solidification occurring. The question, therefore, arises as to the position of the equilibrium curve for the metastable, supercooled liquid phase.

The answer to this question can at once be given when we reflect that at temperatures at which the two liquid phases are metastable, the stable system, solid + liquid, must be capable of being formed from the metastable by separation of the solid phase. If, however, separation of the solid phase takes place, the residual liquid, which is in equilibrium with the solid phase, must contain a lower proportion of the crystallising component than does the metastable liquid. This was first proved experimentally in the case of benzoic acid and water (Fig. 57). As can be seen from the figure, the prolongation *ba* of the curve for liquid —liquid, which represents the solubility of the supercooled liquid benzoic acid, lies above that for the solubility of the solid benzoic acid in water; the solution saturated with respect to the supercooled liquid is therefore supersaturated with respect to the solid form.

Binary Equilibria at Lower Temperatures. While freezing-point diagrams give valuable information regarding the state of a system within the temperature limits of the diagram, the information obtained for high-melting solids does not necessarily remain valid, for example, at room temperature. For the study of binary systems at lower temperatures, the method is frequently applied of adding a third component which does not react with either of the two solids.[39] The **system** thus becomes one of three components, the inert diluent (**frequently** water) functioning as a solvent. Such systems will be considered under three-component systems (Chap. XVII).

III. Factors Affecting Solubility.

From what has been said earlier it will be clear that in aqueous systems of the type represented in Fig. 38, p. 135, in which no compound is formed between the components, *the so-called solubility curve, or the curve which represents the composition of solutions in equilibrium with the solid solute at different temperatures, is identical with the equilibrium curve or freezing-point curve of the fused solute in presence of water.* While it is of importance always to bear this fact in mind, it is nevertheless advantageous to give separate and special consideration to the question of solubility and solubility curves, owing both to differences in experimental method and to the special interests involved in their study.

When a solid is brought into contact with a liquid in which it can dissolve, a certain amount of it passes into solution; and the process continues until the concentration reaches a definite value independent of the amount of solid present. A condition of equilibrium is established between the solid and the solution; the solution becomes *saturated*. Since the number of components is two, and the number of phases three, viz. solid, liquid solution, vapour, the system is univariant. If, therefore, one of the factors, pressure, temperature, or concentration of the components (in the solution),[40] is arbitrarily fixed, the state of the system becomes perfectly defined. Thus, at any given temperature, the vapour pressure of the system and the concentration of the components have a definite value. If the temperature is altered, the vapour pressure and also, in general, the concentration, will undergo change. Likewise, if the pressure varies, while the system is isolated so that no heat can pass between it and its surroundings, the concentration and the temperature must also undergo variation until they attain values corresponding to the particular pressure.

Considering, for the present, those systems in which only solid and liquid phases are present, it is clear that the system solid—

liquid (solution) will be bivariant. If the pressure is maintained constant, the composition of the solution will vary with the temperature; or, on the other hand, if the temperature is maintained constant, the composition of the solution will vary with the pressure. The influence of temperature on the solubility of a solid in water is sufficiently appreciated; the effect of pressure, although not so well known, is no less certain.

The Saturated Solution. From what has been said above, it will be seen that the condition of saturation of a solution can be defined only with respect to a certain solid phase; if no solid is present, the system is undefined, for it then consists of only two phases, and is therefore bivariant. Under such circumstances not only can there be at one given temperature solutions of different concentration, all containing less of one of the components than when that component is present in the solid form, but there can also exist solutions containing more of that component than corresponds to the equilibrium when the solid is present. In the former case the solutions are *unsaturated,* in the latter case they are *supersaturated with respect to a certain solid phase;* in themselves, the solutions are stable, and are neither unsaturated nor supersaturated. Further, if the solid substance can exist in different allotropic modifications, the particular form of the substance which is in equilibrium with the solution must be known, in order that the statement of the solubility may be definite; for each form has its own solubility, and, as we shall see presently, the less stable form has the greater solubility (*cf.* p. 183). In all determinations of the solubility, therefore, not only must the concentration of the components in the solution be determined, but equal importance should be attached to the characterisation of the solid phase present.

In this connection, also, one other point may be emphasised. For the production of the equilibrium between a solid and a liquid, time is necessary, and this time not only varies with the state of division of the solid and the efficiency of the stirring, but is also dependent on the nature of the substance.[40] Considerable care must therefore be taken that sufficient time is allowed for equilibrium to be established. Such care is more especially needful when changes may occur in the solid phase, and neglect of it has greatly diminished the value of many of the older determinations of solubility.[41]

(a) The Pressure Factor.

The direction in which change of concentration will occur with change of pressure can be predicted by means of the principle of Le Chatelier, if it is known whether increase or diminution of volume takes place when the substance dissolves in an almost saturated solution. If diminution of the total volume of the system occurs on solution, increase of pressure will increase the solubility; in the reverse case, increase of pressure will diminish the solubility.

The effect of pressure on the solubility has been made the subject of both mathematical and experimental investigation. The following equation is easily derived thermodynamically:

$$\left(\frac{\partial L}{\partial p}\right)_T \bigg/ \left(\frac{\partial L}{\partial T}\right)_p = - T \cdot \frac{\Delta V}{\Delta H}$$

where $(\partial L/\partial p)_T$ is the pressure coefficient of solubility, $(\partial L/\partial T)_p$ the temperature coefficient of solubility, ΔV the total change of volume when one mole of the solute goes into solution under equilibrium conditions (that is, into an infinite amount of the nearly saturated solution), ΔH the heat absorbed when one mole dissolves under the same conditions, and T the absolute temperature. Because at least two of the above quantities may have different algebraic signs in any one case, it is apparent that the quantity $(\partial L/\partial p)_T$ may be positive or negative, depending on the substance investigated, that is, the solubility may increase or may decrease with increasing pressure, depending on the system investigated.

Accurate determinations of the influence of pressure on solubility, extending over a great range of pressure, have been carried out by Cohen and his collaborators[42] and by others. Some of their results are given in the following tables (p. 180).

The values of Δv for thallous sulphate — water, naphthalene — tetrachlorethane, and *m*-dinitrobenzene → ethylacetate are -0.0491, + 0.1313, and + 0.0442 c.c. per gram respectively.

From the values of the solubility, more especially of *m*-dinitro-

Pressure in atm.	Solubility of mannitol at 24·05° (grams of solute in 100 grams of water).	Solubility of thallous sulphate at 30·00° (grams of solute in 100 grams of saturated solution).	Solubility of naphthalene in tetrachlorethane at 30·00° (grams of solute in 100 grams of solution).
I	20·66	5·83	35·07
250	20·92	—	30·26
500	21·14	7·48	26·40
1000	21·40	9·03	20·89
1500	21·64	10·50	—

Pressure.	Solubility of m-dinitrobenzene in ethyl acetate at 30·00° (grams of solute in 100 grams of solvent).
0	52·54
100	49·97
220	47·06
300	45·39
480	42·02

benzene in ethyl acetate and of naphthalene in tetrachlorethane, it will be clear that the pressure may, in some cases, bring about a very considerable change in the solubility. For all practical purposes, however, the solubility determined under atmospheric pressure may be taken as equal to the solubility when the system is under the pressure of its own vapour.

(b) The Temperature Factor.

The solubility curve—that is, the curve representing the change of concentration of the components in the solution with the temperature — differs markedly from the curve of vapour pressure (p. 21), in that it possesses no general form, but may vary in the most diverse manner. Not only may the curve have an almost straight and horizontal course, or slope or curve upwards at varying angles; but it may even slope downwards, corresponding to a decrease in the solubility with rise of temperature (known as retrograde solubility); may exhibit maxima or minima of solubility, or may, as in the case of some hydrated salts, pass through a point of maximum temperature. In the latter case the salt may possess two values of solubility at the same temperature. Examples of this type belong to the class of congruently melting compounds (*cf.* Figs. 40 and 41).

The great variety of form shown by solubility curves is at once apparent from Fig. 58, in which the solubility curves of various substances (not, however, drawn to scale) are reproduced.

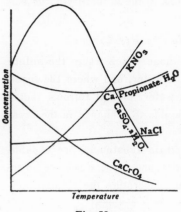

Fig. 58

Varied as is the form of the solubility curve, its *direction*, nevertheless, can be predicted by means of the principle of Le Chatelier; for in accordance with that theorem (p. 22) increase of solubility with the temperature must occur in those cases where the process of solution is accompanied by an *absorption* of heat; and a decrease in the solubility with rise of temperature will be found in cases where solution occurs with *evolution* of heat. Where there is no heat effect accompanying solution, change of temperature will be without influence on the solubility; and if the sign of the heat of solution changes, the direction of the solubility curve must also change, *i.e.* must show a maximum or minimum point. This has in all cases been verified by experiment.

When applying the principle of Le Chatelier to the course of the solubility curve, the partial molal heat of solution to be considered is the heat absorption attending the solution of a mole of solute in a very large quantity of almost saturated solution: it is obvious that this quantity cannot be obtained by direct experiment, but it can by graphical extrapolation. Not only may be the magnitude of this so-called "last heat of solution" be very different from that of dissolving solute in pure solvent, but it may even differ as to sign.

Despite its many forms, it should be particularly noted that the solubility curve is, for any given substance, *continuous*, so long as the solid phase, or solid substance in contact with the solution, remains unchanged. If any "break" or discontinuous change in the direction of the curve occurs, it is a sign that the *solid phase has undergone alteration.* Conversely, if it is known that a change takes place in the solid phase, a break in the solubility curve can be predicted

(c) The Nature of the Solid Phase (Allotropy).

If the discussion is limited to those cases where the solute forms no compound (hydrate) with the water, and where the fused solute is completely miscible with water, then it follows that a break in the solubility curve must be due to a change in the crystalline form of the solid solute.

We have already learned that certain substances are capable of existing in various crystalline forms, and these forms are so related to one another that at a given temperature the relative sta-

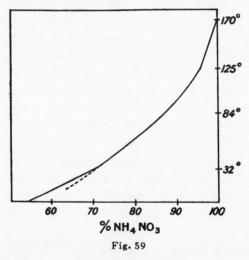

Fig. 59

bility of each pair of allotropic forms undergoes change. Since each crystalline variety of a substance must have its own solubility, there must be a break in the solubility curve at the temperature of transition of the two enantiotropic forms (*cf.* p. 154). At this point the two solubility curves must cut, for since the two forms are in equilibrium with respect to their vapour (p. 37), they must also be in equilibrium with respect to their solutions.

The break in the solubility curve of an enantiotropic substance has been verified, more especially in the case of ammonium nitrate[43] and thallous picrate.[44]

In the following table are given the values of the solubility of ammonium nitrate in water from 0° to the melting-point, 169.6°:

SOLUBILITY OF AMMONIUM NITRATE.

Temperature.	Solid phase.	Solubility (grams of NH₄NO₃ in 100 grams of solution).
0°	NH_4NO_3 (β-rhombic)	54·2
6·2°	„ „	59·70
24·5°	„ „	68·03
31·9°	„ „	71·05
34·3°	NH_4NO_3 (α-rhombic)	71·84
43·7°	„ „	75·71
58·4°	„ „	80·24
72·4°	„ „	84·43
83·8°	„ „	87·11
100·1°	NH_4NO_3 (rhombohedral)	91·10
120·8°	„ „	95·23
135·8°	NH_4NO_3 (regular)	97·14
157°	„ „	98·95
170°	„ „	100·0

On plotting these values, the curve shown in Fig. 59 is obtained. The curve shows distinct breaks at 32° (transition point for β- and α-rhombic) and at 125° (transition point for rhombohedral and regular or cubic). No detectible break, however, was observed at 84° (transition point for α-rhombic and rhombohedral), showing that the temperature coefficients of solubility of α-rhombic and rhombohedral ammonium nitrate are practically the same.

Suspended Transformation and Supersaturation. As has already been learned, the transformation of the one crystalline form into the other does not necessarily take place immediately the transition point has been passed; and it has therefore been found possible in a number of cases to follow the solubility curve of a given crystalline form beyond the point at which it ceases to be the most stable modification. Now, it will be evident from Fig. 59 that if the solubility curves for rhombohedral and regular ammonium nitrate be prolonged beyond the point of intersection, the solubility of the less stable form is greater than that of the more stable (*cf.* p. 153). Above 125°, for example, rhombohedral ammonium nitrate (meta-

stable) is more soluble than regular ammonium nitrate (stable). A
solution, therefore, which is saturated with respect to the less
stable form, *i.e.* which is in equilibrium with that form, is *supersaturated with respect to the more stable modification.* If, therefore, a small quantity of the more stable form is introduced into the
solution, the latter must deposit such an amount of the more stable
form that the concentration of the solution corresponds to the solubility of the stable form at the particular temperature. Since, however, the solution is now *unsaturated* with respect to the less stable
variety, the latter, if present, must pass into solution; and the two
processes, deposition of the stable and solution of the metastable
form, must go on until the latter form has entirely disappeared and a
saturated solution of the stable form is obtained. There will thus
be a conversion, through the medium of the solvent, of the less
stable into the more stable modification. This behaviour is of
practical importance in the determination of transition points.

From the above discussion it will be seen how important is the
statement of the solid phase for the definition of saturation and
supersaturation.[45]

NOTES

1. Washburn and Read, *Proc. Nat. Acad. Sci.*, 1915, 1, 191; Hildebrand,
Solubility (Chemical Catalog Co.); van Laar, *Z. physikal. Chem.*, 1908, **63**,
216; 1908, **64**, 257; 1909, **66**, 197.

2.   The temperature of the eutectic point will vary with the pres-
sure in accordance with the Clapeyron equation $d\mathrm{T}/dp = \mathrm{T} \cdot \triangle v/Q$ where
Q is the heat absorbed when c gram-molecules of component A and $(1 - c)$
gram-molecules of component B melt to yield the eutectic mixture, and
$\triangle v$ is the change of volume accompanying this change. On the other hand,
if the temperature is kept constant, the concentration of the eutectic solution will change with pressure in accordance with the expression
$d\log_e c/dp = - \triangle v/\mathrm{RT}$, assuming that the vapour of the solution obeys the
gas laws. (See Puschin and Grebenschtschikov, *Z. physikal. Chem.*, 1925,
118, 276; Puschin, *ibid.*, p. 447.) As, however, the eutectic temperature
varies with pressure, this equation cannot be used to calculate the eutectic
curve, except perhaps in the immediate neighbourhood of the (normal)

eutectic temperature. The exact equations connecting eutectic temperature, eutectic composition, and pressure have been deduced by McKay and Higman. (*Phil. Mag.*, 1935, (7), **19**, 367). An equation has been established by Kordes (*Z. physikal. Chem.*, 1932, **162**, 103) by means of which the complete crystallisation diagrams of binary eutectic systems can be calculated.

3. *Z. physikal. Chem.*, 1907, **58**, 350.

4. *Proc. Roy. Soc.*, 1935 (A), **152**, 81.

5. Stoffel, *Z. anorg. allg. Chem.*, **53**, (1907), 149; Fischer, *Z. techn. Physik*, **6**, (1925), 146.

6. Bowen, *Am. J. Sci.*, **40**, 161, (1915).

7. The solid phase other than ice is not always the anhydrous salt. Frequently it is a hydrate.

8. If in the neighbourhood of the eutectic point solution should be accompanied by an evolution of heat, then as the solubility would in that case increase with fall of temperature, salt would pass into solution.

9. Aten, *Proc. K. Akad. Wetensch. Amsterdam*, 1904, **7**, 468.

10. Kurnakov and Solovev, *Proc. J. Russ. Phys. Chem. Soc.*, 1916, **48**, 1333; Stortenbeker, *Z. physikal. Chem.*, 1892, **10**, 194.

11. Bancroft, *J. Physical Chem.*, 1899, **3**, 72; Roozeboom and Aten, *Z. physikal. Chem.*, 1905, **53**, 463; Kremann, *Z. Elektrochem.*, 1906, **12**, 259; Findlay and Hickmans, *J. Chem. Soc.*, 1907, **91**, 905; Kendall and Booge, *J. Chem. Soc.*, 1925, **127**, 1768; Ross and Somerville, *J. Chem. Soc.*, 1926, p. 2770.

12. In the case of the fusion of a compound of two components with formation of a liquid phase of the same composition, the temperature is a maximum; in the case of liquid mixtures of constant boiling-point, the temperature may be a minimum.

13. The hypothetical maximum on this metastable curve, known as a "concealed maximum," represents the temperature at which the compound would melt congruently, if it did not previously melt incongruently (decompose) at the transition temperature of the point E.

14. This solid phase may be another compound, or it may be a pure component. It is the latter case which is represented in **Fig. 42.**

15. E. Rinck, *Compt. rend.*, 1933, **197**, 49.

16. Richards, *Z. physikal. Chem.*, 1898, **26**, 690; Richards and Wells, *ibid.*, 1903, **43**, 465; Dickinson and Mueller, *J. Amer. Chem. Soc.*, 1907, **29**, 1381.

17. *Z. physikal. Chem.*, 1903, **46**, 818.

18. Richards, *Z. physikal. Chem.*, 1898, **26**, 690. A number of other salt hydrates, having transition points ranging from $20°$ to $78°$, which might be used for the same purpose, have been given by Richards and Churchill, *ibid.*, 1899, **28**, 313; Richards and Wells, *ibid.*, 1906, 56, 348; Richards and Wrede, *ibid.*, 1908, **61**, 313; Richards and Fiske, *J. Amer. Chem. Soc.*, 1914, **36**, 485.

19. Meusser, *Ber.*, 1901, **34**, 2440.

20. Mylius and von Wrochem, *Ber.*, 1900, **33**, 3693.

21. Bruni and Padoa, *Atti Accad. Lincei*, 1902 [5], **11**, 1, 565.

22. It should be remarked that the behaviour described here will hold strictly only when the solid solution undergoes change (by diffusion) sufficiently rapidly to be always in equilibrium with the liquid. This, however, is not always the case (see Reinders, *Z. physikal. Chem.*, 1900, 32, 494; van Wyk, *Z. anorgan. Chem.*, 1905, **48**, 25), and complete solidification will not in this case take place at the temperature corresponding with the line *dc* in Fig. 46 but only at a lower temperature. See also Tammann, *Z. physikal. Chem.*, 1898, **26**, 314; von Lepkowski, *Z. anorgan. Chem.*, 1908, **59**, 285. For a study of the spontaneous crystallisation of solid solutions, see Miers and Isaac, *J. Chem. Soc.*, 1908, **93**, 927; F. Isaac, *Proc. Roy. Soc.*, 1913, A, **88**, 205. See, also Kordes, *Z. physikal. Chem.*, 1931, **152**, 161.

23. J. J. van Laar, *Z. physikal. Chem.*, 1906, **55**, 435.

24. H. Seltz, *J. Amer. Chem. Soc.*, 1934, **56**, 307. For non-ideal solid solutions see Seltz, ibid., 1935, **57**, 391.

25. For an example see Campbell and Prodan, *ibid.*, 1948, **70**, 553.

26. Adriani, *Z. physikal. Chem.*, 1900, **33**, 469.

27. van Laar, *Z. physikal. Chem.*, 1908, **63**, 216; Jänecke, "Kurzgefasstes Handbuch aller Legierungen", p. 20 (Spamer, Leipzig, 1937); Campbell, Nature, 1944, **153**, 530.

28. Timmermans, Nature, 1944, **154**, 24.

29. Ferguson and Buddington, *Amer. J. Sci.*, 1920 (4), **50**, 131.

30. Briscoe and Madgin, *J. Chem. Soc.*, 1923, **123**, 1608.

31. Clendinnen and Rivett, *J. Chem. Soc.*, 1923, **123**, 1344.

32. Hissink, *Z. physikal. Chem.*, 1900, **32**, 542.

33. Ricci, *J. Amer. Chem. Soc.*, 1935, **57**, 807.

34. Sachs, *Z. Metallk.*, 1932, **24**, 241.

35. Campbell and Campbell, *Can. J. Research*, 1946, B **24**, 93.

36. Grahmann, Jahrb. Min., 1920, **1**, 1.

37. Campbell and Campbell, *J. Amer. Chem. Soc.*, 1937, **59**, 2481.

38. Rhodes and Markley, *J. Phys. Chem.*, 1921, **25**, 530.

39. Cf. Freeth, *J. Physical Chem.*, 1925, **29**, 497.

40. Since this is the only phase of variable composition present.

41. Van't Hoff, *Arch. néerland*, 1901 [2], **6**, 471; Hill, *J. Am. C. S.*, 1937, **59**, 2243; Hill, Smith and Ricci, *J. Am. C. S.*, 1940, **62**, 862.

42. Cohen and Sinnige, *Z. physikal. Chem.*, 1909, **67**, 432; Cohen, Inouye and Euwen, *ibid.*, 1910, **75**, 257; Cohen and Moesveld, *ibid.*, 1919, **93**, 385; Cohen, Voller, and Moesveld, *ibid.*, 1923, **104**, 323; Cohen, Ishikawa, and Moesveld, *ibid.*, 1923, **105**, 155; Cohen, Hetterschij, and Moesveld, *ibid.*, 1920, **94**, 210; Cohen, de Meester, and Moesveld, *ibid.*, 1924, **114**, 321; Cohen and van den Bosch, *ibid.*, 1925, **114**, 453. Adams and Hall, *Jour. Wash. Acad. Sci.*, 1931, **21**, 183. See also Cohen, *Physico-chemical Metamorphosis and Problems in Piezochemistry.* Cohen and Schut, *Piezochemie kondensierter Systeme*, Leipzig, 1919.

43. Müller and Kaufmann, *Z. physikal. Chem.*, 1903, **42**, 497; Millican, Joseph, and Lowry, *J. Chem. Soc.*, 1922, **121**, 959.

44. Rabe, *Z. physikal. Chem.*, 1901, **38**, 175.

45. With regard to the limits of supersaturation and the spontaneous crystallisation of the solute from supersaturated solutions, see Jaffé, *Z. physikal. Chem.*, 1903, **43**, 565; Miers and Isaac, *J. Chem. Soc.*, 1906, **89**, 413; 1908, **93**, 384; Hartley, Jones, and Hutchinson, *ibid.*, 825; Jones, *ibid.*, 1739; Fouquet, *Compt. rend.*, 1910, **150**, 280, Campbell and Campbell, *T. Faraday Soc.*, 1937, **33**, 299. For a theoretical discussion of super-saturation, see Jones and Partington, *Phil., Mag.*, 1915, **29**, 35. See also

Cohen and Moesveld, *Z. physikal. Chem.*, 1920, **94**, 482. A formula for the crystallisation velocity constant has been deduced by E. N. Gapon, *J. Russ. Phys. Chem. Soc.*, 1929, **61**, 2327.

CHAPTER IX

MISCELLANEOUS EXAMPLES OF FREEZING-POINT CURVES

In this chapter it is proposed to discuss the application of the principles of the Phase Rule, as developed in the preceding pages, to a number of systems of two components, so as to show more fully how the Phase Rule has been applied to the elucidation of certain problems connected with the equilibria between two components and how it has been employed for the interpretation of the data obtained by experiment. It is hoped that the practical value of the Phase Rule may thereby become more apparent, and its application to other cases be rendered easier.

I. Optically Active Substances.

The question as to whether a resolvable inactive body is a mixture of the two oppositely active constituents (a *dl*-mixture), or a racemate, is one which has given rise to considerable discussion; and several investigators have endeavoured to establish general rules by which the question could be decided. In the case of inactive liquids it is a matter of great difficulty to arrive at a certain conclusion as to whether one is dealing with a mixture or a compound, for in this case the usual physical methods give but a dubious answer. There is, however, no doubt that racemic molecules exist in the liquid state in certain cases. [1] Their existence in solution is more doubtful.

Even in the case of crystalline substances, where the differences between the various forms are greater, it is not always easy to discriminate between the *dl*-mixture and the racemate. The occurrence of hemihedral faces was considered by Pasteur to be a sufficient criterion for an optically active substance. It has, however, been found that hemihedry in crystals, although a frequent accompaniment of optical activity, is by no means a necessary or constant expression of this property. Other rules, also, which were given, although in some cases reliable, were in other cases insufficient; and all were in so far unsatisfactory that they lacked a theoretical basis.

With the help of the Phase Rule, however, it is possible from a study of the solubility or fusion curves of the optically active and inactive substances, to decide the nature of the inactive substance, at least under certain conditions. On account of the interest and importance which these compounds possess, a brief description of the application of the Phase Rule to the study of such substances will be given here; [2] the two optical antipodes being regarded as the two components.

In the present chapter we shall consider only the fusion curves, the solubility curves being discussed in the next section on three-component systems. The rules which are hereby obtained have reference only to the nature of the inactive substance in the neighbourhood of the melting-points.

(a) The inactive substance is a dl-mixture.

In this case the fusion curves will have the simple form shown in Fig. 38. A and B in Fig. 38 would represent the melting-points of the two optical isomerides (the temperature, however, being the

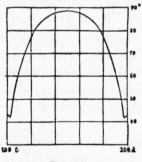

Fig. 60

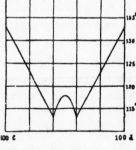

Fig. 61

same for both isomerides), and C the eutectic point at which the inactive mixture (conglomerate), consisting of equal amounts of d- and l- form, melts. Owing to the similar effect of the one form on the freezing-point of the other, the figure is symmetrical. The only known example of this type of system is found in the case of *d*- and *l*-pinene.[3] The melting-point of the active isomerides is −63° to −64°, and the eutectic temperature is about −120°.

(b) The two components form a racemate.

In this case there will be three melting-point curves as in Fig. 40. In this case also the figure must be symmetrical.

As examples of this there may be taken dimethyl tartrate and mandelic acid, the freezing-point curves of which are given in Figs. 60 and 61.[4] As can be seen, the curve for the racemic tartrate occupies a large part of the diagram, while that for racemic mandelic acid is much smaller. In the case of dimethyldiacetyl tartrate, this middle portion is still less.

Active dimethyl tartrate melts at 43.3°; racemic dimethyl tartrate at 89.4°. Active mandelic acid melts at 132.8°; the racemic acid at 118.0°. In the one case, therefore, the racemic compound has a higher, in the other a lower, melting-point than the active forms.

Camphoric acid and *o*-methylhydrogen camphorate also yield curves indicating the formation of a crystalline racemate with a congruent melting-point.[5]

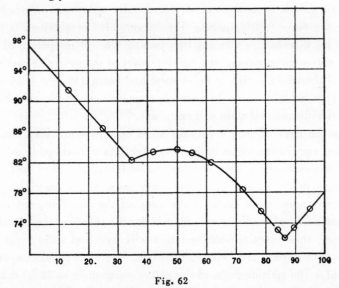

Fig. 62

In the case of partially racemic compounds (*i.e.* the compound of a racemate with an optically active substance) the type of curve will be the same, but the figure will no longer be symmetrical. Such a curve has been found in the case of the *l*-menthyl esters of *d*- and *l*-mandelic acid (Fig. 62). [6] The freezing-point of *l*-menthyl *d*-mandelate is 97.2°, of *l*-menthyl *l*-mandelate 77.6°, and of *l*-menthyl *r*-mandelate 83.7°. It will be observed that the summit of the curve for the partially racemic mandelate is fairly flat, indicating that the compound is dissociated to a considerable extent in the liquid state.

(c) The inactive substance is a pseudo-racemic mix-crystal (solid solution).

In cases where the active components can form mix-crystals or solid solutions, the freezing-point curve will exhibit one of the forms given in Figs. 45, 51 and 53. The inactive mix-crystal containing 50 per cent. of the dextro and lævo compound, is known as a pseudo-racemic mix-crystal. [7] So far, only curves of the types I. and II. have been obtained.

The two active camphor oximes are of interest from the fact that they form a continuous series of solid solutions, *all of which have the same melting-point*. The curve which is obtained in this case is, therefore, a straight line joining the melting-points of the pure active components; the melting-point of the active isomerides and of the whole series of solid solutions being 118.8°. Curves of this type are also given by borneol, camphor, camphoric anhydride, bornyl hydrogen phthalate and camphene. [8]

In the case of the carvoximes solid solutions are also formed, but the equilibrium curve in this case exhibits a maximum (Fig. 47). At this maximum point the composition of the solid and of the liquid solution is the same. Since the curve must be symmetrical, this maximum point must occur in the case of the solution containing 50 per cent. of each component, which will therefore be inactive. Further, this inactive solid solution will melt and solidify at the same temperature, and behave, therefore, like a chemical compound (p. 161). The melting-point of the active compounds is 72°; that of the inactive pseudo-racemic mix-crystal is 91.4°. A similar behaviour is shown by the monobornyl malonates. [9]

Transformations. As has already been remarked, the conclusions which can be drawn from the fusion curves regarding the nature of the inactive substances formed, hold only for temperatures in the neighbourhood of the melting-points. At temperatures below the melting-point transformation may occur; *e.g.* a racemate may break up into a *dl*-mixture, or a pseudo-racemic mix-crystal may form a racemate. We shall at a later point meet with examples of a racemate changing into a *dl*-mixture at a definite transition point; and the pseudo-racemic mix-crystal of camphoroxime is an example of the second transformation. Although at temperatures in the neighbourhood of the melting-point the two active camphoroximes form only mix-crystals but no compound, [10] a racemate is formed at temperatures below $103°$. At this temperature the inactive pseudo-racemic mix-crystal changes into a racemate; and in the case of the other solid solutions transformation to racemate and (excess of) active component also occurs, although at a lower temperature than in the case of the inactive solid solution.

Here, as in so many other cases, the X-ray method may be applied in order to decide definitely whether a given inactive solid form contains racemic molecules. [11] The existence or non-existence of racemic molecules in the liquid state may also be decided by the same method of investigation.

II. Alloys.

One of the most important classes of substances in the study of which the Phase Rule has been of very considerable importance, is that formed by the mixtures or compounds or solid solutions of metals with one another known as alloys. Although in the investigation of the nature of these bodies various methods are employed, one of the most important is the determination of the character of the freezing-point curve; for from the form of this valuable information can, as we have already learned, be obtained regarding the nature of the solid substances which separate out from the molten mixture.

Although it is impossible here to discuss fully the experimental results and the oftentimes very complicated relationships which the study of the alloys has brought to light, a brief reference to these bodies will be advisable on account both of the scientific interest and of the industrial importance attaching to them.[12]

The essential problem in metallurgy is a knowledge of the phases present in the cold alloy. Thermal analysis and a knowledge of the freezing-curve provide important information in this respect, at least as regards temperatures in the neighbourhood of the freezing-point of the alloy. Thermal analysis can also provide information regarding changes in the completely solidified alloy, *i.e.* changes in the solid phases, provided the thermal effects accompanying these changes are sufficiently marked. (Cf. Appendix II for thermal analysis.)

Although the method of thermal analysis retains its importance as a standard metallurgical method, it is less frequently used than formerly and is nowadays supplemented by several other techniques, notably that of X-ray analysis, (Cf. section on X-ray analysis, p. 229,), while the microscopic examination and microphotographic examination of the solidified alloy have long been used in conjunction with the method of thermal analysis. As subsidiary aids may be mentioned the determination of: (1) the electrical conductivity, (2) the magnetic susceptibility, (3) the electrode potential, (4) the heat of mixture of the molten metals, (5) the intensity of reflection of light, (6) the atomic heats of the components and of the alloy, (7) the specific volumes of alloy and components.

We have already seen that there are three chief types of freezing-point curves in systems of two components, viz. those obtained when (1) the pure components crystallise out from the molten mass; (2) the components form one or more compounds; (3) the components form solid solutions. In the case of the metals, representatives of these three classes are also found. A mathematical analysis of the freezing-point curves on the basis of the formulæ for ideal solutions (p. 160) has been carried out by Andrews and Johnston.[38]

(a) The components separate out in the pure state.

In this case the freezing-point curve is of the simple type (Fig. 38). This type of alloy is not so common as was at one time supposed, since the tendency of metals to form solid solutions is very marked. It appears, however, that in the case of bismuth—cadmium there is little or no formation of solid solution.

(b) *The two metals can form one or more compounds.*

In this case there will be obtained not only the freezing-point curves of the pure metals, but each compound formed will have its own freezing-point curve. If the compound have a congruent melting-point, the equilibrium curve will exhibit a point of maximum temperature, and will end, on either side, in an eutectic point. The simplest curve of this type will be obtained when only one compound is formed, as is the case with zinc and magnesium.

(c) *The two metals form solid solutions.*

The simplest case in which the metals crystallise out together in solid solution is found in silver and gold.[13] The freezing-point curve in this case is an almost straight line joining the freezing-points of the pure metals (*cf.* curve I., Fig. 45 p. (159). These two metals, therefore, can form an unbroken series of solid solutions.[14]

In some cases, however, the two metals do not form an unbroken series of solid solutions. In the case of zinc and silver,[15] for example, the addition of silver *raises* the freezing-point of the mixture, until a transition point is reached. This corresponds with Fig. 51. Silver and copper, and gold and copper, on the other hand, do not form unbroken series of mixed crystals, but the freezing-point curve exhibits an eutectic point, as in Fig. 53. In these cases, liquid mixtures having the composition of the point C deposit, on freezing, a mixture of *two solid solutions*, the composition of which is represented diagrammatically by the points D and E.

Not only may there be these three different types of curves, but there may also be combinations of them. Thus the two metals may not only form compounds, but one of the metals may not separate out in the pure state at all, but form solid solutions. In this case the freezing-point may rise (as in the case of silver and zinc), and one of the eutectic points will be absent.

The equilibrium diagram of the system aluminium – gold[16] forms an interesting study for the beginner, since it presents in one diagram most of the variations hitherto discussed, namely, two congruently melting compounds, at least two incongruently melting compounds and limited solid solubility accompanied by eutectics. The equilibrium diagram, simplified for the purpose of clarity, is reproduced in Fig. 63. The isoplethal behaviour and the nature of the

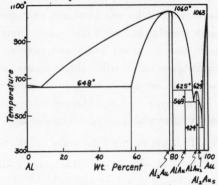

Fig. 63

cooling curves, together with the interpretation of the stable condition of any completely solidified alloy, should form an instructive exercise for the reader.

The Brasses. [17]   Common brass is an alloy of copper and zinc. The (complete) equilibrium diagram is given in Fig. 64, and it's

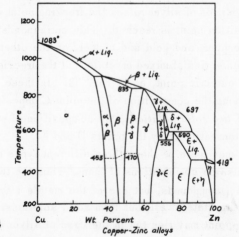

Fig. 64

Copper-Zinc alloys

interpretation should now present no difficulty.   There are six regions of homogeneous solid solution, described as α, β, γ, δ, ϵ, and η.   The true brasses, containing about 30 to 33% zinc, consist therefore of homogeneous α crystals.   One of the advantages of brass is that it is ductile and can be drawn into tubes and wires.

Before this operation is performed, it is usual to anneal the brass, that is, to heat it up to 600-650° and then to allow it to cool slowly. Since no phase change takes place in ordinary brass, up to its melting point (say 900°), the only effect of the annealing process is to homogenise the α crystals, which may have been "cored" through rapid chilling in the original casting, and to cause them to grow in size, but this increase in particle size renders the alloy more ductile.

Another group of alloys belonging to this system, and known as Muntz metal and similar alloys, contain from 37 to 46% zinc. Examination of the equilibrium diagram shows that alloys of this series, when in equilibrium at room temperature (annealed) consist of a mixture of α and β crystals.

The question of the chemical nature of these homogeneous systems naturally arises. The α-series might be described, though not necessarily correctly, as a solid solution of zinc in copper, and the η-series as a solid solution of copper in zinc, since the space lattices of the solid forms are essentially those of pure copper and pure zinc. Such an explanation cannot, however, be applied to the intermediate regions of solid solution, since they possess lattice structures fundamentally different. Here it is usual to assume the existence of intermetallic compounds, e.g. the γ region is supposed to contain the compound Cu_5Zn_8 in solid solution with excess of copper or zinc. The experimental evidence for the existence of such compounds rests chiefly on microscopic and X-ray work: a pronounced change in structure can only receive some such explanation.

(d) Amalgams.

When one of the constituents of an alloy is mercury, the alloy is referred to as an amalgam. Commercial amalgams are usually of a liquid or semiliquid (pasty) consistency, which has given rise to the description of them as solutions of metals in mercury. Apart, however, from the fact that mercury is liquid at ordinary temperatures, there is no reason why its alloys should be treated as different from the alloys of any other metal. Mercury may form compounds, congruently or incongruently melting, and solid solutions, with other metals, and the equilibrium diagrams are similar in character to those of other binary alloys. For example, Figure 65 rep-

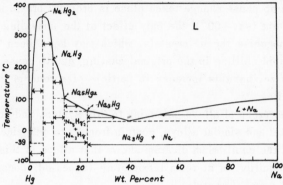

Fig. 65

resents the equilibrium diagram of the system sodium—mercury. [18]

There are two congruently melting compounds, $NaHg_2$ and Na_3Hg, and two incongruently melting compounds, $NaHg$ and Na_5Hg_2. The composition of the eutectic formed between Na_5Hg_2 and Na_3Hg is so close to the composition of Na_3Hg that the two are indistinguishable on the diagram. Similarly the liquid compositions at the incongruent melting points of $NaHg$ and Na_5Hg_2 are indistinguishable from the compositions of these compounds.

The Nature and Formulae of Intermetallic Compounds. The existence of a maximum on a freezing-point curve is unquestionable evidence of the existence of a true chemical compound of the metals, if we rule out the very rare case of the occurrence of a maximum associated with complete solid solubility. The existence of a peritectic point on the freezing curve means that the nature of the solid phase has changed, and this may involve the assumption of the formation of an intermetallic compound, to which a formula is assigned which is most consistent with the position of the peritectic point. Again any discontinuity in the succession of physical properties as a function of concentration seems to point to the existence of a chemical compound. It is difficult, however, to assign exact formulae to these so-called compounds for they almost all seem to have the power of forming solid solutions with adjacent compounds or component metals. A region of homogeneity is thus produced and the question of where within this region the exact composition of the compound lies becomes a very real one. The application of X-rays to the problem has only added to the difficulty. It appears that, within limits, different atoms can replace one another within the lattice without disturbing its fundamental structure. From this point of view it is difficult to visualise anything of the nature of a compound of the orthodox kind.

Another difficulty with intermetallic compounds lies in the formulae assigned to them, which are often not compatible with any ordinary chemical valence of the metal. In fact, Dalton's law of multiple proportions, which calls for a *small* whole number ratio between the components in two or more intermetallic compounds of the same elements, no longer applies. Order has been introduced, to some extent, into this confused subject by the application of a principle due to Hume-Rothery,[19] but the subject is one with which Phase Rule, as such, is scarcely concerned.

(e) The Components are not Completely Miscible in the Liquid State.

The theoretical aspects of this case have already been dealt with in connection with the system phenol — water. A good example in the field of alloys is that of the system iron — tin. The equilibrium diagram, as given by Ehret and Gurinsky,[20] is reproduced in

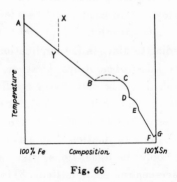

Fig. 66

Fig. 66 (liquidus only). A and G are the melting points of iron and tin respectively. F is the eutectic lying very close to the melting point and composition of pure tin. BC is the miscibility gap, D and

E peritectic points indicating phase change in the solid alloy at the corresponding temperatures. It is instructive to follow the fate of alloy X from a temperature of about 1400°C. On cooling, the completely molten alloy follows the isopleth XY. At the temperature of Y, solid begins to separate in the form of a solid solution of tin in α-iron. This process continues until the temperature of the point B is reached. At this temperature, a second liquid of the composition C begins to make its appearance and the temperature remains constant until all liquid B has transformed to C. Further separation of the α-iron solid solution continues along CD until the peritectic point D is reached. The temperature now remains constant, the liquid of composition D reacting with separated solid to produce a compound of iron and tin described as γ. Since the composition of the compound γ is well to the right of the composition X, solidification now goes to completion at constant temperature, with formation of a completely solid heterogeneous mixture of solid solution of tin in α-iron and compound γ. This heterogeneous mixture then undergoes further phase changes with falling temperature.

III. Iron-Carbon Alloys.[21]

Of all the different binary alloys, probably the most important are those formed by iron and carbon: alloys consisting not of two metals, but of a metal and a non-metal. On account of the importance of these alloys, an attempt will be made to describe in brief some of the most important relationships met with.

Before proceeding to discuss the application of the Phase Rule to the study of the iron-carbon alloys, however, the main facts with which we have to deal may be stated very briefly.

Iron is capable of existing in three distinct solid phases, known as α-, γ- and δ-ferrite respectively. α-ferrite and δ-ferrite have been shown by X-ray examination[22] to have body-centred cubic lattices, varying only in dimensions with temperature,[23] while γ-ferrite has a face-centred cubic lattice. δ-ferrite[24] is the stable form of iron above 1400°, and undergoes change to γ-ferrite below this temperature. Between 1400° and 910°C γ-ferrite is stable while below 910° α-ferrite becomes the stable form.

With regard to β-ferrite, it has been fully established that the change formerly spoken of as the A_2 or $\alpha \to \beta$ change, does not represent a phase transformation at all, but a magnetic transformation which, unlike a polymorphic or phase transformation, does not take place at a definite temperature, but is a progressive change, the velocity of which is a function of the temperature. β-ferrite, therefore, does not exist as a distinct phase.

Owing to the fact that the phase changes $\delta \to \gamma$ and $\gamma \to \alpha$ are accompanied by evolution of heat, the cooling curve of iron, below its melting-point, shows an arrest at the temperatures at which the phase changes occur. The arrest on the cooling curve corresponding with the change $\delta \to \gamma$ is referred to as Ar_4 (A = arrêt = arrest; r = refroidissement = cooling); and the arrest at the temperature of change $\gamma \to \alpha$ is known as Ar_3. Similarly, the arrests on the heating curve (*chauffage*) are known as Ac_4 and Ac_3. For Ar_4 and Ar_3 the values are 1400° and 910° respectively.

A short description may now be given of the application of the Phase Rule to the two-component system iron—carbon; and of the diagram showing how the different systems are related, and with the help of which the behaviour of the different mixtures under given conditions can be predicted.

The most important equilibrium relations met with in the case of the iron-carbon alloys are represented graphically in Figs. 67 and 68.

In Fig. 67 are represented the equilibrium relations for δ-ferrite, determined by Ruer and Goerens[25] and by Andrew and Binnie:[26] in the diagram the figures of Andrew and Binnie are preferred. In this diagram, D represents the transition point for δ- and γ-ferrite (1400°C.). This transition point is greatly raised by addition of small amounts of carbon, as indicated by the curve DE, until at the point E, when the amount of carbon is about 0.1 per cent., the transition point lies at 1494°, and the transition curve ends in the curve of complete solidification, AE.[27] This curve, AE, gives the composition of the solid solutions of δ-ferrite and carbon in equilibrium with the molten solutions AB. At the temperature of the horizontal EFB (1494°), the molten solution is in equilibrium with the two solid phases, δ-ferrite solid solutions (E) and γ-ferrite solid solutions (F). At B, the melt contains about 0.71 per cent. of carbon. The position of F (composition of the γ-ferrite solid solutions) is not known with accuracy.

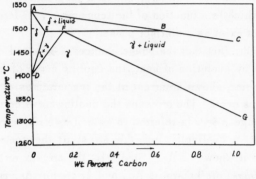

Fig. 67

From melts containing less than 0.1 per cent. of carbon (E), δ-solid solutions first separate out, and these then, on cooling, undergo transformation (along ED) into γ-solid solutions. From melts containing between 0.1 and 0.2 per cent. of carbon, δ-ferrite solid solutions first separate, and these on cooling to 1494°, change, through reaction with the melt, into δ- and γ-solid solutions (E and F). It is here assumed that equilibrium is constantly being established (see p. 186). From melts containing more than 0.71 per cent. of carbon, γ-solid solutions only separate out (curve FG).

The area ADE represents the region of stability of δ-ferrite; the area DEF the region in which δ-ferrite solid solutions and γ-ferrite solid solutions are in equilibrium; and the area AEB is the area for δ-solid solutions and liquid.

In Fig. 68 is given the more complete equilibrium diagram.[28] The curves AB and BC are the freezing-point curves for solutions of carbon in iron (δ-ferrite and γ-ferrite respectively), starting from the melting-point of pure iron (δ-ferrite). C is a eutectic point. Suppose that we start with a molten mixture of iron and carbon, represented by the point x, containing more than 0.71 per cent. of carbon.[29] On allowing the temperature to fall, a point, y, will be reached at which solid begins to separate out. This solid phase, however, is not pure iron, but a solid solution of carbon in γ-ferrite known as austenite, having a composition represented by γ' (cf. p. 186). As the temperature continues to fall, the composition of the liquid phase changes in the direction yC, while the composition of the solid phase which separates out changes in the direction γ'E; and, finally, when the composition of the molten mass is that of the point C (4.3 per cent. of carbon), the whole mass solidifies to a heterogeneous mixture of saturated austenite (saturated solution of carbon in γ-ferrite) and cementite, Fe_3C, represented respectively by E and by a point on an extension of the line EC corresponding with 6.7 per cent. of carbon (F). The saturated austenite (point E) contains 1.7 per cent. of carbon. The temperature of the eutectic point is 1130° to 1145°.[30] An alloy which crystallises with the eutectic composition is known as ledeburite.

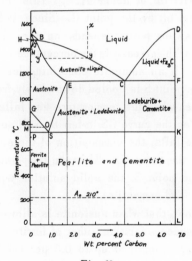

Fig. 68

Even below the solidification point, changes can take place. As the saturated austenite is cooled below 1125°, separation of cementite takes place along ES, the percentage of carbon in the saturated austenite diminishing with fall of temperature, until at about 700°,[31] the limit of saturation is reached at 0.89 per cent.

of carbon (point S). Below this eutectoid point S, separation into
α-ferrite and cementite takes place (A_1 transformation). This eutectoid mixture is known as pearlite.

From the above discussion it follows that if we start with a
molten mixture of iron and carbon, the composition of which is
represented by any point between E and C (1.7 to 4.3 per cent. of
carbon), we shall obtain, on cooling the mass, first of all solid
solutions, the composition of which will be represented by points
on the curve JE; then, after the mass has completely solidified at
1130°, further cooling will lead to a separation of cementite and a
change in the composition of the austenite (from 1.7 to 0.89 per
cent. of carbon), until, at temperatures below about 700° the
austenite becomes heterogeneous and forms pearlite and cementite.

It has already been mentioned that γ-ferrite undergoes transformation into α-ferrite at about 912°. This transition point is
represented in Fig. 68 by the point G. Since γ-ferrite dissolves
carbon, the transition point depends on the amount of carbon
present, and falls with increase in the percentage of carbon as shown
by the curve GS. If an austenite containing less carbon than is
represented by the point S is cooled down slowly from a temperature
of, say, 912°, then when the temperature has fallen to that represented by a point on the curve GS, α-ferrite will separate out; and,
as the temperature falls, the composition of the solid solution will
alter as shown by the curve GS. When the temperature reaches that
represented by the point S, the solid solution will break up into
pearlite (α-ferrite and cementite).

We see, therefore, that when austenite is allowed to cool *slowly*,
it yields a heterogeneous mixture either of ferrite and pearlite (when
the original mixture contained up to 0.8 per cent. of carbon), or
pearlite and cementite (when the original mixture contained between
0.9 and 1.7 per cent. of carbon). These heterogeneous mixtures
constitute soft steels, or, when the carbon content is low, wrought
iron.

The case, however, is different if the solid solution of carbon in
iron is *rapidly* cooled (quenched) from a temperature above the curve
GSE to a temperature below this curve. In this case, although the

rapid cooling does not completely prevent the resolution of the solid solution, austenite, into ferrite or cementite, the resolution is not so complete as when cooling takes place slowly; and in this way hard steel is obtained. By varying the rapidity of cooling, as is done in the tempering of steel, varying degrees of resolution of the austenite are produced, and so varying degrees of hardness obtained. [32]

The diagram below the curve AHJECF represents a completely solid system and it will be observed that this area is divided up into smaller areas marked "austenite", "ferrite", "pearlite", "cementite", and "ledeburite", These names, as shown above do not all represent homogeneous phases of the system. There are only three phases in this part of the diagram, viz. ferrite (a component), austenite (a solid solution) and cementite (a compound). The remaining terms refer to mixtures; they might be described as the names of microscopic "constituents". For example, the term "ledeburite" refers to the eutectic mixture C. This mixture consists of two phases, saturated austenite, E, and pure cementite. Nevertheless, eutectic mixtures have a fine grained structure recognisable in the microscope and it is sometimes convenient to treat eutectic mixtures as if they were individuals. Thus the mixture, x (Fig. 68), on cooling, will give a primary crystallisation of austenite, followed by the eutectic crystallisation of ledeburite. This completely solidified alloy is thus described as a mixture of proeutectic austenite and ledeburite, as long as the temperature remains above that of the line PSK. At the temperature of the line PSK, the austenite (which has been diminishing in carbon content along ES) breaks up completely into pearlite (a mixture of ferrite and cementite). Since ledeburite is itself a mixture of cementite and austenite this likewise breaks up into a mixture of cementite and pearlite, so that the alloy as a whole is now a mixture of cementite and pearlite.

Similarly a hypereutectic alloy (one containing more carbon than the eutectic mixture C) gives a proeutectic crystallisation of cementite, followed by ledeburite. Above the temperature of PSK it is therefore described as a mixture of cementite and ledeburite.

Again, on further cooling, the ledeburite breaks up into a mixture of cementite and pearlite.

An alloy containing less carbon than corresponds to the point E will give a primary crystallisation of austenite, but complete solidification will take place before the eutectic temperature is reached, to give a homogeneous austenite. When the vertical line of falling temperature (isopleth) crosses ES, primary or proeutectoid separation of cementite begins, followed, at the temperature of the point S, by complete decomposition of the austenite into pearlite. The cold alloy is therefore a mixture of proeutectoid cementite and pearlite. Finally, an alloy containing less carbon than the mixture S will give a proeutectoid crystallisation of ferrite followed by eutectoid transformation of austenite into pearlite: such alloys are therefore described as mixtures of ferrite and pearlite.

The horizontal dotted line MO shown in Fig. 68 represents what is known as the A_2 transformation. This, as has already been mentioned, was formerly thought to be a phase transformation of α- into β-ferrite, but it is now known to represent merely a magnetic transformation, which takes place progressively, beginning at a low temperature and ending at about 768°C.[33] This transformation differs from a phase transformation in the fact that it begins but does not progress to completion with time at temperatures below 768°. This is the temperature at which the A_2 transformation begins on cooling and ends on heating, and it is independent of the carbon content, as shown by the horizontal, dotted line. This line was first detected by Carpenter and Keeling,[34] but has been more fully studied in recent times by Honda.[35]

The dotted line marked "A_0 210°" represents a magnetic transformation of cementite, in every way similar to the magnetic transformation of pure iron, represented by the line MO.

IV Minerals.

Important and interesting as is the application of the Phase Rule to the study of alloys, its application to the study of the conditions regulating the formation of minerals is no less so; and although we do not propose to consider different cases in detail here, attention must be drawn to certain points connected with this interesting subject.

In the first place, it will be evident from what has already been said, that the mineral which first crystallises out from a molten magma is not necessarily the one with the highest melting-point. The *composition* of the fused mass must be taken into account. When the system consists of two components which do not form a compound, one or other of these will separate out in a pure state, according as the composition of the molten mass lies on one or other side of the eutectic composition; and the separation of the one component will continue until the composition of the eutectic point is reached. Further cooling will then lead to the simultaneous separation of the two components.

If, however, the two components form a stable compound (*e.g.* orthoclase, from a fused mixture of silica and potassium aluminate), then the freezing-point curve will resemble that shown in Fig. 40, *i.e.* there will be a middle curve possessing a dystectic point, and ending on either side at a eutectic point. This curve would represent the conditions under which orthoclase is in equilibrium with the molten magma. If the initial composition of the magma is represented by a point between the two eutectic points, orthoclase will separate first. The composition of the magma will thereby change, and the mass will finally solidify to a mixture of orthoclase and silica, or orthoclase and potassium aluminate, according to the initial composition.[36]

A subject closely allied to that of geology is ceramics. Reference to such a publication as "Phase Diagrams for Ceramists." (J. Amer. Ceramic Soc., 1947, **30**, No. 11, 1-152), will show that the equilibria are described in terms of the now familiar Phase Rule diagrams. It should always be borne in mind however that phase rule deals only with true (thermodynamic) equilibrium and that to attain this melts must cool very slowly and in contact with the solid which separates. In practice, this is frequently not the case. The separated solid may be removed before solidification is complete, so that further interaction of magma and solid is impossible, or the chemical nature of the environment may change during the long history of a cooling magma, so that chemical interaction between the magma and the surrounding rock may take place. Rapid chilling may result in "coring" or "zoning", that is, the deposition of successive layers which are not in equilibrium with one another. Finally, siliceous materials are very prone to supercooling with formation of the vitreous state. This latter phenomenon is so marked, indeed, that the method of thermal analysis is not usually applicable. (See Appendix II on "Determination of the Equilibrium Curve in Binary Systems.")

The study of the formation of minerals from the point of view of the Phase Rule is now attracting considerable attention,[37] and reference to some recent work in this department will be made later (p. 334).

NOTES

1. Campbell, *J. Chem. Soc.*, 1929, 1111.

2. Roozeboom, *Z. physikal. Chem.*, 1899, **28**, 494; Adriani, *ibid.*, 1900, **33**, 453. See also van Laar, *ibid.*, 1908, **64**, 257; Tammann, *ibid.*, 1914, **87**, 357.

3. Ross and Somerville, *J. Chem. Soc.*, 1926, 2770.

4. Adriani, *Z. physikal. Chem.*, 1900, **33**, 453.

5. Ross and Somerville, *J. Chem. Soc.*, 1926, 2770; 1936, 718.

6. A. Findlay and Miss E. Hickmans, *J. Chem. Soc.*, 1907, **91**, 905. See also Dutilh, *Verhandelingen K. Akad. Wetensch. Amsterdam*, 1912, **11**, Sect. I; Abbott, McKenzie, and Ross, *Ber.*, 1937, **70**, 163.

7. Kipping and Pope, *J. Chem. Soc.*, 1897, **71**, 993.

8. Ross and Somerville, *ibid.*, 1926, 2770; 1936, 718; Abbott, Christie and McKenzie, *Ber.*, 1938, **71**, 9.

9. Abbot, McKenzie and Ross, *Ber.*, 1938, **71**, 16.

10. That is, no compound capable of existing as solid phase in equilibrium with liquid mixtures. A racemate may be formed which yields solid solutions with the optically active isomerides.

11. Tammann, *Z. physikal. Chem.*, 1914, **87**, 364, 365.

12. A bibliography of the alloys is given in *Z. anorgan. Chem.*, 1903, **35**, 249, and by Estis, *Met. and Chem. Eng.*, 1917, **16**, 273. See also the vol-

ume on *Metallography*, and the monograph on *Inter-metallic Compounds*, by C. H. Desch; Mlodziejowski, *Z. physikal. Chem.*, 1925, **117**, 361; Jänecke, *Kurzgefasstes Handbuch aller Legierungen*.

13. Roberts-Austen and Rose, *Proc. Roy. Soc.*, 1903, **71**, 161.

14. Since diffusion takes place relatively slowly in a solid solution, the solid which is deposited from a molten mixture will not be uniform. By "annealing" such an alloy, that is, by heating for some time to a temperature below the melting-point, diffusion takes place and a homogeneous solid solution is produced.

15. Heycock and Neville, *J. Chem. Soc.*, 1897, **71**, 414; Owen and Edwards, *J. Inst. Met.*, London, 1935, **57**, 305.

16. West and Peterson, *Z. Kristallogr.*, 1934, **88**, 93; Eisenhut and Kaupp, *Z. Elektrochem.*, 1931, **37**, 472.

17. Hansen and Stenzel, *Metallwirtsch.*, 1933, **12**, 539; Olander, *Z. phys. Chem.*, 1933, A **164**, 428; Ruer and Kremers, *Z. anorg. allg. Chem.*, 1929, **184**, 194; Johansson and Westgren, *Metallwirtsch.*, 1933, **12**, 539.

18. Vanstone, *Trans. Faraday Soc.*, 1911, **7**, 42; Bornemann and Müller, *Metallurgie*, 1910, **7**, 399, 738, 767.

19. *J. Inst. Metals.*, 1926, **35**, 195; Mott and Jones, "*The Theory of the Properties of Metals and Alloys.*", Oxford, 1936.

20. *J. A. C. S.*, 1943, **65**, 1226. More recent work by Cambell, Wood and Skinner assigns somewhat different values to the liquidus, *ibid.*, 1949, **71**, 1729.

21. See S. Epstein, *The Alloys of Iron and Carbon*, Vol. I; Desch, *Metallography*, 4th Edit., 345.

22. Bain, *Chem. and Met. Eng.*, 1921, **25**, 663; Westgren, *J. Iron and Steel Inst.*, 1921, **103**, 303; Westgren and Phragmen, *ibid.*, 1922, **105**, 241; *Z. physikal. Chem.*, 1922, **102**, 1.

23. It has been shown by Honda (*Sci. Rep. Tôhoku Imp. Univ.*, 1925, **13**, 363) that δ-ferrite lies on the same curve of properties as α-ferrite, and that it is therefore identical with it as a phase. See also Sato, *Phil. Mag.*, 1926 [7], **1**, 996; *Sci. Rep. Tôhoku Imp. Univ.*, 1925, **14**, 513.

24. Osmond, *J. Iron and Steel Inst.*, 1890, I. 102; Ruer and Klesper, *Ferrum*, 1914, **11**, 257; Ruer and Goerens, *ibid.*, 1916, **14**, 161.

25. *Ferrum,* 1916, **14**, 161.

26. *J. Iron and Steel Inst.,* 1929, **119**, 309.

27. The melting-point of pure iron (δ-ferrite) is shown here at about 1525° C., the value of 1527° was found by Jenkins and Gayler, *Proc. Roy. Soc.,* 1930, A. **129**, 91.

28. Taken from Epstein: *"Alloys of Iron and Carbon.,* Vol. I., *Constitution."* McGraw-Hill, New York, 1936., p. 43.

29. The behaviour which is found when the molten mixtures contain less than 0.71 per cent. of carbon has already been discussed.

30. According to Ruer and Goerens(*Ferrum* ,1916, **14**, 161), the temperature is 1145°.

31. See Ruer and Goerens, *Ferrum,* 1916, **14**, 161; Saldaou and Goerens, *J. Russ. Met. Soc.,* 1914, 1, 789; *Rev. de Métal.,* 1917, **14**, E., 65; Honda, *J. Iron and Steel. Inst.,* 1922, **105**. 381.

32. See Humphrey (*Chem. News,* 1914, **110**, 271) for the part played by the amorphous phase in the hardening of steels.

33. See Maurer, *Mitt. K. W. Inst. Eisenforsch.,* 1920, **1**, 39.

34. *J. Iron and Steel Inst.,* 1904, **65**, 224.

35. *Sci. Rep. Tôhoku Imp. Univ.,* 1915, **4**, 169; *J. Iron and Steel Inst.,* 1915, **91**, 199; **92**, 181; *Sci. Rep. Tôhoku Imp. Univ.,* 1917, **6**, 213; *J. Iron and Steel Inst.,* 1922, **105**, 381; *ibid.,* 1925, **112**, 345.

36. For a study of the binary system $MgO - SiO_2$, see Bowen and Andersen, *Amer. J. Sci.,* 1914 [4], **37**, 487. For the system $Al_2O_3-SiO_2$, see Bowen and Greig, *J. Amer. Cer. Soc.,* 1924, **7**, 238.

37. In this connection,see Doelter, *Physikalisch-chemische Mineralogie* (Barth, 1901); Meyerhoffer, *Z. Krist.,* 1902, **36**, 593; Guthrie, *Phil. Mag.,* 1884 [5]., **17**, 479; LeChatelier, *Compt. rend.,* 1900, **130**, 85; and especially E. Baur, *Z. physikal. Chem.,* 1903, **42**, 567; J. H. L. Vogt, *Z. Elektrochem.,* 1903, **9**, 852. and *Die Silikatschmelzlösungen,* Parts I. and II. (Christiania, 1903, 1904). See also N. V. Kultascheff, *Z. anorgan. Chem.,* 1903, **35**, 187; Doelter, *Monatsh.,* 1906, **27**, 433; Day and Allen, *Z. physikal. Chem.,* 1905, **54**, 1; Day and Shepherd, *J. Amer. Chem. Soc.,* 1906, **28**, 1089; Reiter, *Jahrb. Min.,* 1906, *Beil.-Bd.,* **22**, 183; Lebedeff, *Z-anorgan. Chem.,* 1911, **70**, 301; Bowen, *ibid.,* 1913, **82**,

283; Deleano, *ibid.*, 1914, **84**, 401; Day, *Fortschr. d. Min. Kristall., Petrog.*, 1914, **4**, 115; Rastall, *Physico-chemical Geology* (Arnold); Bowen and Schairer, *Amer. Jour. Sci.*, 1935, **29**, 151.

38. Inst. Met., 1924, **32**, 385.

CHAPTER X

SYSTEMS CONSISTING OF SOLID AND GAS PHASES ONLY

I. Two Volatile Solids which do not Interact Chemically or Form Solid Solutions.

At constant temperature, the vapour pressure of a pure solid is constant. If, therefore, to excess of solid A, a small quantity of B is added, so that B volatilises completely, the total pressure will be increased in accordance with Dalton's law. As more of B is added this will continue until the partial pressure of B in the gas phase exceeds its vapour pressure, when solid B will deposit. When both solid A and solid B are present, the total vapour pressure is constant, at constant temperature, in accordance with the Phase Rule. Similarly, if successive additions of A are made to excess of B, the total vapour increases in the same way until isothermal invariance is produced. Hence, the p-x diagram assumes the form of Fig. 69, where the ordinate of C equals the sum of the vapour pressures of pure A and B, and where the composition of C corresponds to a ratio of A to B equal to the ratio of the vapour pressures of the respective solids.

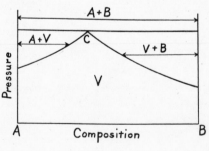

Fig. 69

If, on the other hand, the total pressure is kept constant, say at one atmosphere, then, as successive additions of B to A are made, it will be necessary to lower the temperature, in order to lower the vapour pressure of A (present in excess) and keep the total pressure constant. When, however, B is also present in excess, the vapour pressure of each is constant at constant temperature, and therefore at only one temperature will the total pressure be equal to the assigned constant pressure. The system is now isobarically invariant. The *t-x* diagram which is an approximate mirror image of the *p-x* diagram, is given in Fig. 70. The resem-

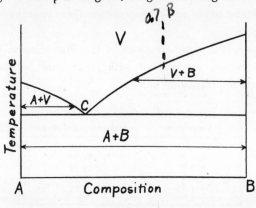

Fig. 70

blance of the point C to a eutectic point, in its appearance and characteristics, is obvious.

II. A Gaseous and a Solid Component which can only Form Compounds.

As an example of this, we may first consider the system formed by the two components CaO and CO_2, which can combine to form the compound $CaCO_3$. This substance, on being heated, dissociates into calcium oxide and carbon dioxide, and gives rise to the equilibrium $CaCO_3 \rightleftharpoons CaO + CO_2$. In accordance with the definition given on p. 7, there are present here two solid phases, the carbonate and the quicklime, and one vapour phase; the system is therefore univariant. To each temperature, therefore, there will correspond a certain definite maximum pressure of carbon dioxide (dissociation pressure) and this will follow the same general law as the vapour pressure of a pure liquid (pp. 20 and 21). More particularly, it will be independent of the relative or absolute amounts of the two solid phases, and of the volume of the vapour phase. If the temperature is maintained constant, increase of volume will cause the dissociation of a further amount of the carbonate until the pressure again reaches its maximum value corresponding to the given temperature. Diminution of volume, on the other hand, will bring about the combination of a certain quantity of the carbon dioxide with the calcium oxide until the pressure again reaches its original value.[1]

The most recent determinations of the dissociation pressure of calcium carbonate, carried out with great care by Southard and Royster[2] gave the following values·

Temperature.	Pressure in cm. of mercury.
900.3°	82.60
877.8°	59.87
854.6°	42.23
774.8°	10.93

The experimental numbers are in close agreement with the equation:

$$\log p = -9140/T + 0.382 \log T - 0.668 \times 10^{-3} T + 9.3171$$

If p is plotted against t, using the above equation, a steeply ascending curve, exactly similar to the vapour pressure curve of a pure liquid, is obtained. Indeed, the Clapeyron equation applies to dissociation pressure, just as it does to vapour pressure, and the heat of dissociation can be calculated from experimental measurements of dissociation pressure at different temperatures in the same way that the latent heat of evaporation of a liquid can be calculated.

The temperature at which the dissociation pressure is equal to 1 atm. is 894.4°C. In an atmosphere of carbon dioxide, therefore, under one atmosphere pressure, decomposition of the calcium carbonate would not take place below this temperature. If, however, the carbon dioxide is removed as quickly as it is formed, say by a current of air, the entire decomposition can be made to take place at a much lower temperature. For the dissociation equilibrium of the carbonate depends only on the partial pressure of the carbon dioxide, and if this is kept small, then the decomposition can proceed, even at temperatures at which the pressure of the carbon dioxide is less than atmospheric pressure. From the above equation, and taking the mean partial pressure of carbon dioxide in the atmosphere as 0.3 mm., decomposition should result above about 520°.

Cadmium carbonate behaves similarly to calcium carbonate and, on being heated, gives rise to the equilibrium $CdCO_3 \rightleftharpoons CdO + CO_2$. The equilibrium pressure at different temperatures has been determined by Centnerszwer and Andrusov,[3] who find that the dissociation pressures are expressed by the formula $\log p = -12.44 + 0.02439\ T$. The reaction $CdO + CO_2 \rightarrow CdCO_3$ takes place about fifty times more slowly than the reaction $CdCO_3 \rightarrow CdO + CO_2$.

In the case of the systems $CaO-CO_2$ and $CdO-CO_2$, only one compound is formed by the components, and only two solid phases, therefore, are possible.[4] In many cases, however, more than one dissociating compound can be formed between a solid and a gaseous component, and two or more stable univariant systems may therefore be produced consisting of two solid phases and one gas phase. The behaviour which is found in such cases will best be understood by the consideration of definite systems which have been investigated experimentally.

Ammonia Compounds of Metal Chlorides. Ammonia possesses the property of combining with various substances, chiefly the halides of metals, to form compounds which again yield up the ammonia on being heated. Thus, for example, on passing ammonia over silver chloride, absorption of the gas takes place with formation of the compounds $AgCl \cdot NH_3$, $2AgCl \cdot 3NH_3$ and $AgCl \cdot 3NH_3$, according to the conditions of the experiment. These were the first known substances belonging to this class, and were employed by Faraday in his experiments on the liquefaction of ammonia. Similar compounds have also been obtained by the action of ammonia on silver bromide, iodide, cyanide, and nitrate, and on the halogen compounds of calcium, zinc, magnesium and other metals. The behaviour of the ammonia compounds of silver chloride is typical of the compounds of this class, and may be briefly considered here.[5]

The equilibria in the two-component system $AgCl - NH_3$ have been most fully investigated by Biltz and Stollenwerk,[6] who have established the existence of the three compounds $AgCl.3NH_3$, $2AgCl.3NH_3$ and $AgCl.NH_3$. On being heated, these compounds decompose and give rise to the equilibria:

$$2[AgCl.(NH_3)_3] \rightleftharpoons (AgCl)_2.(NH_3)_3 + 3NH_3$$
$$(AgCl)_2.(NH_3)_3 \rightleftharpoons 2(AgCl.NH_3) + NH_3.$$
$$AgCl.NH_3 \rightleftharpoons AgCl + NH_3.$$

In each case, therefore, there are three phases present, two solid phases and one gas phase. The systems are, therefore, univariant and to each temperature there must correspond a definite pressure of dissociation, quite irrespective of the amounts of the phases present. The values of these dissociation pressures are given in the following tables (p. 217).

Since the dissociation pressure of the triammonia mono-chloride becomes equal to atmospheric pressure at a temperature of about $20°$, this compound cannot be formed at temperatures above $20°$ by the passage of ammonia at atmospheric pressure over silver chloride. The triammonia di-chloride, however, can be formed, for at this temperature its dissociation pressure amounts to only about 160 mm.

Emphasis may again be laid on the fact that *two* solid phases are necessary in order that the dissociation pressure at a given temperature shall be definite; *and for the exact definition of this pressure it is necessary to know, not merely what is the substance undergoing dissociation, but also what is the solid product of dissociation formed.* For the definition of the equilibrium, the latter is as important as the former. We shall presently find proof of this in the case of an analogous class of phenomena, viz. the dissociation of salt hydrates.

The behaviour which is observed when ammonia is withdrawn from or added to the system $AgCl - NH_3$ at constant temperature is of interest and importance. If, at constant temperature, the volume of the system is increased, or, if the ammonia which is evolved is

$2\left[AgCl.(NH_3)_3\right] \rightleftharpoons$ $(AgCl)_2.(NH_3)_3 + 3NH_3$		$(AgCl)_2.(NH_3)_3 \rightleftharpoons$ $2(AgCl.NH_3) + NH_3$	
Temperature.	Pressure in mm.	Temperature.	Pressure in mm.
− 25°	56·5	0°	42
− 16°	84	5·0°	55
0°	271	16·3°	116
+ 9·5°	464	19·0°	159
+ 14·0°	632	26·0°	231
+ 16·3°	701	32·8°	366

$AgCl.NH_3 \rightleftharpoons AgCl + NH_3$.	
Temperature.	Pressure in mm.
0°	17
16·3°	42
32·8°	118
42°	240
43°	252
59°	613
63°	653

pumped off, the pressure will remain constant so long as two solid phases are present, i.e. until the compound richer in ammonia is completely decomposed. There will then ensue a sudden fall in the pressure to the value appropriate to the next system of lower ammonia content. On continually withdrawing ammonia at constant temperature, therefore, there will be a step-wise diminution of the ammonia pressure.

The reverse changes take place when the pressure of the ammonia is gradually increased. If ammonia is passed into a vacuous vessel containing silver chloride at a suitable and constant temperature, the pressure will increase until it has reached a certain value; the compound $AgCl.NH_3$ is then formed, and the pressure

will now remain constant until all the silver chloride has combined
with ammonia. On continuing to add ammonia, the pressure will
again rise until it has reached the value at which the compound
$2AgCl.3NH_3$ can be formed, and it will again remain constant
until the lower compound has entirely disappeared. Thereafter,
the pressure will increase, and will become constant when the
compound $AgCl.3NH_3$ begins to be formed. *There is no gradual
change of pressure* on passing from one system to another; the
changes are abrupt, as is demanded by the Phase Rule (*cf*.p. 222), and
as experiment has conclusively proved. These relationships are
represented graphically in Fig. 71 which is based on the measurements of Biltz and Stollenwerk at 16.3°. On passing ammonia into
a vessel containing silver chloride at 16.3°, the pressure rises
until it reaches the value of 42 mm. of mercury. The compound

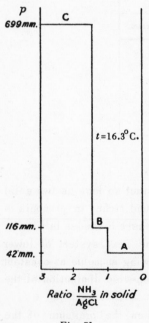

Fig. 71

$AgCl.NH_3$ is then formed, and as there
are now two solid phases present, the
pressure remains constant (line A).
Continued addition of ammonia leads
to the complete conversion of AgCl to
$AgCl.NH_3$. When this has taken place,
i.e. when the ratio $NH_3/AgCl$ in the
solid equals unity, further addition of
ammonia produces an increase of pressure up to 116 mm., when the compound
$2AgCl.3NH_3$ begins to be formed.
Again, the pressure remains constant
(line B) until the compound $AgCl.NH_3$
has been completely converted into
$2AgCl.3NH_3$ and the ratio $NH_3/AgCl$
in the solid becomes 1.5. Thereafter,
the pressure rises to 701 mm. and remains constant at this value until conversion of $2AgCl.3NH_3$ into $AgCl.3NH_3$
has taken place (line C).[7]

The reverse series of changes is observed on withdrawing
ammonia from the system at 16.3°. It is important to note that the

step-wise change in equilibrium pressure (dissociation pressure) at constant temperature *is indicative of the formation of more than one definite, dissociating compound.*

At temperatures above 33°, solid solutions are formed between $2AgCl \cdot 3NH_3$ and $AgCl \cdot NH_3$, and the changes of pressure, as shown in Fig. 71 ,are no longer so abrupt. The behaviour shown in such a case will be mentioned later in the case of water and silicates (p. 228).

Formation of Oxy-carbonates. The step-wise change in equilibrium pressure (dissociation pressure) at constant temperature which is shown by the systems formed from AgCl and NH_3, and which *is indicative of the formation of more than one dissociating compound,* is shown also by certain carbonates. Thus lead carbonate, on being heated, gives rise not only to carbon dioxide and the solid phase, PbO, but also to the oxy-carbonates $3PbO \cdot 5PbCO_3$, $PbO \cdot PbCO_3$, and $2PbO \cdot PbCO_3$; and there exist, as Centnerszwer, Falk, and Awerbach[8] have shown, the following equilibria:

Temperature at which the
dissociation pressure
equals 1 atm.

A.	$8PbCO_3 \rightleftharpoons 3PbO \cdot 5PbCO_3 + 3CO_2$ . . .			274°
B.	$3PbO \cdot 5PbCO_3 \rightleftharpoons 4[PbO \cdot PbCO_3] + CO_2$.		.	286°
C.	$3[PbO \cdot PbCO_3] \rightleftharpoons 2[2PbO \cdot PbCO_3] + CO_2$		.	360°
D.	$2PbO \cdot PbCO_3 \rightleftharpoons 3PbO + CO_2$ . . .		.	412°

The relationships are shown in Fig. 72, where the dissociation temperatures are plotted against the total composition of the solid, considered as a mixture of PbO and $PbCO_3$. Points *a*, *b*, and *c* on the composition axis represent the composition of the compounds $3PbO \cdot 5PbCO_3$, $PbO \cdot PbCO_3$ and $2PbO \cdot PbCO_3$ respectively, and the letters A, B, C, and D refer to the systems mentioned in the above table. From the diagram it will be seen that when lead carbonate is heated in an open vessel under a pressure of one atmosphere of carbon dioxide, decomposition does not take place till the temperature has risen to 274°. At this temperature the pressure of the carbon dioxide becomes equal to that of the atmosphere, and continuous decomposition of the $PbCO_3$ takes place with formation of $3PbO \cdot 5PbCO_3$ and CO_2.

If the pressure is constant, the temperature also will remain constant so long as the two solid phases are present (system A). When all the $PbCO_3$ has undergone decomposition, the temperature must be raised to 286° before the oxy-carbonate, $3PbO \cdot 5PbCO_3$, undergoes decomposition into $PbO \cdot PbCO_3$ and CO_2. The temperature will again remain constant until complete decomposition of $3PbO \cdot 5PbCO_3$ has taken place (System B). At 360°, decomposition of $PbO \cdot PbCO_3$ takes place (System C), and at 412° decompo-

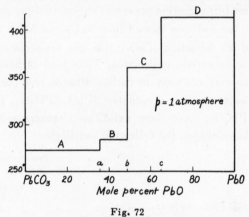

Fig. 72

sition of $2PbO \cdot PbCO_3$ (System D). At 412°, therefore, complete decomposition of lead carbonate to lead oxide and carbon dioxide can take place.

Magnesium carbonate, also, on being heated, gives rise to oxy-carbonates, and shows a behaviour similar to that found in the case of lead carbonate.[9]

Salts with Water of Crystallisation. In the case of the dehydration of crystalline salts containing water of crystallisation, we meet with phenomena which are in all respects similar to those just studied. A salt hydrate on being heated dissociates into a lower hydrate (or anhydrous salt) and water vapour. Since we are dealing with two components — salt and water[10] — in three phases, viz., hydrate a, hydrate b (or anhydrous salt), and vapour, the system is univariant, and to each temperature there will correspond a certain definite vapour pressure (the dissociation pressure), which will be independent of the relative or absolute amounts of the phases, *i.e.* of the amount of hydrate which has already undergone dissociation or dehydration.

The constancy of the dissociation pressure had been proved experimentally by several investigators a number of years before the theoretical basis for its necessity had been given.[11] In the case of salts capable of forming more than one hydrate, we should obtain a series of dissociation curves (*p-t* curves), as in the case of the

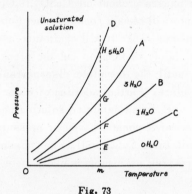

Fig. 73

different hydrates of copper sulphate. In Fig. 73 there are represented diagrammatically the vapour pressure curves of the following univariant systems of copper sulphate and water:

Curve OA : $CuSO_4, 5H_2O \rightleftharpoons CuSO_4, 3H_2O + 2H_2O.$
Curve OB : $CuSO_4, 3H_2O \rightleftharpoons CuSO_4, H_2O + 2H_2O.$
Curve OC : $CuSO_4, H_2O \rightleftharpoons CuSO_4 + H_2O.$
Curve OD : Sat. Solution $\rightleftharpoons CuSO_4 \cdot 5H_2O + xH_2O.$

Let us now follow the changes which take place on increasing the pressure of the aqueous vapour in contact with anhydrous copper sulphate, the temperature being meanwhile maintained constant. If, starting from the point *m*, we slowly add water vapour to the system, the pressure will gradually rise, without formation of hydrate taking place; for at pressures below the curve OC only the anhydrous salt can exist. At E, however, the hydrate $CuSO_4,H_2O$ will be formed, and as there are now three phases present, viz. $CuSO_4$, $CuSO_4,H_2O$, and vapour, the system becomes *univariant;* and since the temperature is constant, the pressure must also be constant. Continued addition of vapour will result merely in an increase in the amount of the hydrate, and a decrease in the amount of the anhydrous salt. When the latter has entirely disappeared, *i.e.* has passed into hydrated salt, the system again becomes *bivariant,* and passes along the line EF; the pressure gradually increases, therefore, until at F the hydrate $3H_2O$ is formed, and the system again becomes univariant. The three phases present are $CuSO_4,H_2O$, $CuSO_4,3H_2O$, vapour. The pressure will remain constant, therefore, until the hydrate $1H_2O$ has disappeared, when it will again increase till G is reached; here the hydrate $5H_2O$ is formed, and the pressure once more remains constant until the complete disappearance of the hydrate $3H_2O$ has taken place. Further addition of water vapour causes the pressure to rise to D, when saturated solution begins to form. The pressure again remains constant (vapour pressure of the saturated solution), until all solid $CuSO_4 \cdot 5H_2O$ has dissolved, after which the pressure increases as a progressively more dilute solution is formed.

Conversely, on dehydrating a dilute aqueous solution of copper sulphate at constant temperature (say at $50°$), we should find that the pressure would at first fall along the curve LM (Fig. 74) as the dilute solution becomes more concentrated. (Point L is, of course, the vapour pressure of pure water at $50°$.) At point M the solution has become saturated as a consequence of the loss of water vapour. Crystals of $CuSO_4 \cdot 5H_2O$ then deposit and the vapour pressure remains constant (MN) until the last trace of liquid has evaporated. Further dehydration results in the formation of some $CuSO_4 \cdot 3H_2O$ and the pressure drops suddenly to that of the invariant system $CuSO_4 \cdot 5H_2O - CuSO_4 \cdot 3H_2O - vapour$ (OP), and the pressure maintains the value corresponding to the dissociation pressure (47 mm.) of this system, until all the hydrate $5H_2O$ has disappeared. Further removal of water then causes the pressure to fall *abruptly* to the pressure (30 mm.) of the system $CuSO_4,3H_2O - CuSO_4,H_2O - vapour$, (QR), at which value it again remains constant until the trihydrate has passed into the monohydrate, when a further sudden diminution of the pressure occurs. The line of constant pressure, ST, gives the value of the vapour pressure (4.4 mm.) of the system $CuSO_4 \cdot H_2O - CuSO_4 - H_2O$ at $50°$.[12]

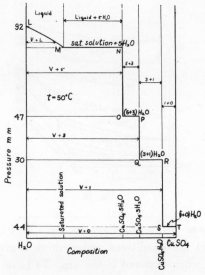

Fig. 74

To the dissociation pressure of a salt hydrate we may apply the equation (p. 24), $d \log_e p / dT = Q/RT^2$, where Q is the heat of dissociation per gram molecule of water vapour. Since, for the vaporisation of pure water, we have the expression $d \log_e p_w / dT = L/RT^2$, where L is the latent heat of vaporisation per gram-molecule, it follows that

$$\frac{d \log_e \dfrac{p}{p_w}}{dT} = \frac{Q - L}{RT^2}.$$

Q - L represents the heat of combination of the salt with one gram-molecule of liquid water (heat of hydration).

In Fig. 73, pressure is plotted against temperature, and in Fig. 74, pressure against composition. A third plot would be that of composition against temperature (pressure constant). All these plane diagrams, however, are merely projections or sections of the solid model which expresses all three variables. This solid model is given in Fig. 75.[13] It is obvious that the plane diagrams of Figs. 73 and 74 result from Fig. 75.

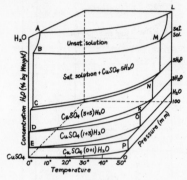

Fig. 75

Efflorescence. From p-t diagrams such as Fig. 73 we are enabled to predict the conditions under which a given hydrated salt will effloresce when exposed to the air. We have just learned that copper sulphate pentahydrate, for example, will not be formed unless the pressure of the aqueous vapour reaches a certain value; and that, conversely, if the vapour pressure falls below the dissociation pressure of the pentahydrate, this salt will undergo dehydration. From this, then, it is evident that a crystalline salt hydrate will effloresce when exposed to the air, if the partial pressure of the water vapour in the air is lower than the dissociation pressure of the hydrate. At room temperature the dissociation pressure of copper sulphate pentahydrate is ordinarily less than the pressure of water vapour in the air, and therefore copper sulphate does not effloresce. In the case of sodium sulphate decahydrate, however, the dissociation pressure is greater than the normal vapour pressure in a room, and this salt therefore effloresces.

Indefiniteness of the Vapour Pressure of a Hydrate. Reference has already been made (p. 216), in the case of the ammonia compounds of the metal chlorides, to the importance of the solid product of dissociation for the definition of the dissociation pressure. Similarly also in the case of a hydrated salt. A salt hydrate in contact with vapour constitutes only a bivariant system, and can exist therefore at different values of temperature and pressure of vapour, as is seen from Fig. 73. Anhydrous copper sulphate can exist in contact with water vapour at all values of temperature and pressure lying in the field below the curve OC; and the hydrate $CuSO_4, H_2O$ can exist in contact with vapour at all values of temperature and pressure in the field BOC. Similarly, each of the other hydrates can exist in contact with vapour at different values of temperature and pressure.

From the Phase Rule, however, we learn that, in order that at a given temperature the pressure of a two-component system may be constant, there must be three phases present. Strictly, therefore, we can speak only of the vapour pressure of a *system;* and since, in the cases under discussion, the hydrates dissociate into a solid and a vapour, any statement as to the vapour pressure of a hydrate has a definite meaning *only when the second solid phase produced by the dissociation is given.* The everyday custom of speaking of the vapour pressure of a hydrated salt acquires a meaning only through the assumption, tacitly made, that the second solid phase, or the solid produced by the dehydration of the hydrate, is the *next lower* hydrate, where more hydrates than one exist. That a hydrate always dissociates in such a way that the next lower hydrate is formed is, however, by no means certain; indeed, cases have been met with where apparently the anhydrous salt, and not the lower hydrate (the existence of which was possible), was produced by the dissociation of the higher hydrate.

That a salt hydrate can exhibit different vapour pressures according to the solid product of dissociation, can not only be deduced theoretically, but it has also been shown experimentally to be a fact. Thus $CaCl_2, 6H_2O$ can dissociate into water vapour and either of two lower hydrates, each containing four molecules of water of crystallisation, and designated respectively as $CaCl_2, 4H_2O\alpha$ and $CaCl_2, 4H_2O\beta$.

By reason of the non-recognition of the importance of the solid dissociation product for the definition of the dissociation pressure of a salt hydrate, many of the older determinations lose much of their value.

The constancy of vapour pressure (at constant temperature) of a hydrate in contact with the next lower hydrate has given rise to a method of preserving any given hydrate unchanged. It is apparent that if a given hydrate is placed in a desiccator over water it will deliquesce (cf. p. 237), whereas placed over sulphuric acid it will dehydrate progressively. The practical problem is that of drying a hydrate without dehydrating it. This can be accomplished by placing the moist hydrate on a tray above a mixture of the hydrate with the next lower hydrate, in a desiccator. For example, if moist copper sulphate pentahydrate is placed over a mixture of pentahydrate and trihydrate, water will pass from the pentahydrate solution until nothing but dry pentahydrate is left, some of the trihydrate at the same time transforming to pentahydrate. Similarly, the trihydrate could be preserved indefinitely over a mixture of trihydrate and monohydrate.

Suspended Transformation. Just as in systems of one component we found that a new phase was not necessarily formed when the conditions for its existence were established, so also we find that even when the vapour pressure is lowered below the dissociation pressure of a system, dissociation does not necessarily occur. This is well known in the case of Glauber's salt, first observed by Faraday. Undamaged crystals of $Na_2SO_4, 10H_2O$ could be kept unchanged in the open air, although the vapour pressure of the system $Na_2SO_4, 10H_2O \longrightarrow Na_2SO_4 \longrightarrow$ vapour is greater than the ordinary pressure of aqueous vapour in the air. That is to say, the possibility of the formation of the new phase Na_2SO_4 was given; nevertheless, this new phase did not appear, and the system therefore became metastable, or unstable with respect to the anhydrous salt. When, however, a trace of the new phase — the anhydrous salt — was brought in contact with the hydrate, transformation occurred; the hydrate effloresced.

Range of Existence of Hydrates. In Fig. 73 the vapour pressure curves of the different hydrates of copper sulphate are represented.

as maintaining their relative positions throughout the whole range of temperatures. But this is not necessarily the case. It is possible that at some temperature the vapour pressure curve of a lower hydrate may cut that of a higher hydrate. At temperatures above the point of intersection, the lower hydrate would have a higher vapour pressure than the higher hydrate, and would therefore be metastable with respect to the latter. The range of stable existence of the lower hydrate would therefore end at the point of intersection. This appears to be the case with the two hydrates of sodium sulphate, to which reference will be made later.

Constancy of Vapour Pressure and the Formation of Compounds. We have seen in the case of the systems discussed in this section that the continued addition of the vapour phase to the system, at constant temperature, causes an increase in the pressure until at a definite value of the pressure a dissociating compound is formed; the pressure then becomes constant, and remains so, until one of the solid phases has disappeared. Conversely, on withdrawing the vapour phase, the pressure remains constant so long as any of the dissociating compound is present, independently of the degree of the decomposition (p. 222). In other words, when compounds are formed which dissociate with formation of a solid and of a gaseous phase, there is a step-wise change in the equilibrium pressure when the gas phase is added to or withdrawn from the system at constant temperature. This behaviour has been employed for the purpose of determining whether or not definite chemical compounds are formed. Bancroft[14] has employed the method in studying reactions between proteins and hydrogen chloride.

III. (a) The Gas is Absorbed by the Solid Component and
No Compound is Formed.

As only one solid phase is formed when the gas is absorbed by the solid component without formation of a compound, the system is bivariant. There will therefore be no "breaks" in the pressure-composition curve. Continued addition of the vapour phase will lead to a continuous change in the composition of the solid phase (a solid solution), and to a continuous increase of the pressure. Similarly, withdrawal of the gaseous product of dissociation will lead

to a continuous change in the composition of the solid phase and
diminution of the gas or vapour pressure. Thus, Tammann[15] found
that when the hydrated silicates, known as zeolites, are dehydrated
at constant temperature, there is a continuous diminution of the vapour pressure. Similarly, the dehydration curve of the so-called
white tungstic acid is continuous and gives no indication of the
existence of the compound $WO_3 . 2H_2O$.[16] Continuous dehydration
curves are obtained also in the case of the hydrates of silicic acid,
and of the oxalates of thorium, zirconium, lanthanum, yttrium, and
cerium[17], also with calcium sulphate hemihydrate.[18]

(b) The Gas is Absorbed by the Solid Component and a Compound is also Formed.

When sodium ammonium ferric oxalate, $Na_3(NH_4)_3Fe_2(C_2O_4)_6,$
$7H_2O$, and sodium ammonium aluminium oxalate,

$$Na_3(NH_4)_3Al_2(C_2O_4)_6,7H_2O,$$

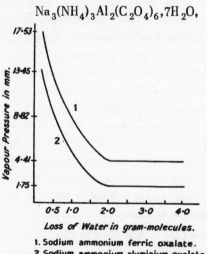

Loss of Water in gram-molecules.

1. Sodium ammonium ferric oxalate.
2. Sodium ammonium aluminium oxalate.

Fig. 76

are dehydrated at $25°$, the vapour pressure diminishes continuously
with loss of water from the hydrated salts until two gram molecules
of water have been lost. The vapour pressure then remains constant
until the pentahydrate has been converted into the monohydrate
(Fig. 76).[19]

Application of X-ray Analysis to Phase Rule Problems. As a result of the classical experiment of von Laue on the diffraction of X-rays by the crystal lattice, methods have been developed by W.H. and W.L. Bragg[20] (the reflection method) and by Debye and Scherrer[21] (the powder method), whereby the arrangement of structural units in the crystal lattice, as well as the absolute dimensions of the crystal lattice can be determined. Apart from the obvious application of this to the science of crystallography, its importance here lies in the fact that it enables a change in the nature of the solid phase to be demonstrated with certainty, even although that solid phase may be opaque and microcrystalline in structure.[22] Prior to the introduction of the X-ray method, the determination of a change in a solid phase rested on the fact that many physical properties (such as density, colour, optical properties), change discontinuously at the transition point. Other properties, such as solubility, vapour pressure, electrode potential, although the same for both forms at the transition point, vary differently with respect to temperature, so that an inflection is obtained at the transition point. All these methods, though in many cases entirely satisfactory, frequently fail to give the desired information, either because the magnitude of the discontinuous change is small, or because the system remains obstinately meta-stable. This behaviour is frequently met with in the case of the allotropic modifications of the metals.[23]

Nevertheless, however small the difference between the physical properties of two crystalline solid phases may be, their existence as two separate phases requires that they possess different space lattices. This property is the most fundamental of all.[24] The importance of this behaviour for the sciences of metallurgy and mineralogy, where the crystal forms are frequently opaque and distorted, will be obvious. For details of the X-ray method, the special treatises dealing with this subject should be consulted.[25] The method has also been applied to the structure of liquids.[26]

As an example of the application of this method to problems of heterogeneous equilibria, we shall consider the work of G. Hägg[27] on the sorption of nitrogen by manganese. The behaviour is formally similar to the sorption of ammonia by the halides of silver (p. 215) although it is complicated somewhat by the occurrence of solid solutions. It remains true, however, that the occurrence of a second solid phase will always produce constancy of gas pressure at constant temperature. The principal difficulty is, as very frequently, the persistence of metastability. Although manganese takes up nitrogen readily at high temperatures (above 600°), at lower temperatures the nitride or solid solution produced does not come into equilibrium with the gaseous phase.

Hägg heated manganese in a closed tube with nitrogen to a temperature sufficiently high to ensure the absorption of the nitrogen. In this way he procured solutions of nitrogen in manganese of varying concentrations up to a limit. Still higher concentrations of nitrogen can be obtained by heating in a stream of ammonia gas. These solutions were caused to assume internal equilibrium by appropriate heat treatment and then examined by the method of X-ray analysis. Starting with pure manganese, the dimensions of the unit crystal and its crystal system were obtained. In the neighbourhood of 0 per cent. nitrogen two allotropic forms of manganese, alpha and beta, exist. Investigation of the changes between 0 and about 14 per' cent. nitrogen by weight, revealed four crystallographically distinct nitride phases. The phase poorest in nitrogen is the delta phase, which shows homogeneity in the region of 2 per cent. nitrogen by weight. It exists only above 500°, and decomposes below this temperature to give alpha manganese and the epsilon phase. The epsilon phase occurs in the neighbourhood of concentration of 6 per cent. nitrogen by weight. The homogeneous state of the next richest nitride phase, the zeta phase, begins at about 9 per cent. nitrogen. The fourth nitride phase, the eta phase, was only found in the homogenised, highly nitrogenated phase, obtained by the action of ammonia. The formulae which correspond to the various phases may be written as follows: eta phase, Mn_3N_2 (14.2 per cent. nitrogen); zeta phase, Mn_5N_2 (9.2 per cent. nitrogen); epsilon phase Mn_4N (6.8 per cent. nitrogen). No formula can be written for the delta phase. This is thought to be either a solid solution, or a crystalline modification of the epsilon phase.

An interesting example of the simultaneous application of the three techniques, viz.: phase-rule, microscopy and X-ray analysis, is presented in the study by Bunn, Clark and Clifford,[28] of the old problem of the constitution of bleaching powder.

NOTES

1. See Sosman, Hostetter, and Merwin, *J. Washington Acad. Sci.*, 1915, 5, 563; Jolibois and Bouvier, *Compt. rend.*, 1921, 172, 1182.

2. *J. Phys. Chem.*, 1936, 40, 435. See also, Johnston, *J. Amer. Chem. Soc.*, 1910, 32, 938; Smyth and Adams, *J. Amer. Chem. Soc.*, 1923, 45, 1167.

3. *Z. physikal. Chem.*, 1924, 111, 79; *Acta Univ. Latviensis*, 1924, 10, 495.

4. If one excludes for the moment the possibility of polymorphism in the case of the compound.

5. For an experimental method of determining the equilibria in such systems see Hüttig, *Z. anorgan. Chem.*, 1920, 114, 161.

6. *Z. anorgan. Chem.*, 1920, 114, 174.

7. For the study of other systems similar to $AgCl - NH_3$, see Biltz and Stollenwerk, *Z. anorgan. Chem.*, 1920, 114, 174; 1921, 119, 97; Biltz and Hüttig, *ibid.*, 1921, 119, 115; Loyd, *J. Physical Chem.*, 1908, 12, 398.

8. *Z. physikal. Chem.*, 1925, 115, 29.

9. Centnerszwer and Bružs, *Z. physikal. Chem.*, 1924, 114, 237.

10. For the reasons for choosing anhydrous salt and water instead of salt hydrate and water as components, see p. 12.

11. For the most accurate recent figures, see Logan, *J. Phys. Chem.*, 1932, 36, 1035.

12. The hydrates of copper sulphate have also been studied by treating copper sulphate with sulphuric acid of varying concentration (Foote, *J. Amer. Chem. Soc.*, 1915, 37, 288).

13. Reproduced by permission from "Outlines of Physical Chemistry," by F. Daniels, published by John Wiley & Sons, Inc. 1948.

14. *J. Physical Chem.*, 1930, 34, 449, 753; Bancroft and Barnett, *Proc. Nat. Acad. Sci.*, 1930, 16, 118.

15. *Z. physikal. Chem.*, 1898, 27, 323.

16. Hüttig, *Z. anorgan. Chem.*, 1923, **122**, 44.

17. Löwenstein, *ibid.*, 1909, **63**, 69.

18. Gibson and Holt, *J. Chem. Soc.*, 1933, 638.

19. *Z. anorgan. Chem.*, 1909, **63**, 69.

20. See W. H. Bragg's *Introduction to Crystal Analysis* (Bell).

21. *Physik. Z.*, 1916, **17**, 277; 1917, **18**, 291.

22. It is interesting to find that twenty years before the introduction of the method of X-ray analysis of crystals as a systematic procedure, Heycock and Neville (*J. Chem. Soc.*, 1898, **73**, 714) had already made use of the method as a qualitative means of examination.

23. See E. Cohen, *Physico-chemical Metamorphosis, and Problems in Piezochemistry* (1926).

24. For the study of allotropy by means of X-rays, see U. Dehlinger, *Ergebnisse der exakten Naturwissenschaften*, 1931, **10**, 325.

25. For example, Bragg, *An Introduction to Crystal Analysis;* Wyckoff, *The Structure of Crystals;* Compton and Allison, *X-rays in Theory and Experiment.*

26. Randell, *The Diffraction of X-rays and Electrons by Amorphous Solids, Liquids and Gases* (Chapman and Hall, 1934).

27. *Z. physikal. Chem.* 1929, B. **4**, 346.

28. *Proc. Roy. Soc.*, 1935, [A] **151**, 141.

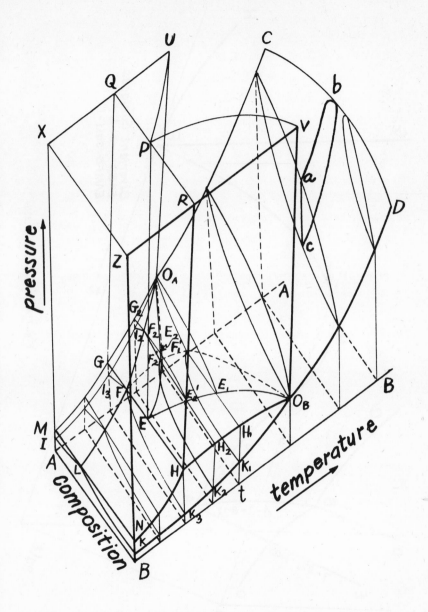

Fig. 84

[*To face page* 232.]

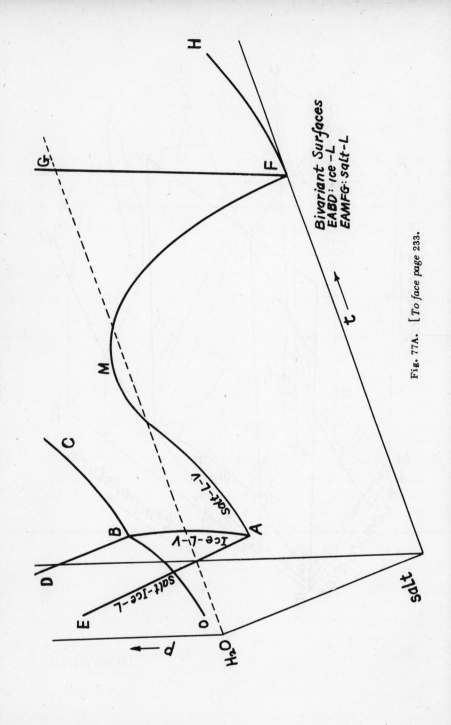

Fig. 77A. [*To face page 233.*]

Bivariant Surfaces
EABD: ice — L
EAMFG: salt — L

CHAPTER XI

E. COEXISTENCE OF SOLID, LIQUID AND GAS PHASES.

I. Only One Component is Volatile.

Pressure–Temperature–Concentration Model. Since, in a two-component system there are three variables, viz. temperature, pressure and concentration, the complete and simultaneous representation of these variables requires three axes, that is, a solid model. The solid model is given in Fig. 77A for the case of water and an involatile salt which forms no hydrate. The lines BC, BD and BO all lie on the back face of the solid; they are, in fact, the vapour pressure curve, melting-point curve and sublimation curve, respectively, of water. Point B is therefore the triple point of water. Similarly FH and FG are the vapour pressure curve and melting-point curve for the salt so that F is its triple point, lying at zero pressure because of the assumed involatility of the salt. The curve FH is included for purposes of clarity but actually it would more or less coincide with the edge of the solid model, again because of involatility. As usual, on this model points correspond to invariance, lines to univariance and surfaces to bivariance. It therefore follows that every surface represents the coexistence in equilibrium of two phases, every space curve the coexistence of three phases, and every point (within the model) the coexistence of four phases. The nature of these phases is sufficiently described on the diagram. Only one invariant point is to be found on the diagram, viz., point A, which marks the conditions of coexistence of four phases: salt, ice, solution and vapour. Such a point is called a quadruple point (cf. triple point in unary systems). It is also a eutectic point (cf. p. 136). If each of these four phases is eliminated in turn, $4C_3 = 4$ systems of univariant behaviour are obtained, each corresponding to the equilibrium of three phases. Three of these are shown in the

Figure by the lines AB, AMF and AE, and are appropriately labelled.

Changes at the Quadruple Point. Since the invariant system solid solvent—solute—solution—vapour can exist only at a definite temperature, addition or withdrawal of heat must cause the disappearance of one of the phases, whereby the system will become univariant. So long as all four phases are present the temperature, pressure, and concentration of the components in the solution must remain constant. When, therefore, heat is added to or withdrawn from the system, mutually compensatory changes will take place within the system whereby the condition of the latter is preserved. These changes can in all cases be foreseen with the help of the principle of Le Chatelier; and, after what was said on pages 22 and 23, need only be briefly referred to here. In the first place, addition of heat will cause solvent to melt, and the concentration of the solution will be thereby altered; solute must therefore dissolve until the original concentration is reached, and the heat of fusion of solvent will be counteracted by the heat of solution of the solute. Changes of volume of the solid and liquid phases must also be taken into account; an alteration in the volume of these phases being compensated by condensation or evaporation. All four phases will therefore be involved in the change, and the final state of the system will be dependent on the amounts of the different phases present; the ultimate result of addition or withdrawal of heat or of change of pressure at the quadruple point will be one of the four univariant systems: solid solvent — solution — vapour; solute—solution —vapour; solid solvent—solute—vapour; solid solvent— solute — solution. If the vapour phase disappear, there will be left the univariant system solid solvent—solute—solution, and the temperature at which this system can exist will alter with the pressure. Since in this case the influence of pressure is comparatively slight, the temperature of the quadruple point will differ only slightly from that of the eutectic point as determined under atmospheric pressure.

Pressure—Temperature Plane Diagram. If the space curves of the solid model, Fig. 77A, are projected on the p-t plane a plane representation of pressure as a function of temperature is obtained, the concentration variable being sacrificed. This is frequently done, but it is advisable to introduce the solid model first, in order that it may be clear that the curves are really space curves, that is, they do not really lie in one plane.

Since in systems of two components the two phases, solution and vapour, constitute a bivariant system, the vapour pressure is undefined, and may have different values at the same temperature, depending on the concentration. In order that there may be for each temperature a definite corresponding pressure of the vapour, a third phase must be present. This condition is satisfied by the system solid—liquid (solution)—vapour; that is, by the saturated solution (*v. infra*). In the case of a saturated solution, therefore, the pressure of the vapour at any given temperature is constant.

Vapour Pressure of Solid–Solution–Vapour.   It has long been known that the addition of a non-volatile solid to a liquid in which

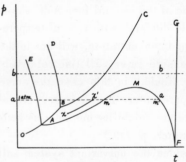

Fig. 77B

it is soluble lowers the vapour pressure of the solvent; and the diminution of the pressure is approximately proportional to the amount of substance dissolved. The vapour-pressure curve, therefore, of a solution of a salt in water must lie below that for pure water. Further, in the case of a pure liquid, the vaporisation curve is a function only of the temperature (p. 21), whereas, in the case of a solution, the pressure varies both with the temperature and the *concentration*. These two factors, however, act in opposite directions; for although the vapour pressure in all cases increases as the temperature rises, increase of concentration, as we have seen, lowers the vapour pressure. For *saturated* solutions, therefore, since the concentration itself varies with the temperature, two cases have to be considered, viz. where the concentration increases, and where the concentration diminishes, with rise of temperature.

The relations which are found here will be best understood with the help of Fig. 77B,[1] which is a projection of Fig. 77A on the *p-t* plane of the model. In this figure, OB represents the sublimation curve of ice, and BC the vaporisation curve of water; the curve for the saturated solution must lie below this, and must cut the sublimation curve of ice at some temperature below the melting-point. The point of intersection A is the eutectic point. If the solubility increases with rise of temperature, the increase of the vapour pressure due to the latter will be partially annulled. Since at first the effect of increase of temperature more than counteracts the depressing action of increase of concentration, the vapour pressure will increase on raising the temperature above the eutectic point. If the elevation of temperature is continued, however, to the melting-point of the salt, the effect of increasing concentration makes itself more and more felt, so that the vapour-pressure curve of the solution falls more and more below that of the pure liquid, and the pressure will ultimately become equal to that of the pure salt; that is to say, practically equal to zero. The curve will therefore be of the general form AMF shown in Fig. 77B. If the solubility should diminish with rise of temperature, the two factors, temperature and concentration, will act in the same direction, and the vapour-pressure curve will rise relatively more rapidly than that of the pure liquid; in this case the curve must end on the face representing pure water. In this case, critical phenomena may be observed, before the solubility has become zero. (Cf. the system sodium sulphate—water, p. 243.)

Other Univariant Systems. Besides the univariant system salt —solution—vapour already considered, three others are possible, viz. ice—solution—vapour, ice—salt—solution, and ice—salt—vapour.

The fusion-point of a substance is lowered, as we have seen, by the addition of a foreign substance, and the depression is all the greater the larger the quantity of substance added. The vapour pressure of the water, also, is lowered by the solution in it of other substances, so that the vapour pressure of the system ice—solution —vapour must decrease as the temperature falls from the fusion-point of ice to the eutectic point. This curve is represented by BA(Fig. 77B), and is coincident with the sublimation curve of ice.

The curve AO represents the pressures of the system ice—salt—vapour. This curve will also be coincident with the sublimation curve of ice, on account of the non-volatility of the salt.

The equilibria of the fourth univariant system ice—salt—solution are represented by AE. Since this is a condensed system, the effect of a small change of temperature will be to cause a large change of pressure, as in the case of the fusion point of a pure substance. The direction of this curve will depend on whether there is an increase or diminution of volume on solidification; but the effect in any given case can be predicted with the help of the principle of Le Chatelier, and calculated by means of the Clapeyron equation.

Bivariant Systems. Besides the univariant systems already discussed, $4C_2 = 6$ bivariant systems are possible, representing the coexistence of the two phases. For at least two of these the equilibrium conditions as to temperature, pressure and composition, are shown in the solid model of Fig. 77A and the key to them given on the side of the diagram. It is difficult and misleading to interpret the pressure-temperature relations of the bivariant systems from the projection diagram of Fig. 77B however, since some of the surfaces cover one another, when projected. For instance, a bivariant point in the area CBAMFG, of Fig. 77B may refer to either of the binary equilibria, solution—vapour or salt—solution, as well as to either of the component unary systems; but no such ambiguity exists on the solid model (if the construction lines are shown.)

Deliquescence. The conditions under which a salt will deliquesce may now be considered. As is evident from Fig. 77B, salt can exist in contact with water vapour at pressures and temperatures lying below OAMF. If, however, at a constant temperature higher than that of the eutectic A, the pressure of water vapour is increased until it reaches a value lying on this curve, solution will be formed; for this curve AMF represents the equilibrium salt—solution—vapour. From this, therefore, it is clear that if the pressure of the aqueous vapour in the atmosphere is greater than that of the saturated solution of a salt, that salt will, on being placed in the air, form a solution: it will deliquesce.

Whether or not any given salt will deliquesce, depends on the vapour pressure lowering of its saturated solution, that is, on whether a point on AMF, representing the vapour pressure of a saturated solution of the salt at the given temperature (usually room temperature) is above or below the point representing the pressure of aqueous vapour in the atmosphere. This again depends on the vertical displacement of curve AMF below BC, and this will be a function of the concentration of the salt in saturated solution. Generally speaking, the more soluble the salt, the lower the vapour pressure, and hence we find that all deliquescent substances are very soluble; the converse, however, does not always appear to be true.

Separation of Salt on Evaporation. With the help of Fig. 77B it is possible to state in a general manner whether or not salt will be deposited when a solution is evaporated under a constant pressure.

The curve AMF (Fig. 77B) is the vapour-pressure curve of the saturated solutions of the salt, *i.e.* it represents, as we have seen, the maximum vapour pressure at which salt can exist in contact with solution and vapour. The dotted line *aa* represents atmospheric pressure.

Since the boiling-point is defined as that temperature at which the vapour pressure is equal to the superincumbent pressure, it is obvious that, in this case, the solution has two boiling-points, that is, two solutions exist, differing distinctly in concentration, which possess the same vapour pressure at two different temperatures: this has been verified experimentally for silver nitrate solutions in water, whose boiling-points, under atmospheric pressure, are 133° and 191 °C.[17]. If, now, an unsaturated solution, the composition of which is represented by the point x, is heated in an open vessel, the temperature will rise, and the vapour pressure of the solution will increase. The system will, therefore, pass along a line represented diagrammatically by xx'. At the point x' the vapour pressure of the system becomes equal to 1 atm.; and as the vessel is open to the air, the pressure cannot further rise; the solution boils. If the heating is continued water passes off, the concentration increases, and the boiling-point rises. The system will therefore pass along the line $x'm$, until at the point m solid salt separates out (provided supersaturation is excluded). The system is now invariant, the pressure being constant, and continued heating will no longer cause an alteration of the concentration; as water passes off, solid salt will be deposited, and the solution will evaporate to dryness.

If, however, the atmospheric pressure is represented not by aa but by bb, then, as Fig. 77B shows, the maximum vapour pressure of the system salt—solution—vapour never reaches the pressure of 1 atm. Further, since the curve bb lies in the area of the bivariant system solution—vapour, there can at no point be a separation of the solid form; for the system solid—solution—vapour can exist only along the curve AMF.

On heating the solution of such a salt continuously in an open vessel, therefore, there is no separation of the solid. Only a homogeneous fused mass is obtained. This is found to be the behaviour of aqueous solutions of sodium hydroxide and of potassium hydroxide, under atmospheric pressure. If, however, the heating is carried out under a pressure which is lower than the maximum pressure of the saturated solution, separation of the solid substance will be possible.

The System Sodium Sulphate-Water. The consideration of the pressure-temperature relations of two components, such as sodium sulphate and water, where the formation of crystalline hydrates takes place, must include not only the vapour pressure of the saturated solutions, but also that of the hydrates. The vapour pressures of salt hydrates have already been treated in a general manner (Chap. X), so that it is only necessary here to point out the connection between the two classes of systems.

In most cases the vapour pressure of a salt hydrate, *i.e.* the vapour pressure of the system hydrate—anhydrous salt (or lower hydrate)— vapour, is at all temperatures lower than that of the system anhydrous salt (or lower hydrate)—solution—vapour. This, however, is not a necessity; and cases are known where the vapour pressure of the former system is, under certain circumstances, equal to or higher than that of the latter. An example of this is found in sodium sulphate decahydrate.

On heating $Na_2SO_4,10H_2O$ a point is reached at which the dissociation pressure into anhydrous salt and water vapour becomes equal to the vapour pressure of the saturated solution of the anhydrous salt. This occurs at $32.6°$, where the vapour pressures of the two systems

$$Na_2SO_4,10H_2O - Na_2SO_4 - vapour,$$
$$Na_2SO_4 - solution - vapour$$

are, therefore, equal; at this temperature the four phases, Na_2SO_4, $10H_2O$; Na_2SO_4; solution; vapour, can coexist. From this it is evident that when sodium sulphate decahydrate is heated to $32.6°$, in a closed system the two new phases, anhydrous salt and solution, will be formed (suspended transformation being supposed excluded), and the hydrate will appear to undergo *partial fusion;* and during the process of "melting" the vapour pressure and temperature will remain constant.

The vapour pressure of the different systems of sodium sulphate and water can best be studied with the help of the diagram in Fig. 78. The curve ABCD represents the vapour pressure curve of the saturated solution of anhydrous sodium sulphate. GC is the pressure curve of decahydrate + anhydrous salt, which, as we have seen, cuts the curve ABCD at the quadruple point, $32.6°$, Since at this point the solution is saturated with respect to both the anhydrous salt and the decahydrate, the vapour pressure curve of the saturated solution of the latter must also pass through the point C. As at temperatures below this point the solubility of the decahydrate is less than that of the anhydrous salt, the vapour pressure of the solution will, in accordance with Babo's law, be higher than that of the solution of the anhydrous salt; which was also found experimentally to be the case (curve HC).

In connection with the vapour pressure of the saturated solutions of the anhydrous salt and the decahydrate, attention must be drawn to a conspicuous deviation from what was found to hold in the case of one-component systems in which a vapour phase was present (p. 48). There, it was seen that the vapour pressure of the more stable system was always *lower* than that of the less

stable; in the present case, however, we find that this is no longer
so. We have already learned that at temperatures below 32.6° the
system decahydrate—solution—vapour is more stable than the system anhydrous salt—solution—vapour; but the vapour pressure of
the latter system is, as has just been stated, lower than that of the
former. At temperatures above the transition point the vapour pressure of the saturated solution of the decahydrate will be lower than
that of the saturated solution of the anhydrous salt.

This behaviour depends on the fact that the less stable form is
the more soluble, and that the diminution of the vapour pressure increases with the amount of salt dissolved.

With regard to sodium sulphate heptahydrate, the same considerations will hold as in the case of the decahydrate. Since at 24° the
four phases heptahydrate, anhydrous salt, solution, vapour can coexist, the vapour pressure curves of the systems hydrate—anhydrous
salt—vapour (curve EB) and hydrate—solution—vapour (curve FB)
must cut the pressure curve of the saturated solution of the anhydrous salt at the above temperature, as represented in Fig. 78 by

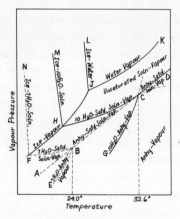

Fig. 78

the point B. This constitutes, therefore, a second quadruple point,
which is, however, metastable.

From the diagram it is also evident that the dissociation pressure of the heptahydrate is higher than that of the decahydrate,

although it contains less water of crystallisation. The system hep-tahydrate—anhydrous salt—vapour must be metastable with respect to the system decahydrate—anhydrous salt—vapour, and will pass into the latter. Whether or not there is a temperature at which the vapour pressure curves of the two systems intersect, and below which the heptahydrate becomes the more stable form, is not known.

It is apparent that Fig. 78 is the projection of a solid model, since the concentration variable is ignored. For the sake of com-pleteness, several other curves are drawn. Thus, J is the triple point of the system water, H is the binary eutectic of the system sodium sulphate—water, at which ice, solid decahydrate, solution and vapour are in equilibrium, HM represents the effect of pressure on the condensed system ice— decahydrate— solution, and FN is the corresponding curve for the system ice—heptahydrate—solution.

We now turn from the projection on the pressure-temperature face of the solid model to the projection on the temperature-concentration face, thereby supplementing the short discussion already given on pp. 235 and 236. Using the results obtained by Wuite[2] Fig. 79 is ob-tained. In this figure, at A we have a eutectic point at which ice and sodium sulphate decahydrate coexist with solution and vapour. The temperature is -1.286°, and the solution contains 4.669 grams (0.58 moles) of anhydrous sodium sulphate in 100 grams of water.

The curve AB is the equilibrium curve for the decahydrate in contact with solution and vapour, and ends at the point B (32.6°), where transition to the rhombic form of anhydrous sodium sulphate occurs. The equilibrium curve for rhombic anhydrous sodium sul-phate in contact with solution and vapour shows a minimum at about 125°, and ends at E (234°), the vapour pressure at this point being 27.5 atm.. Here transition of rhombic to monoclinic sodium sulphate takes place, the solubility of the latter decreas-ing with rise of temperature (EF). At these high temperatures and pressures the concentration of sodium sulphate in the coexisting vapour becomes noticeable. This is shown by the curve GF, which, below about 320°, coincides with the water axis. GF therefore rep-resents vapour compositions and EF the coexisting liquid composi-tions in the three-phase system monoclinic sodium sulphate — liquid—vapour. (Point F is actually nearer the water axis than shown on the diagram.) The liquid and vapour compositions become identical at F, which is therefore a critical point, and must lie on the critical curve which runs from H (the critical point of water, 374°) to the critical point of sodium sulphate, although the portion immediately to the right of F is metastable. (See the discussion of critical phenomena, p. 257. Point F in Fig. 79 corresponds to point p in Fig. 89 (b).

Potassium Iodide and Sulphur Dioxide. In order still further to

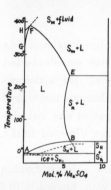

Fig. 79

illustrate the application of the principles of the Phase Rule to the study of systems formed by a volatile and a non-volatile component, a brief description may be given of the behaviour of sulphur dioxide and potassium iodide. After it had been found that liquid sulphur dioxide has the property of dissolving potassium iodide, and that the solutions thus obtained present certain peculiarities of behaviour, the question arose as to whether or not compounds are formed between the sulphur dioxide and the potassium iodide, and if so, what these compounds are. To find an answer to this ques-

tion, Walden and Centnerszwer[3] made a complete investigation of the solubility curves of these two components, the investigation extending from the freezing-point to the critical point of sulphur dioxide. For convenience of reference, the results which they obtained are represented diagrammatically in Fig. 80. The freezing-point (A) of pure sulphur dioxide was found to be -72.7°. Addition of potassium iodide lowered the freezing-point, but the maximum depression obtained was very small, and was reached when the concentration of the potassium iodide in the solution was only 0.336 mols. per cent. Beyond this point, an increase in the concentration of the iodide was accompanied by an elevation of the freezing-point, the change of the freezing-point with the concentration being represented by the curve BC. The solid which separated from the solutions represented by BC was a bright *yellow* crystalline

substance.   At the point C (-23.4°) a temperature-maximum was
reached; and as the concentration of the potassium iodide was continuously increased, the temperature of equilibrium first fell and then

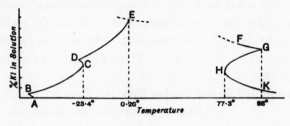

Fig. 80

slowly rose, until at +0.26° (E) a second temperature-maximum was
registered. On passing the point D, the solid which was deposited
from the solution was a *red* crystalline substance. On withdrawing sulphur dioxide from the system, the solution became turbid, and
the temperature remained constant. The investigation was not pur-
sued further at this point, the attention being then directed to the
equilibria at higher temperatures.

When a solution of potassium iodide in liquid sulphur dioxide
containing 1.49 per cent. of potassium iodide was heated, solid
(potassium iodide) was deposited at a temperature of 96.4°. Solutions containing more than about 3 per cent. of the iodide separated,
on being heated, into two layers, and the temperature at which the
liquid became heterogeneous fell as the concentration was increased, a temperature-minimum being obtained with solutions containing 12 per cent. of potassium iodide. On the other hand, solutions containing 30.9 per cent. of the iodide, on being heated, deposited potassium iodide; while a solution containing 24.5 per
cent. of the salt first separated (metastably) into two layers at
89.3°, and then, on cooling, solid was deposited and one of the
liquid layers disappeared.

Such are, in brief, the results of experiment; their interpretation,
with the aid of Fig. 80 should present no difficulty to the reader, as
far, at least, as concerns the low temperature part of the diagram.
Passing to higher temperatures, FG is the solubility curve of potassium iodide in sulphur dioxide; at G two liquid phases are formed,

and the system therefore becomes invariant (*cf.* p. 174). The curve GHK is the solubility curve for two partially miscible liquids; and since complete miscibility occurs on *lowering* the temperature, the curve is similar to that obtained with triethylamine and water (p. 98. K is also an invariant point at which potassium iodide is in equilibrium with two liquid phases and vapour.

The complete investigation of the equilibria between sulphur dioxide and potassium iodide, therefore, shows that these two components form two compounds $(KI . 14SO_2$ and $KI . 4SO_2)$;   and that when solutions having a concentration between those represented by the points G and K are heated, separation into two layers occurs.

II. Both Components are Volatile.

General.   In the preceding pages certain restrictions were imposed on the discussion of the equilibria between two components;

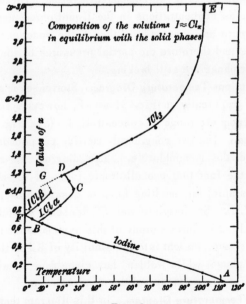

Fig. 81

but in the present section the restriction that only one of the components is volatile will be allowed to fall, and the general behaviour of two volatile[4] components, each of which is capable of forming a liquid solution with the other, will be studied. As we shall see, however, the removal of the previous restriction produces no alteration in the general aspect of the equilibrium curves for concentration and temperature, but changes to some extent the appearance of the pressure-temperature diagram. The latter will become still more complicated when account is taken not only of the total pressure but also of the partial pressures of the two components in the vapour phase. In the example we are about to describe, viz. the system iodine-chlorine, we shall not introduce this complication, in other words, the concentration of the vapour will not be shown. We shall, however, refer to it later (p. 248).

Iodine and Chlorine.

The different systems furnished by iodine and chlorine, rendered classical by the studies of Stortenbeker,[5] form an instructive example of equilibria in a two-component system. The study is complete, as far as concentrations in the liquid phase and total equilibrium pressure are concerned, although the concentrations in the vapour phase and therefore the partial pressures of the components in the vapour phase are still lacking.

Concentration—Temperature Diagram Stortenbeker's results are represented graphically in Fig. 81 which, however, covers only a part of the complete range of concentration. (See Fig. 82 for complete diagram.) The two congruently melting compounds are the trichloride and the monochloride. The diagram is slightly complicated by the fact that two allotropic forms of the monochloride exist. The stable, high-melting form, is described as IClα, the unstable as IClβ. So complete was Stortenbeker's work that there has been little or no further study of this system, although Karsten[6] has given a clearer insight into the stability of ICl in the liquid and the gaseous phase, while Walden[7] has given more detailed data on the states of stable existence of the monochloride.

Pressure—Temperature Diagram. In this diagram there are represented the values of the vapour pressure of the saturated solutions of chlorine and iodine. To give a complete picture of the relations between pressure, temperature, and concentration, a solid model would be required, with three axes at right angles to one another along which could be measured the values of pressure, temperature, and concentration of the components in the solution. Instead of this, however, there may be employed the accompanying projection figure (Fig. 82), the lower portion of which shows the projection of the equilibrium curve on the surface containing the concentration and temperature axes, while the upper portion is the projection on the plane containing the pressure and temperature axes. The lower portion is therefore a concentration-temperature diagram; the upper portion, a pressure-temperature diagram. The corresponding points of the two diagrams are joined by dotted lines.

Corresponding to the point C, the melting-point of pure iodine, there is the point C_1 which represents the vapour pressure of iodine at its melting-point. At this point four curves cut: (1) the sublimation curve of iodine; (2) the vaporisation curve of fused iodine; (3) C_1B_1, the vapour pressure curve of the saturated solutions in equilibrium with solid iodine; and (4), the melting curve of iodine under pressure. Starting, therefore, with the system solid iodine — liquid iodine, addition of chlorine will cause the temperature of equilibrium to fall continuously, while the vapour pressure will first increase, pass through a maximum[8] and then fall continuously until the eutectic point, $B(B_1)$, is reached.[9] At this point the system is invariant, and the pressure will therefore remain constant until all the iodine has disappeared. As the concentration of the chlorine increases in the manner represented by the curve BfH, the pressure of the vapour also increases as represented by the curve $B_1f_1H_1$. At H_1, the eutectic point for iodine monochloride and iodine tri-chloride, the pressure again remains constant until all the mono-chloride has disappeared. As the concentration of the solution passes along the curve HF, the pressure of the vapour increases as represented by the curve H_1F_1; F_1 represents the pressure of the vapour at the melting-point of iodine trichloride. If the concentration of the chlorine in the solution is continuously increased from this point, the vapour pressure first increases and then decreases, until the eutectic point for iodine trichloride and solid chlorine is reached (D_1). Curves Cl_2 — solid and Cl_2 — liquid repre-

sent the sublimation and vaporisation curves of chlorine, the melting-point of chlorine being −102°.

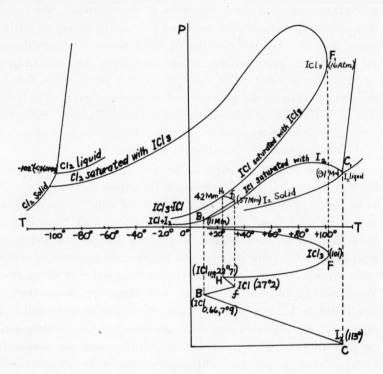

Fig. 82

Although complete measurements of the vapour pressure of the
different systems of pure iodine to pure chlorine have not been
made, the experimental data are nevertheless sufficient to allow
of the general form of the curves being indicated with certainty.

**Partial Pressures of the Components and the Composition of
the Vapour Phase.** Although Fig. 82 contains an axis of composition, the composition-temperature diagram is of course that of the
liquid phase. It would be interesting and instructive to plot a
similar diagram for the vapour phase, but the data, viz. the analyses
of the vapour phase, are lacking for this.

The same data, assuming the validity of Dalton's law of partial pressure, would also permit of the calculation of the partial pressures of the components in the vapour phase, and these could be plotted on the same pressure-temperature diagram which expresses the total vapour pressure. It could then be said that the study of this system was complete.

Bivariant Systems. To these, only a brief reference need be made. Since there are two components, two phases will form a bivariant system. The fields in which these systems can exist are shown in Fig. 82 and Fig. 83, which is a more diagrammatic representation of a portion of Fig. 82.

    I. Iodine—vapour.

    II. Solution—vapour.

    III. Iodine trichloride—vapour.

    IV. Iodine monochloride—vapour.

The conditions for the existence of these systems will probably be best understood from Fig. 83. Since the curve $B'A'$ represents the pressures under which the system iodine — solution — vapour can exist, increase of volume (diminution of pressure) will cause the volatilisation of the solution, and the system iodine — vapour will remain. If ,therefore, we start with a system represented by a, dim-

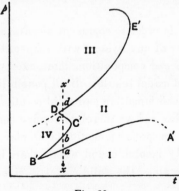

Fig. 83

inution of pressure at constant temperature will lead to the condition represented by x. On the other hand, increase of pressure at a will lead to the condensation of a portion of the vapour phase. Since the concentration of chlorine in the vapour is greater than in the solution, condensation of vapour would increase the concentration of chlorine in the solution; a certain amount of iodine must therefore pass into solution in order that the composition of the latter shall remain unchanged.[10] If, therefore, the volume of vapour be sufficiently great, continued diminution of volume will ultimately lead to the disappearance af all the iodine, and there

will remain only solution and vapour (field II.). As the diminution
of volume is continued, the vapour pressure and the concentration
of the chlorine in the solution will increase, until, when the pressure has reached the value b, iodine monochloride can separate out.
The system, therefore, again becomes univariant; and at constant
temperature the pressure and composition of the phases must remain
unchanged. Diminution of volume will therefore not effect an increase of pressure, but a condensation of the vapour; and since
this is richer in chlorine than the solution, solid iodine monochloride
must separate out in order that the concentration of the solution remain unchanged.[11] As the result, therefore, we obtain the bivariant
system iodine monochloride—vapour.

A detailed discussion of the effect of a continued increase of
pressure will not be necessary. From what has already been said,
and with the help of Fig. 83, it will readily be understood that this
will lead successively to the univariant system (c), iodine monochloride—solution—vapour; the bivariant system solution—vapour
(field II.); the univariant system (d), iodine trichloride—solution—
vapour; and the bivariant system x', iodine trichloride—vapour.
If the temperature of the experiment is above the melting-point of
the monochloride, then the systems in which this compound occurs
will not be formed.

Generalised p, t, x Model. [12] In order to represent simultaneously and completely the behaviour of any system with respect to
variations in temperature, pressure and composition, three axes of
reference are necessary and a solid model results. If all possibilities are considered, such as compound formation and solid solution,
the model becomes extremely complex and we therefore confine ourselves to the simple case where no compound formation takes place,
where the solid forms are mutually insoluble and where there is
complete miscibility in the liquid state. The solid model is given
in Fig. 84.

It is apparent that a vertical plane parallel to the plane of XAA
gives a t-p diagram (constant composition), that a vertical plane
parallel to the plane of XABZ gives a p-x diagram (temperature
constant) and that a horizontal plane parallel to the plane of AABB

gives a *t-x* diagram (pressure constant). All these plane diagrams have already been discussed and, although it is perhaps illogical to discuss the sections before dealing with the solid model, it would be practically impossible to discuss the solid model until physical meaning had been given to the subject by a discussion of the sections. It remains then to consider the solid model in its totality.

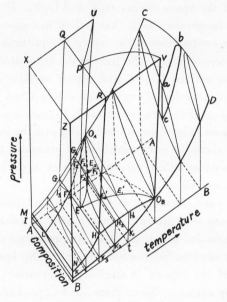

Fig. 84 – (An enlarged view will be found facing p. 232).

O_A and O_B are the triple points and C and D the critical points of A and B respectively. The regions of liquid and vapour are separated by two curved surfaces forming an irregular lens-shaped envelope within which both liquid and vapour can coexist. This envelope is bounded by the critical curve CD (see p. 257), the plane curves CO_A and DO_B (vapour pressure curves of pure liquid A and B respectively), the space curves O_AF and O_BF, the space curves O_AE and O_BE and the straight line EF (E and F being the respective liquid and vapour compositions at the eutectic point).[18]

The liquid region is limited by the planes UO_AC and VO_BD, the upper surface of the envelope just described, the surface UO_AEP which represents the coexistence of liquid and solid A, and the surface VO_BFP which is the corresponding surface for solid B. The line EP therefore gives the conditions for equilibrium between solids A and B and liquid.

The region of vapour is limited in one direction by the vapour surface which corresponds to the limit of existence of liquid, that is the surface bounded by the critical curve CD, the plane curves CO_A and DO_B and the space curves O_AF and O_BF. F is at the same pressure and temperature as E, but differs in composition, since it represents the composition of the vapour in equilibrium with a liquid of eutectic composition E. The limit in the other direction is formed by the vapour surface IO_AFL and vapour surface KO_BFL, which represent the equilibrium of vapour with solids A and B respectively. The resemblance of the space curves O_AFO_B to a eutectic diagram has already been pointed out when dealing with the vapour pressures of solids: F gives the only conditions of pressure, temperature and concentration under which vapour can be in equilibrium with solid A and solid B and liquid.

It will be seen, therefore, that the region of liquid only and the region of vapour only are both volumes and, as such, represent trivariant systems for which all three of pressure, temperature and concentration need be fixed in order to define the system.

Systems of two phases in equilibrium (bivariant behaviour) are represented by surfaces. Since there are four possible phases, there are $4C_2 = 6$ systems of two phases. Owing to the fact that the composition of the two phases is not in general the same, each system of two phases is represented by two surfaces, in which the equilibrium concentrations of the two phases refer to the same p,t values. The two-phase systems and corresponding surfaces are as follows:

1. Vapour + Liquid: surfaces FO_ACDO_BF and EO_ACDO_BE.
2. Vapour + solid A: surfaces IO_AFL and IO_AGM.
3. Vapour + Solid B: surfaces KO_BFL and KO_BHN.
4. Liquid + Solid A: surfaces UO_AEP and UO_AGQ.
5. Liquid + Solid B: surfaces VO_BEP and VO_BHR.
6. Solid A + Solid B: surfaces MGQX and NHRZ.

If corresponding points of these pairs of surfaces are joined by horizontal lines, all points on these lines represent systems of these pairs of phases. The spaces enclosed by the surfaces representing the coexistence of the six pairs of phases fill up the space in the solid model not occupied by the regions of homogeneous liquid and vapour.

The three liquid surfaces cut in pairs in the three curves O_AE, O_BE and EP, and the vapour surfaces in pairs in the curves O_AF, O_BF and FL. Each curve represents the univariant behaviour of a system of three phases, in three of which liquid is always present and in the other three vapour. Since, in general, the three phases will have different composition, at the same temperature and pressure, any one curve must always be associated with two others. There will be $4C_3 = 4$ such univariant systems for the complete representation of each of which, three curves will be necessary, as follows:

1. Solid A + liquid + vapour: curves O_AG, O_AE, O_AF.
2. Solid Ḃ + liquid + vapour: curves C_BH, O_BE, O_BF.
3. Solid A + solid B + vapour: curves GM, HN, FL.
4. Solid A + solid B + liquid: curves GQ, HR, EP.

Finally, for the type of system under consideration there is only one invariant point at which four phases coexist and for which, of course, temperature, pressure and concentration are fixed. Since, however, the four phases will have different (though fixed) composition, four points, having the same temperature and pressure coordinates, will be necessary for the complete representation of this invariant point. The points are G, expressing the composition of pure A, H that of pure B, F that of the vapour, and E that of the liquid.

Only a solid model can give full information as to the values of the variables of a system, but since it is practically almost impossible to work with such a model, it is usual to project on one or other of the planes of reference, thus, projection on the rear vertical plane gives a diagram, such as has been given for the iodine — chlorine system, which represents the variation of equilibrium pressure with respect to temperature, but ignores composition: similarly projection on the horizontal base gives a diagram which represents change of composition as a function of temperature, but ignores change of pressure. Finally, isothermal, isobaric or isoplethal sections can be drawn. A number of isothermal sections are drawn in the figure, at points of interest, but their interpretation may be left to the reader, since many of them have already been given. For a more detailed discussion of the model, the reader should consult the reference to Roozeboom, "Die Heterogenen Gleichgewichte", given at the commencement of this section. It is suggested that the student draw the isotherm at temperature t (Fig. 84) to give a type which has not been discussed.

Pressure – Temperature – Composition Model for Aniline and Sulphur Dioxide. This system has been studied very fully by A.E. Hill,[13] and is a good example of a complete representation of the behaviour of a binary system in the form of a solid model, the three variables being temperature, pressure and concentration.

Sulphur dioxide combines with anhydrous aniline to form the compound $C_6H_5NH_2 . SO_2$; and on adding sulphur dioxide to aniline the isothermal vapour pressure curve (Fig. 85) is obtained. The initial sloping portion of the curve represents the vapour pressures of solutions of sulphur dioxide in liquid aniline.

When the pressures corresponding to the horizontals of such isothermals as that of Fig. 85, are plotted against temperature, the vapour pressure curve of the compound is obtained (Fig. 86).

The complete representation of the system is given by the solid model shown in Fig. 87.[19] The curve b g e is the solubility curve of the compound, which in the case of condensed systems is usually represented as a projection upon the composition-temperature surface. What is left out of the familiar projection, however, is that not only is the solubility curve bg moving in the direction of higher pressures with increase in temperature, but also that ge is moving in the direction of higher pressures with *decrease* in temperature. To the well-known fact that the solid phase may be in equilibrium at a constant temperature with either of two liquid phases of differing composition is to be added the fact that of course, the two liquids have different vapour pressures. The front view of the figure shows in perspective the regions of stability for the solid, for liquid solution and for vapour alone.

A section of the solid model representing a typical isotherm at the temperature t_0 is shown in Fig. 88.[19] This is a complete representation of what is shown in part in Fig. 85. The line a b represents the change in solubility of sulphur dioxide in liquid aniline with increase in pressure; at pressures lower than b the system can consist only of a liquid phase coexisting with vapour of the same pressure and a different composition, expressed by a point on the vapour curve $axyf$. At the pressure b solid appears, and addition

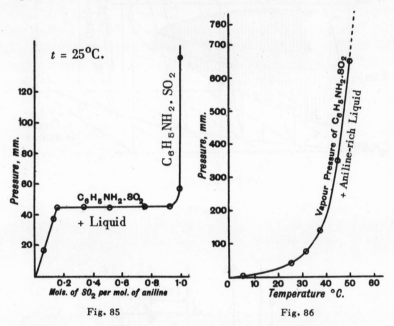

Fig. 85   Fig. 86

of sulphur dioxide results only in variation in the amounts of the three invariant phases, b (saturated solution), c (solid compound), and x (vapour). On addition of sulphur dioxide up to the composition c the liquid has all been changed to solid compound; further additions of sulphur dioxide result only in a change in pressure without any change in composition of the compound, *i.e.*, the system is isothermally univariant and consists of solid coexisting with vapour of the compositions shown along the section xy of the vapour curve. At d, a high pressure not measured in this instance, there is condensation of a new liquid phase e, rich in liquid sulphur dioxide, and the system is again isothermally invariant, consisting of

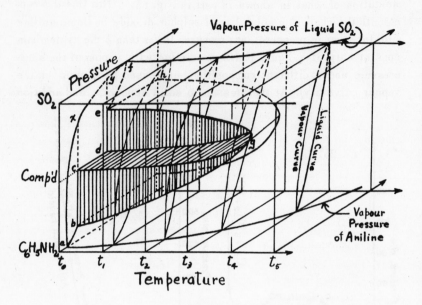

Fig. 87

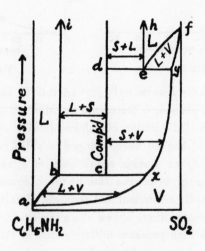

Fig. 88

compound, liquid phase *e*, and gaseous phase *y*. Addition of sulphur dioxide results now in diminishing the amount of the solid and increasing the amount of the liquid until the solid disappears entirely at *e*; and further additions of sulphur dioxide give the isothermally univariant system consisting of liquid represented on the curve *ef* and vapour represented on the curve *yf*. The pressure at *d* may be looked upon not only as the second vapour pressure of the system compound-liquid-vapour, but also as the deliquescence pressure of the compound. The curves *bi* and *eh* are boundary curves between the area for the solid and the areas for the two liquid phases; they will tend to meet or to separate farther according as the volume of the system tends to decrease or increase on solution of the solid phase. If isotherms are drawn at successively higher temperatures, the distance *cd* and the distances *bc* and *de* will become shorter. At the congruent melting-point the four points will· have met at a single point represented by *g* in Fig. 87. Above this temperature only liquid and vapour can exist up to the point where the vapour curve and the liquid curve meet at the critical temperatures for varying solutions of the two liquids.·

III. Critical Phenomena in Binary Systems, in the Presence or Absence of Solid Phases. [14, 20]

Critical phenomena in unary systems are well-known and, as shown on .p. 22, the vaporisation curve for a pure liquid ends abruptly at its critical point beyond which liquid and vapour become indistinguishable. When a second component is present, however, the critical phenomena are more involved.

We consider only the case that both components are completely miscible in the liquid state. There then results a continuous critical curve, in the *p-t-x* model, joining the critical points of the two components. Two cases are to be distinguished.

Figs. 89 (a) and 89 (b) are projections of the solid model on the *p-t* surface; *a* is the critical point of A, *b* of B, and *d* the triple point of solid B. The line *ab* is the critical curve and *cd* the *p-t* curve of the system: solid B—solution—vapour. (*cf.* Fig. 77B, p. 235). Further *ea* is the vapour pressure curve of liquid A, *fd* that of solid B and *db* that of liquid B.

The case of Fig. 89 (a) will occur when the solubility of solid B in liquid A is relatively great, *e.g.* silver nitrate in water. In this case the vapour pressures of the saturated solutions are relatively small, and hence the curve *cd* lies completely under the critical curve.

The curve *cd* runs without a break up to the melting-point of B; the series of saturated solutions of B is not interrupted by the critical phenomena of solutions; the solubility curve continues unin-

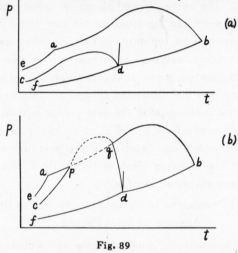

Fig. 89

terruptedly to the triple point of B, and this is the case with the system silver nitrate—water. Similarly, the critical curve is also continuous, as critical phenomena are only observed in solutions which are unsaturated with respect to B.

In the second case, Fig. 89 (b), the solubility of B in A is so slight even at the critical temperature, that *cd* cuts the critical curve above the critical point of A. The intersection occurs at the two points *p* and *q*. This is the case in the system sodium sulphate —water.

The critical temperatures and pressures between *a* and *p* and between *q* and *b* still refer to unsaturated solutions. At *p* and *q*, however, where the *p-t* line of solutions saturated with solid B and in contact with vapour cuts the critical curve, the case arises that the saturated solution has reached its critical temperature; at these points the vapour pressure of the saturated solution and the critical pressure coincide, and hence the saturation temperature and the critical temperature coincide.

If we continue the curve ap from p to q, we shall pass through the region of solutions and vapour, which are supersaturated with respect to solid B. Consequently critical phenomena will only be possible here if the solid phase B does not appear. On the other hand, a continuation of the curve $cpqd$ (the curve of equilibrium between solid B, solution and vapour) between p and q is impossible.

An experimental study of the critical phenomena, in the light of these and further considerations, is that of the system ether—anthraquinone.[15]

At the point p, the first part of the critical curve, ap, ends, and the second part, qb, begins at q. At the points p and q therefore two saturated solutions of different concentrations have reached their critical states. Fluid phases[16] in equilibrium with solid B are the only possible states between p and q.

NOTES

1. For a theoretical discussion of the curves, see Smits, *Z. physikal. Chem.*, 1911, **78**, 708.

2. *Z. physikal. Chem.*, 1914, **86**, 349. See also Smits and Wuite, *Proc. K. Akad. Wetensch. Amsterdam*, 1909, **12**, 244. A similar, and somewhat simpler, diagram is given by the system lithium sulphate—water. (Campbell, *J. Amer. Chem. Soc.*, 1943, **65**, 2269.

3. *Z. physikal. Chem.*, 1903, **42**, 432.

4. Since all substances are no doubt volatile to a certain extent at some temperature, it is to be understood here that the substances are appreciably volatile at the temperature of the experiment.

5. *Z. physikal. Chem.*, 1889, **3**, 11; *Rec. trav. chim. Pays-Bas*, 1888, **7**, 152.

6. *Z. anorgan. Chem.*, 1907, **53**, 365.

7. *Z. anorgan. Chem.*, 1910, **68**, 307.

8. For the calculation of the temperature corresponding to this maximum, *cf.* A. E. Korvezee, *Rec. trav. chim. Pays-Bas*, 1947, **66**, 549.

9. This is different from what we found in the case of non-volatile solutes (p. 236). In the present case the *partial pressure* of the iodine in the vapour will be lowered by addition of chlorine, but the *total pressure* is increased.

10. The diminution of volume is supposed to be carried out at constant temperature. The pressure and the composition of the phases must, therefore, remain unchanged, and only the relative amounts of these can undergo alteration.

11. At point *b* the ratio of chlorine to iodine in the solution is less than in the monochloride, so that by the separation of this the excess of chlorine yielded by the condensation of the vapour is removed.

12. Roozeboom: "Die heterogenen Gleichgewichte", Vol. 2, part 1, pp. 125 et seq. (Vieweg. Braunschweig, 1904.)

13. *J. Amer. Chem. Soc.*, 1931, **53**, 2598.

14. Smits, *Zeit. physikal. Chem.*, 1905, **51**, 193.

15. Smits, *Zeit. phys. Chem.*, 1905, **51**, 193; 1911, **76**, 445.

16. A fluid phase is one which exists above the temperature at which a liquid and a gaseous phase have transformed continuously.

17. Dingemans and van den Berg, Rec. trav. chim., 1942, **61**, 605.

18. Part of a typical isoplethal section of this envelope is shown by *a b c* of Fig. 84, *b* lying *on* the critical curve. The maximum temperature on such an isopleth is called the "cricondentherm" for the given composition; it does not in general coincide with the temperature of *b*.

19. We are indebted to Drs. G. Meyer and I.A.E. Korvezee of the Technische Hogeschool, Delft, Holland for certain modifications in the diagrams of Hill (private communication).

20. A summary of critical phenomena in binary systems is given by Booth and Bidwell, Chem. Rev., 1949, **44**, 477.

CHAPTER XII

DYNAMIC ISOMERIDES AND PSEUDO-BINARY SYSTEMS.

In the systems hitherto discussed (except sulphur and phosphorus), the components behaved, or were regarded as behaving, as strictly unary substances; that is, the molecules of each component in all the phases in which it occurred were identical both physically and chemically. Each component formed only one molecular species, and the number of molecular species was, therefore, equal to the number of the components. The systems were purely unary (one-component) or purely binary (two-component).

There are, however, not a few systems in which the number of molecular species is greater than the number of components; that is, substances which have the same empirical chemical composition (but which are isomeric forms) give rise to different, interconvertible molecular species, between which, in the liquid or vapour state, a condition of equilibrium exists. This fact may alter very markedly the behaviour of a system. Although, therefore, a system may appear to be unary, so far as chemical composition is concerned, it may, as a matter of fact, behave in some respects as a binary system. It forms a pseudo-binary system. The behaviour of these systems, as we shall see, depends largely on the rate at which the internal equilibrium between the different molecular species in the liquid or vapour phase is established. In the present chapter some of the more important aspects of these pseudo-binary systems will be considered.

It has long been known that certain substances, e.g. acetoacetic ester, are capable when in solution or in the fused state of reacting as if they possessed two different constitutions; and in order to explain this behaviour the view was advanced (by Laar) that in such cases a hydrogen atom oscillated between two positions in the molecule, being at one time attached to oxygen, at another time to carbon, as represented by the formula

$$CH_3 \ C\!-\!CH . CO_2C_2H_5$$
$$\overset{\displaystyle O}{\underset{\displaystyle H}{\diagdown}}$$

When the hydrogen is in one position, the substance will act as an hydroxy-compound; with hydrogen in the other position, as a ketone. Substances possessing this double function are called *tautomeric*.

Doubt, however, arose as to the validity of the above explanation, and this doubt was confirmed by the isolation of the two isomerides in the solid state, and also by the fact that the velocity of change of the one isomeride into the other could in some cases be quantitatively measured. These and other observations then led to the view, in harmony with the laws of chemical dynàmics, that tautomeric substances in the dissolved or fused state represent a *mixture* of two isomeric forms, and that equilibrium is established not by *intra-* but by *inter*-molecular change, as expressed by the equation

$$CH_3 . CO . CH_2 . CO_2C_2H_5 \rightleftharpoons CH_3 . C(OH):CH . CO_2C_2H_5.$$

In the solid state, the one or other of the isomerides represents the stable form; but in the liquid state (solution or fusion) the stable condition is an equilibrium between the two forms.

A similar behaviour is also found in the case of other isomeric substances where the isomerism is due to difference of structure, *i.e.* structure isomerism

$$\left(e.g. \text{ in the case of the oximes } \begin{array}{c} C_6H_5 . C . H \\ \| \\ N . OH \end{array} \text{ and } \begin{array}{c} C_6H_5 . C . H \\ \| \\ HO . N \end{array} \right),$$

or to difference in configuration, *i.e.* stereoisomerism (*e.g.* optically active substances), or to polymerism (*e.g.* acetaldehyde and paraldehyde). In all such cases, although the different solid forms correspond to a single definite constitution, in the liquid state a condition of equilibrium between the two modifications is established. As a general name for these different classes of substances, the term "dynamic isomerides" has been introduced; and the different kinds of isomerism are classed together under the title "dynamic isomerism".

By reason of the importance of these phenomena in the study more especially of Organic Chemistry, a brief account of the equilibrium relations exhibited by systems composed of dynamic isomerides may be given here.

In studying the fusion and solidification of those substances which exhibit the relationships of dynamic isomerism, it has to be borne in mind that the phenomena observed will vary somewhat according as the reversible transformation of the one form into the other takes place with measurable velocity at temperatures in the neighbourhood of the melting-points, or only at some higher temperature. If the transformation is relatively very rapid, the system will behave like a one-component system, but if the isomeric change is comparatively slow, the behaviour will be that of a two-component system.

Temperature—Concentration Diagram. The relationships which are met with here will be most readily understood with the help of Fig. 90. Suppose, in the first instance, that isomeric transformation does not take place with appreciable velocity at the temperature of the melting-point, then the freezing-point curve will have the simple form ACB; the formation of compounds being for the present excluded. This is the simplest type of curve, and gives the composition of 'the solutions in equilibrium with the one modification (α-modification) at different temperatures (curve AC); and of the solutions in equilibrium with the other modification (β-modification) at different temperatures (curve BC). C is the eutectic point at which the two solid isomerides can exist side by side in contact with the solution.

Now, suppose that isomeric transformation takes place with measurable velocity. If the pure α-modification is heated to a temperature t' above its melting-point, and the liquid maintained at that temperature until equilibrium has been established, a certain amount of the β-form will be present in the liquid, the composition of which will be represented by the point x'. The same condition of equilibrium will also be reached by starting with pure β. Similarly, if the temperature of the liquid is maintained at the temperature t'', equilibrium will be reached, we shall suppose, when the solution has the composition x''. The curve DE, therefore, which passes through all the different values of x corresponding to different values of t, will represent the change of equilibrium with the temperature. It will slope to the right (as in the figure) if the transformation of α into β is accompanied by absorption of heat; to the left if the transformation is accompanied by evolution of heat, in accordance with the principle of Le Chatelier. If transformation occurs without heat effect, the equilibrium will be independent of the temperature, and the equilibrium curve DE will therefore be parallel to the temperature axis.

We must now find the meaning of the point D. Suppose the pure

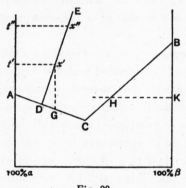

Fig. 90

α- or pure β-form heated to the temperature t', and the temperature maintained constant until the liquid has the composition x' corresponding to the equilibrium at that temperature. If the temperature is now allowed to fall sufficiently slowly so that the condition of equilibrium is continually readjusted as the temperature changes, the composition of the solution will gradually alter as represented by the curve x'D. Since D is on the freezing point curve of pure α, this form will be deposited on cooling; and since D is also on the equilibrium curve of the liquid, D is the only point at which solid can exist in stable equilibrium with the liquid phase. (The vapour phase may be omitted from consideration, as we shall suppose the experiments carried out in open vessels.) All systems consisting of the two hylotropic[1] isomeric substances α and β will, therefore, ultimately freeze at the point D, which is called the "natural" freezing-point[2] of the system; provided, of course, that sufficient time is allowed for equilibrium to be established. From this it is apparent that *the stable modification at temperatures in the neighbourhood of the melting-point is that which is in equilibrium with the liquid phase at the natural freezing-point.*

From what has been said, it will be easy to predict what will be the behaviour of the system under different conditions. If pure α is heated, a temperature will be reached at which it will melt, but this melting-point will be sharp only if the velocity of isomeric transformation is comparatively slow; *i.e.* slow in comparison with the determination of the melting-point. If the substance be maintained in the fused condition for some time, a certain amount of the β-modification will be formed, and on lowering the temperature the pure α-form will be deposited, not at the temperature of the melting-point, but at some lower temperature depending on the concentration of the β-modification in the liquid phase. If isomeric transformation takes place slowly in comparison with the rate at which deposition of the solid occurs, the liquid will become increasingly rich in the β-modification, and the freezing-point will, therefore, sink continuously. At the eutectic point, however, the β-modification will also be deposited, and the temperature will remain constant until all has become solid. If, on the other hand, the velocity of transformation is sufficiently rapid, then as quickly as the α-modification is deposited, the equilibrium between the two isomeric forms in the liquid phase will continuously readjust itself, and the endpoint of solidification will be the natural freezing-point.

Similarly, starting with the pure β-modification, the freezing-point after fusion will gradually fall owing to the formation of the α-modification; and the composition of the liquid phase will pass along the curve BC. If, now, the rate of cooling is not too great, or if the velocity of isomeric transformation is sufficiently rapid complete solidification will not occur at the eutectic point; for at this temperature solid and liquid are not in stable equilibrium with one another. On the contrary, a further quantity of the β-modification will undergo isomeric change, the liquid phase will become richer in the α-form, and the freezing-point will *rise;* the solid phase in contact with the liquid being now the α-modification. The freezing-point will continue to rise until the point D is reached, at which complete solidification will take place without further change of temperature.

The diagram also allows us to predict what will be the result of rapidly cooling a fused mixture of the two isomerides. Suppose that either the α- or the β-modification has been maintained in the fused state at the temperature t' sufficiently long for equilibrium to be established. The composition of the liquid phase will be represented by x'. If the liquid is now *rapidly* cooled, the composition will remain unchanged as represented by the dotted line $x'G$. At the temperature of the point G solid α-modification will be deposited. If the cooling is not carried below the point G, so as to cause complete solidification, the freezing-point will be found to rise with time, owing to the conversion of some of the β-form into the α-form in the liquid phase; and this will continue until the composition of the liquid has reached the point D. From what has just been said, it can also be seen that if the freezing-point curves can be obtained by actual determination of the freezing-points of different synthetic mixtures of the two isomerides, it will be possible to determine the condition of equilibrium in the fused state at any given temperature without having recourse to analysis. All that is necessary is to cool rapidly the fused mass, after equilibrium has been established and to find the freezing-point at which solid is deposited; that is, find the point at which the line of constant temperature cuts the freezing-point curve. The composition corresponding to this temperature gives the composition of the equilibrium mixture at the given temperature.

It will be evident, from what has gone before, that the degree of completeness with which the different curves can be realised will depend on the velocity with which isomeric change takes place, and on the rapidity with which the determinations of the freezing-point can be carried out. As the two extremes we have, on the one hand, practically instantaneous transformation, and on the other, practically infinite slowness of transformation. In the former case, only one melting- and one freezing-point will be found, viz. the natural freezing-point; in the latter case, the two isomerides will behave as two perfectly independent components, and the equilibrium curve

DE will not be realised.

An examination of Fig. 91 will show that under favourable conditions the less stable form may separate from the equilibrium mixture . If the homogeneous equilibrium curve DE slopes as shown in the figure, and cuts the curve AC for the α-modification not very far from the eutectic point; and if, on lowering the temperature through the point D, supercooling takes place and the stable form does not separate out, it may be possible to cool the liquid down to the point D where the equilibrium curve cuts the metastable prolongation of the curve BC, and the less stable, or β-modification, may then crystallise out.

The diagram which is obtained when isomeric transformation does not occur within measurable time at the temperature of the melting-point is somewhat different from that already given in Fig. 90. In this case, the two freezing-point curves AC and BC (Fig. 92) can be readily realised, as no isomeric change occurs in the liquid phase. Suppose, however, that at a higher temperature, t', reversible isomeric transformation can take place, the composition of the liquid phase will alter until at the point x' a condition of equilibrium is reached; and the composition of the liquid at higher temperatures will be represented by the curve $x'F$. Below the temperature t' the position of the equilibrium curve is hypothetical; but as the temperature falls the velocity of transformation diminishes ,and at last becomes *practically* zero. The equilibrium curve can therefore be regarded as dividing into two branches, $x'G$ and $x'H$. At temperatures between G and t' the α-modification can undergo isomeric change leading to a point on the curve Gx'; and the β-modification can undergo change leading to a point on the curve Hx'. The same condition of equilibrium is therefore not reached from each side, and we are therefore dealing not with true but with false equilibrium (p. 6). Below the temperatures G and H isomeric transformation does not occur in measurable time.

Transformation of the Unstable into the Stable Form. As has already been stated, the stable modification in the neighbourhood of the melting-point is that one which is in equilibrium with the liquid phase at the natural freezing-point. In the case of allotropic substances, we have seen (p. 68) that that form which is stable in the neighbourhood of the melting-point melts at the higher temperature. That was a consequence of the fact that the two allotropic forms on melting give identical liquid phases. In the present case, however, the above rule does not apply for the simple reason that the liquid phase obtained by the fusion of the one modification is not identical with that obtained by the fusion of the other. In the case of isomeric substances, therefore, the form of lower melting-point *may* be the more stable; and where this behaviour is found it is a sign that the two forms are isomeric (or polymeric) and not allotropic. An example of this is found in the case of the isomeric benzaldoximes.

Since in Fig. 90 the α-modification has been represented as the stable form, the transformation of the β into the α form will be possible at all temperatures down to the transition point. At temperatures below the eutectic point, transformation will occur without formation of a liquid phase; but at temperatures above the eutectic point liquefaction can take place. This will be more readily understood by drawing a line of constant temperature, HK, at some point be-

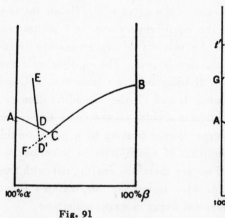

Fig. 91

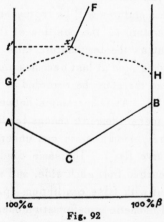

Fig. 92

tween C and B. Then, if the β-modification is maintained for a sufficiently long time at that temperature, a certain amount of the α-modification will be formed; and when the composition of the mixture has reached the point H, fusion will occur. If the temperature is maintained constant, isomeric transformation will continue to take place in the liquid phase until the equilibrium point for that temperature is reached. If this temperature is higher than the natural melting-point, the mixture will remain liquid all the time; but if it is below the natural melting-point, then the α-modification will be deposited when the system reaches the condition represented by the point on the curve AC corresponding to the particular temperature. As isomeric transformation continues, the freezing-point of the system will rise until it reaches the natural freezing-point, or unary freezing-point, as it is also called, D. Similarly, if the α-modification is maintained at a temperature above that of the point D, liquefaction will ultimately occur, and the system will again reach the final state represented by D.

Examples. *Benzaldoximes.* The relationships which have just been discussed from the theoretical point of view will be rendered clearer by a brief description of cases which have been experimentally investigated. The first we shall consider is that of the two isomeric benzaldoximes:[3]

$C_6H_5 . C . H$ $C_6H_5 . C . H$

$\|$ $\|$

$HO . N$ $N . OH$

Benzantialdoxime (α-modification).   Benzsynaldoxime (β-modification).

Fig. 93 gives a graphic representation of the results obtained.

The melting-point of the α-modification is $34°$—$35°$; the melting-point of the unstable β-modification being $130°$. The freezing curves AC and BC were obtained by determining the freezing-points of different mixtures of known composition, and the numbers so obtained are given in the following table:

Grams of the α-modification in 100 gm. of mixture.	Freezing-point.
26·2	101°
49·2	79°
73·7	46°
91·7	26·2°
95·0	28·6°
96·0	30·0°

The eutectic point C was found to lie at $25°$—$26°$, and the natural freezing-point D was found to be 27.7°. The equilibrium curve DE was determined by heating the liquid mixtures at different temperatures until equilibrium was attained, and then rapidly cooling the liquid. In all cases the freezing-point was practically that of the point D. From this it is seen that the equilibrium curve must be a straight line parallel to the temperature axis; and, therefore, isomeric transformation in the case of the two benzaldoximes is not accompanied by any heat effect (p. 264). This behaviour has also been found in the case of acetaldoxime.[4]

The isomeric benzaldoximes are also of interest from the fact that the stable modification has the *lower* melting-point (*v.* p. 268).

Acetaldehyde and Paraldehyde.   As a second example of the equilibria between two isomerides, we shall take the two isomeric (polymeric) forms of acetaldehyde, which have been exhaustively studied.[5]

In the case of these two substances the reaction

$$3CH_3 . CHO \rightleftarrows (CH_3 . CHO)_3$$

takes place at the ordinary temperature with very great slowness. For this reason it is possible to determine the freezing-point curves of acetaldehyde and paraldehyde. The three chief points on these curves, represented graphically in Fig. 94, are:

m.p. of acetaldehyde   −118.45°
m.p. of paraldehyde   + 12.55°
eutectic point   −119.9°

In order to determine the position of the natural melting-point, it was necessary, on account of the slowness of transformation, to employ a catalytic agent in order to increase the velocity with which the equilibrium was established. A drop of concentrated sulphuric acid served the purpose. In presence of a trace of this substance, isomeric transformation very speedily occurs, and leads to the condition of equilibrium. Starting in the one case with fused paraldehyde, and in the other case with acetaldehyde, the same freezing-point, viz. 6.75°, was obtained, the solid phase being paraldehyde. This temperature, 6.75°, is therefore the natural freezing-point, and paraldehyde, the solid in equilibrium with the liquid phase at this point, is the stable form.

With regard to the change of equilibrium with the temperature, it

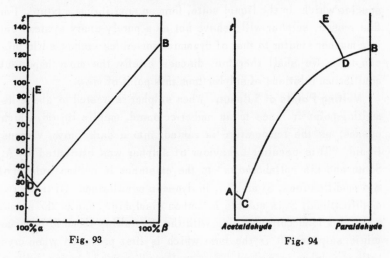

Fig. 93   Fig. 94

was found that whereas the liquid phase contains 11.7 molecules per cent of acetaldehyde at the natural freezing-point, the liquid at the temperature of 41.6° contains 46.6 molecules per cent. of acetaldehyde. As the temperature rises, therefore, there is increased formation of acetaldehyde, or a decreasing amount of polymerisation. This is in harmony with the fact that the polymerisation of acetaldehyde is accompanied by evolution of heat.

While speaking of these isomerides, it may be mentioned that at the temperature 41.6° the equilibrium mixture.has a vapour pressure equal to the atmospheric pressure. At this temperature, therefore, the equilibrium mixture (obtained quickly with the help of a trace of sulphuric acid) boils.[6]

From a more recent investigation by Smits and de Leeuw,[7] it would, however, appear probable that the acetaldehyde-paraldehyde system is not so simple as was found by Hollmann, but that we have here a case of a pseudo-ternary system in which are present not only the simple acetaldehyde molecules ($CH_3 . CHO$), but also the molecules of paraldehyde, ($CH_3 . CHO)_3$, and of metaldehyde, ($CH_3 . CHO)_4$.

SULPHUR.

It has already been indicated (p. 65), that in the case of sulphur we have a substance which can give rise to different molecular species which, in the liquid state, form an equilibrium mixture. For this reason, sulphur will behave not as a purely unary system, but in a manner similar to that of dynamic isomerides discussed in this chapter. We shall therefore discuss briefly the more important equilibrium relations of sulphur from this point of view.

Melting Points of Sulphur. When sulphur is heated to above its melting-point it fuses to an amber-coloured, mobile liquid, which passes, as the temperature is raised, into a dark brown viscous liquid. This peculiar behaviour of sulphur was attributed by A. Smith and his collaborators[8] to the existence in molten sulphur of two modifications, $S\lambda$ and $S\mu$, in dynamic equilibrium. Of these two modifications, $S\lambda$ is soluble in carbon disulphide, and is the normal molecular form corresponding with the crystalline rhombic or monoclinic sulphur. It is the form which is first produced when crystalline sulphur is melted. $S\mu$, on the other hand, is insoluble in carbon disulphide, and is formed in increasing quantity as the temperature is raised.[9] Molten sulphur, therefore, is not a pure liquid consisting of only one kind of molecules, but is a homogeneous mixture or solution of $S\mu$ in $S\lambda$, the composition of which varies with the temperature. The attainment of equilibrium is accelerated by the presence of traces of ammonia, and is retarded by the presence of sulphur dioxide.

The views expressed by Smith and his collaborators regarding the nature of molten sulphur have been modified and extended by A. H. W. Aten,[10] according to whom there exist in molten sulphur not only the $S\lambda$ and $S\mu$ molecules, but also another molecular species, $S\pi$,[11] which is readily soluble in carbon disulphide. At each temperature there exists, in molten sulphur, an equilibrium between these three molecular species in accordance with the numbers shown in the following table[12] (p. 273).

In the solidified melt, $S\pi$ changes very rapidly into $S\mu$, which, in turn, is transformed slowly into the normal $S\lambda$.

The occurrence of "dynamic allotropy" in the case of liquid sulphur is of great importance for the quantitative study of the equilibrium between solid and liquid sulphur. Since, in the case of

Equilibrium Between S_λ, S_μ, and S_π in Molten Sulphur.

Temperature.	Per cent. S_μ.	Per cent. S_π.	Per cent. S_λ.
120°	0·1	3·5	96·4
125°	0·2	4·1	95·7
130°	0·3	4·3	95·4
140°	1·3	5·0	93·7
145°	1·6	5·3	93·1
160°	4·1	6·7	89·2
170°	13·3	5·8	80·9
180°	20·4	6·5	73·1
184°	23·6	6·3	70·1
196°	28·6	6·3	65·1
220°	32·2	5·3	62·7
445°	36·9	4·0	59·1

molten sulphur, we are dealing with a homogeneous solution of three molecular species, S_λ, S_μ, and S_π, from which solid, soluble sulphur, corresponding with S_λ, crystallises out, it follows that the system will no longer behave like a one-component or unary system, but rather will simulate the behaviour of a three-component or ternary system. The system may therefore be said to be a pseudo-ternary system. If, however, for the sake of simplicity we group the two molecular species S_μ and S_π as one, we can treat the system as a pseudo-binary one; and this method of treatment is justified by the fact that in the neighbourhood of the freezing-point of molten sulphur, S_μ is present in very small amount and may be neglected.

From what has just been said, therefore, we see that the equilibrium relations between crystalline sulphur and liquid sulphur will be similar to those found in the case of dynamic isomerides. As in the case of such substances, the crystalline forms of sulphur may exhibit various melting- or freezing-points, and only when there is complete absence of the molecular species S_π or S_μ do we obtain the ideal or true freezing-point; that is, the equilibrium temperature between crystalline sulphur and molten S_λ. Under ordinary conditions, the melting-point is found lower than the ideal melting-point, owing to the formation, and presence in the molten sulphur, of S_π.[13] The natural freezing-point is therefore the temperature at which crystalline sulphur coexists with the equilibrium mixture of S_λ and S_π.

The following values for the ideal and natural freezing point of rhombic (S_I), monoclinic (S_{II}), and mother of pearl sulphur $(S_{III}$ or nacreous sulphur) are given in the following table:[14]

Solid phase.	Ideal freezing-point.	Natural freezing-point.
Rhombic sulphur (S_I) . .	$112 \cdot 8°$	$110 \cdot 2°$
Monoclinic sulphur (S_{II}) . .	$119 \cdot 25°$ ($118 \cdot 95°$)	$114 \cdot 5°$
Mother of pearl sulphur (S_{III}) .	$106 \cdot 8°$	$103 \cdot 4°$

As a result of the investigations of the pseudo-binary systems of the substance sulphur we obtain the diagram shown in Fig. 95. Here, the points A, D, and G represent the ideal freezing-points of monoclinic, rhombic, and nacreous sulphur respectively, or the tem-

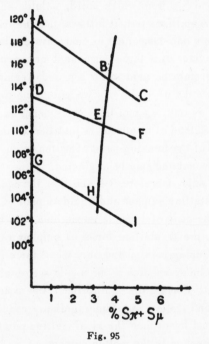

Fig. 95

peratures at which these three crystalline forms are in equilibrium with pure molten S_λ. The curve HEB represents the dynamic equilibrium curve for S_λ, S_μ, and S_π in molten sulphur; and the points B, E, and H, where this equilibrium curve cuts the freezing-point curves, represent the natural freezing-points of the three modifications of sulphur.

The above facts are of essential importance in connection with the equilibrium diagram of sulphur, Fig. 15 (p. 66). In this figure, the data represent-ed in the diagram relate neither to the "ideal" equilibrium conditions in which the solid phase is in equilibrium with S_λ, nor to the "natural" equilibrium conditions in which the solid phase is in equilibrium with the equilibrium mixture of $S_\lambda, S_\mu,$ and S_π; they refer, rather, to conditions in which unknown and variable amounts of S_μ and S_π are present in the liquid phase. The actual values found by Tammann, therefore, for the curves bC, CD, BC, which are represented in Fig. 15, are not quite correct, although they may be taken as representing qualitatively the relationships involved.

NOTES

1. Hylotropic substances are such as can undergo transformation into other substances of the same composition (Ostwald, *Lehrbuch*, II, 2, 298).

2. Also call Equilibrium Point (Lowry).

3. Cameron, *J. Physical Chem.*, 1898, **2**, 409; Schoevers, *Dissertation*, Amsterdam, 1907.

4. Carveth, *J. Physical Chem.*, 1898, **2**, 159. See also Dutoit and Fath, *J. Chim. phys.*, 1903, 1, 358; Findlay, *J. Chem. Soc.*, 1904, **85**, 403.

5. Hollmann, *Z. physikal. Chem.*, 1903, **43**, 129.

6. For other examples of the application of the Phase Rule to isomeric substances, see *J. Physical Chem.*, vol. 2 *et seq.*; Findlay, *J. Chem. Soc.*, 1904, **85**, 403; Atkins and Werner, *ibid.*, 1912, **101**, 1167; Smits and Kettner, *Proc. K. Akad. Wetensch.*, *Amsterdam*, 1912, **15**, 683; Dutoit and Fath, *J. Chim. phys.*, 1903, 1, 358.

7. *Z. physikal Chem.*, 1911, **77**, 269.

8. *J. Amer. Chem. Soc.*, 1905, **27**, 801, 983; *Z. physikal. Chem.*, 1903, **42**, 469; 1905, **52**, 602; 1906, **54**, 257; 1907, **57**, 685; 1907, **61**, 200, 209.

9. Smith and Carson, *Z. physikal Chem.*, 1906, **57**, 685. A different view, however, is put forward by Hammick and collaborators, *J. Chem. Soc.*, 1928, p. 797; 1930, p. 273.

10. *Z. physikal. Chem.*, 1912, **81**, 257; 1913, **83**, 442; 1913, **86**, 1; 1914, **88**, 321.

11. S_λ is regarded as having a molecular weight represented by S_8; S_π a molecular weight represented by S_4.

12. Aten, *Z. physikal. Chem.*, 1913, **86**, 10.

13. The view put forward by Aten (*loc. cit.*) that in the neighbourhood of the freezing-point molten sulphur consists essentially of the molecular species S_λ and S_π (see Table on **p. 273**), and that the lowering of the melting-point of sulphur is due to the presence of S_π, and not of S_μ as was thought by Smith and Carson, has been confirmed, cryoscopically, by Beckmann, Paul, and Liesche (*Z. anorgan. Chem.*, 1918, **103**, 189). According to these investigators, the composition of the melt at the natural freezing-point is $S_\pi = 2.78$ per cent., $S_\lambda = 97.22$ per cent. So-called amorphous sulphur, S_μ, when added to molten sulphur at the natural freezing-point does not alter the freezing-point of the melt, owing to the fact that it undergoes a rapid transformation into the equilibrium mixture of S_λ and S_π. Another molecular form of sulphur, Engel's sulphur or S_ρ, obtained by the action of hydrochloric acid on sodium thiosulphate (Engel, *Compt. rend.*, 1891, **112**, 866), and having the molecular weight of 192 (S_6), when added to the equilibrium mixture, lowers the freezing-point; but S_ρ also undergoes transformation into S_λ and S_π by way of S_μ.

14. Smith and Carson, *Z. physikal. Chem.*, 1911, **77**, 670. See also Kruyt, *ibid.*, 1909, **67**, 338; 1912, **81**, 726; Wigand, *ibid.*, 1910, **75**, 242; Aten, *ibid.*, 1912, **81**, 257; Smits, *ibid.*, 1913, **83**, 221; Nernst, *ibid.*, 1913, **83**, 546; de Leeuw, *ibid.*, 1913, **83**, 245.

CHAPTER XIII

General. It has already been made evident that an increase in the number of the components from one to two gives rise to a considerable increase in the possible number of systems, and introduces not a few complications into the equilibrium relations of these. No less is this the case when the number of components increases from two to three; and although examples of all the possible types of systems of three components have not been investigated, nor, indeed, any one type fully, nevertheless, among the systems which have been studied experimentally, cases occur which not only possess a high scientific interest, but are also of great industrial importance.

On applying the Phase Rule

$$F = C - P + 2$$

to the systems of three components, we see that in order that the system shall be invariant, no fewer than five phases must be present together, and an invariant system will therefore exist at a *quintuple* point. Since the number of liquid phases can never exceed the number of the components,[1] and since there can be only one vapour phase, it is evident that at the quintuple point, as in the case of other invariant systems, there must always be at least one solid phase present. As the number of phases diminishes, the variance of the system can increase from one to four, so that in the last case the condition of the system will not be completely defined until not only the temperature and the total pressure of the system, but also the concentrations of two of the components have been fixed. Or, instead of the concentrations, the partial pressures of the components may also be taken as independent variables.

Graphic Representation. Hitherto the concentrations of the components have been represented by means of rectangular co-ordinates, although the numerical relationships have been expressed in two different ways. In the one case, the concentration of the one component was expressed in terms of a fixed amount of the other component. Thus, the solubility of a salt was expressed by the number of grams of salt dissolved by 100 grams of water or other solvent; and the numbers so obtained were measured along one of the co-ordinates. The second co-ordinate was then employed to indicate the change of another independent variable, *e.g.* temperature. In the other case, the combined weights of the two components A and B were put equal to unity, and the concentration of the one expressed as a fraction of the whole amount. This method allows of the representation of the complete series of concentrations, from pure A to pure B, and was employed, for example, in the graphic representation of the freezing-point curves.

Even in the case of three components, rectangular co-ordinates can also be employed, and, in some respects, are more convenient, *e.g.*, in those cases where the behaviour of two of the components to one another is very different from their behaviour to the third component; as, for example, in the case of two salts and water. In these cases, the composition of the system can be represented by measuring along two co-ordinates at right angles to each other the amounts of each of the two components in a given weight of the third; and the change of the system with the temperature can then be represented by a third axis at right angles to the first two. In those cases, however, where the three components behave in much the same manner towards one another, the rectangular co-ordinates are not at all suitable, and instead of these a *triangular diagram* is employed.

Of the various modes of representation on a triangle[2] we shall only describe the one in common use, namely that of Roozeboom. This method consists in employing an equilateral triangle, the length of whose side is made equal to one hundred; the sum of the fractional or percentage amounts of the three components, either in weight percent or mole percent, is being represented, therefore, by a side of the triangle. The composition of a ternary (or three-component) mixture (point P, Fig. 96) is obtained by determining its distance from the three sides of the triangle in a direction parallel to the sides of the triangle. Conversely, in order to represent a mixture consisting of *a*, *b*, and *c* percentages of the components A, B, and C respectively, one side of the triangle, say AB, is first of all divided into one hundred parts; a portion, B*x* = *a*, is then measured off, and represents the percent of A present. Similarly, a portion, A*x'* = *b*, is measured off and represents the per cent of B, while the remainder, *xx'* = *c*, represents the amount of C. From *x* and *x'* lines are drawn parallel to the sides of the triangle, and the point of intersection, P, represents the composition of the ternary mixture of given composition; for, as is evident from the figure, the distance of the point P from the three sides of the triangle, when measured in directions *parallel* to the sides, is equal to *a*, *b*, and *c* respectively. From the division marks on the side AB it is seen that the point P in this figure represents the mixture

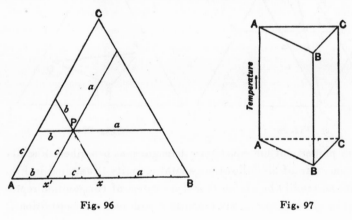

Fig. 96   Fig. 97

50% A, 20% B, and 30% C.

If it is desired to represent at the same time the change of another independent variable, *e.g.* temperature, this can be done by measuring the latter along axes drawn perpendicular to the corners of the triangle. In this way a right prism (Fig. 97) is obtained, and each section of this cut parallel to the base represents therefore an isotherm.

In employing the triangular diagram, it will be of use to note a

property of the equilateral triangle. A line drawn from one corner of the triangle to the opposite side represents the composition of all mixtures in which the *relative* amounts of two of the components remain unchanged. If in Fig. 98, the component C is added to a mixture x_r in which A and B are present in the proportions of $a:b$, to give a mixture x', the point x', since it still contains A and B in the ratio $a:b$ must still lie on the straight line joining x and C. For the two triangles ACx and BCx are similar to the two triangles HCx' and KCx'; and, therefore, $Ax:Bx = Hx':Kx'$. But $Ax = Dx$ and $Bx = Ex$; further, $Hx' = Fx'$ and $Kx' = Gx'$. Therefore, $Dx:Ex = Fx':Gx' = b:a$. At all points on the line Cx, therefore, the ratio of A to B is the same.

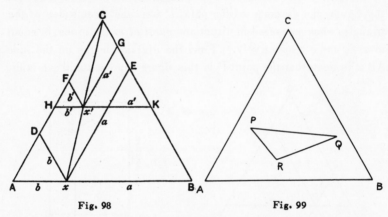

Fig. 98   Fig. 99

The property of the equilateral triangle just described is really a special case of the following general property illustrated in Fig. 99. It can readily be shown that if a system of composition represented by Q be mixed in any proportion with one of composition P the total composition of the mixture will always lie on the *straight* line joining P and Q. This means that the compositions of the phases in any two-phase system will always lie on a straight line through the total composition of the system. Analogously, the total composition of any three-phase system, the respective compositions of which are given by P, Q and R, must lie within the triangle PQR.

A further property of the equilateral triangular diagram has been

pointed out[3] (Fig. 100). The property is best illustrated by a con-
crete example, viz.: the system KNO_3—$Pb(NO_3)_2$—Pb_3O_4. A bi-

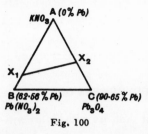

KNO_3 A (0% Pb)

B (62·56% Pb)   C (90·65% Pb)
$Pb(NO_3)_2$ Pb_3O_4

Fig. 100

nary mixture of KNO_3 (0 per cent. Pb)
and $Pb(NO_3)_2$ (62.56 per cent. Pb) containing X per cent. Pb is represented by
a point X_1 on the side AB, such that
$AX_1 = 100X/62.56$. Similarly, a binary
mixture of KNO_3 and Pb_3O_4 (90.65 per
cent. Pb) which contains X per cent. Pb
is represented by X_2 on AC where $AX_2 =$
$100X/90.65$. All points on X_1X_2 represent mixtures containing X
per cent. total Pb. This theorem can be applied to any ternary system in which the same radical occurs in two or three of the components.

NOTES

1. Cf. p. 8.

2. G. G. Stokes, *Proc. Roy. Soc.*, 1891, **49**, 174; Gibbs, *Trans. Conn.
Acad.*, 1876, **3**, 176; Roozeboom, *Z. physikal. Chem.*, 1894, **15**, 147. For
another suggested method of representation, see Lodočnikov, *Z. anorgan.
Chem.*, 1926 ,**151**, 185; 1928, **169**, 177. Some explanation of the method
of Lodočnikov will be found on p. 406.

3. Freeman, Laybourn, and Madgin, *J. Chem. Soc.*, 1933, 648.

CHAPTER XIV

A. SYSTEMS CONSISTING OF LIQUID PHASES ONLY.

At the outset it should be pointed out that, as with binary systems, the experimental study of the interactions of three liquids may be conducted in open vessels at constant atmospheric pressure or in sealed vessels in the presence of their vapour, the pressure of which may vary, but in both cases the results are, for practical purposes, the same. The pressure variable, therefore, will be disregarded, and also, in this chapter, the composition of any vapour which may be present.

We have already seen (p. 92) that when two liquids are brought together they may mix in all proportions and form one homogeneous liquid phase; or, only partial miscibility may occur, and two phases be formed consisting of two mutually saturated solutions. In the latter case, the concentration of the components in either phase and also the vapour pressure of the system had, at a given temperature, perfectly definite values. In the case of three liquid components, a similar behaviour may be found, although complete miscibility of three components with the formation of only one liquid phase is of much rarer occurrence than in the case of two components. When only partial miscibility occurs, various cases are met with according as the three components form one, two, or three pairs of partially miscible liquids. Further, when two of the components are only partially miscible, the addition of the third may cause either an increase or a diminution in the mutual solubility of these. An increase in the mutual solubility is generally found when the third component dissolves readily in each of the other two; but when the third component dissolves only sparingly in the other two, its addition diminishes the mutual solubility of the latter (see p. 103).

We shall consider here only a few examples illustrating the three chief cases which can occur, viz. (1) A and B, and also B and C are miscible in all proportions, while A and C are only partially miscible; (2) A and B are miscible in all proportions, but A and C, and B and C are only partially miscible; (3) A and B, B and C, and A and C are only partially miscible. A, B, and C here represent the three components.

I. *The three components form only one pair of partially miscible liquids.* [1]

An example of this is found in the three substances: toluene, water, and acetic acid. [2] Toluene and acetic acid, and water and acetic acid, are miscible with each other in all proportions, but toluene and water are only partially miscible with each other. If, therefore, toluene is shaken with a larger quantity of water than it can dissolve, two layers will be formed consisting one of a saturated solution of water in toluene, the other of a saturated solution of toluene in water. The composition of these two solutions at a temperature of 25° will be represented by the points *a* and *b* in Fig. 101 (schematic), *a* representing a solution nearly 100 per cent toluene and *b* a solution nearly 100 per cent water. When

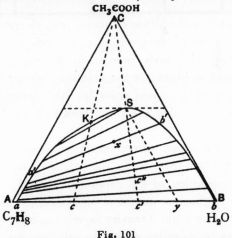

Fig. 101

acetic acid is added, it distributes itself between the two liquid layers, and two conjugate *ternary* solutions, consisting of toluene, water, and acetic acid are thereby produced which are in equilibrium with each other, and the composition of which will be represented by two points inside the triangle. In this way a series of pairs of ternary solutions will be obtained by the addition of acetic acid to the mixture of toluene and water. By this addition, also, not only do the two liquid phases become increasingly rich in acetic acid, but the mutual solubility of the toluene and water increases; so that the layer *a* becomes relatively richer in water, and layer *b* relatively richer in toluene. This is seen from the following table, which gives the percentage composition of different conjugate ternary solutions at 25°:

Aqueous layer			Toluene layer		
Acetic acid	Water	Toluene	Acetic acid	Water	Toluene
21.4	78.4	0.2	1.4	nearly zero	98.6
37.7	61.8	0.5	4.1	nearly zero	95.9
58.1	40.4	1.5	10.4	0.3	89.3
70.6	25.4	4.0	24.9	0.9	74.2
65.3	10.0	24.7	44.4	3.0	52.6

By the continued addition of acetic acid, the composition of the successive conjugate solutions in equilibrium with each other becomes, as the table shows, more nearly the same, and a point is at length reached at which the two solutions become identical. This will therefore be a *critical point* (p. 94). Increased addition of acetic acid beyond this point will lead to a single homogeneous solution.

These relationships are represented graphically by the so-called binodal[3] curve *aKb* (Fig. 101). The points on the branch *a*K represent the composition of the solutions relatively rich in toluene (lighter layer), those on the curve *b*K the composition of solutions relatively rich in water (heavier layer); and the points on these two branches representing conjugate solutions are joined together by "tie-lines". Thus, the points *a'* and *b'* represent conjugate solutions, and the line *a' b'* is a tie line.

Since acetic acid, when added to a heterogeneous mixture of toluene and water, does not enter in equal amounts into the two layers, but in amounts depending on its coefficient of distribution between toluene and water,[4] the tie-lines will not be parallel to AB, but will be inclined at an angle. As the solutions become more nearly the same, the tie-lines diminish in length, and at last, when the conjugate solutions become identical, shrink to a point. For the reason that the tie-lines are, in general, not parallel to the side of the triangle, the critical point at which the tie-line vanishes will not be at the summit of the curve, but somewhere below this, as represented by the point K called the (isothermal) critical point or plait point.

The curve aKb, further, forms the boundary between the heterogeneous and homogeneous systems. A mixture of   toluene, water, and acetic acid, represented by any point outside the curve aKb, will form only one homogeneous phase; while any mixture represented by a point within the curve will separate into two layers having the composition represented by the ends of the tie-line passing through that point. Thus, a mixture of the total composition x will separate into two layers having the composition a' and b' respectively and the ratio of the amount of the layer a' to that of the layer b' is given by the ratio of xb' to xa'.

Outside of the parabolic area two phases (liquid and vapour) coexist (if there is a vapour phase). Such a system is therefore trivariant and three out of the four independent variables (temperature, total pressure and the two independent concentration variables) must be fixed in order to define the system completely. Within the parabolic area the system is bivariant; so that, for example, the composition of the two layers and the total vapour pressure will not depend merely on the temperature, as in the case of two-component systems (p. 92), but also on the composition of the initial mixture. At constant temperature, however, all mixtures, the composition of which is represented by a point on one and the same tie-line, will separate into the same two liquid phases, although the relative *amounts* of the two phases will vary. If we omit the vapour phase, the condition of the system will depend on the pressure as well as on the temperature and composition of the initial mixture. By keeping the pressure constant, *e.g.* at atmospheric pressure (by working with open vessels), the system again becomes bivariant. We see, therefore, that the position of the curve aKb, or, in other words, the composition of the different conjugate ternary solutions, will vary with the temperature, and only with the temperature, if we assume either constancy of pressure or the presence of the vapour phase. Since at the critical point the condition is imposed that the two liquid phases become identical, one degree of freedom is thereby lost, and therefore only one degree of freedom remains (cf. p. 100). The composition of the plait point, therefore, depends on the temperature, and only on the temperature; always on the assumption, of course, that the pressure is constant, or that a vapour phase is present.

It is of importance to note that the composition of the different ternary solutions obtained by the addition of acetic acid to a heterogeneous mixture of toluene and water, will depend not only on the amount of acetic acid added, but also on the relative amounts of toluene and water at the commencement. Suppose, for example, that we start with toluene and water in the proportions represented by the point c' (Fig. 101). On mixing these, two liquid layers having the composition a and b respectively will be formed. Since by the addition of acetic acid the relative amounts of these two substances in the system as a whole cannot undergo alteration, the total composition of the different ternary systems which will be obtained must be represented by a point on the line Cc' (p. 280). Thus by the addition of acetic acid a system may be obtained, the total composition of which is represented by the point c''. Such a system, however, will separate into two conjugate ternary solutions, the compositions of which will be represented by the ends of the tie-line passing through the point c''. So long as the total composition of the system lies below the point S, *i.e.* the point of intersection of the line Cc' with the boundary curve, two liquid layers will be formed; while all systems having a total composition represented by a point on the line Cc', above S, will form only one homogeneous solution. It is evident also that as the amount of acetic acid is increased, the relative amounts of the two liquid layers formed differ more and more until at S a limiting position is reached, when the amount of the one liquid layer dwindles to nought, and only one solution remains.

The same reasoning can be carried through for different initial amounts of toluene and water, but it would be fruitless to discuss all the different systems which can be obtained. The reason for the preceding discussion was to show that although the addition of acetic acid to a mixture of toluene and water will, in all cases, lead ultimately to a limiting system, beyond which homogeneity occurs, that point is not necessarily the plait point. On the contrary, in order that addition of acetic acid shall lead to the critical mixture, it is necessary to start with a binary mixture of toluene and water in the proportions represented by the point c. In this case, addition of acetic acid will give rise to a series of conjugate ternary solutions, the compositions of which will gradually approach one another, and at last become identical.

From the foregoing it will be evident that the amount of acetic acid required to produce a homogeneous solution will depend on the relative amounts of toluene and water with which we start, and can be ascertained by joining the corner C with the point on the line AB representing the total composition of the initial binary system. The point where this line intersects the boundary curve aKb will indicate the minimum amount of acetic acid which, under these particular conditions, is necessary to give one homogeneous solution.

Relationships similar to those described for toluene, water and acetic acid are also found in the case of a number of other systems, e.g. chloroform — water — acetic acid,[5] aniline — phenol — water (over a limited temperature range).[6] They have also been observed in the case of a considerable number of molten metals.[7] Thus, molten lead and silver, as well as molten zinc and silver, mix in all proportions; but molten lead and zinc are only partially miscible with each other. The system lead—silver—zinc is thus similar to the one discussed above in detail, and, incidentally, forms the basis for the well-known Parkes process for the desilverisation of lead.[8]

Retrograde Solubility. As a consequence of the fact that acetic acid distributes itself unequally between toluene and water, and that the plait point K, therefore, does not lie at the summit of the curve, it is possible to start with a homogeneous solution in which the percentage amount of acetic acid is greater than at the plait point, and to produce a small amount of a second layer which subsequently shrinks into non-existence again, merely by altering the relative amounts of toluene and water. This phenomenon, to which the term *retrograde solubility* is applied, will be observed not only in the case of toluene, water, and acetic acid, but in all other sys-

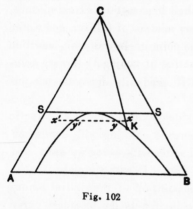

Fig. 102

tems in which the plait point lies below the highest point of the boundary curve for heterogeneous systems. This will be seen from the diagram, Fig. 102. Starting with the homogeneous system represented by x, in which, therefore, the concentration of C is greater than in the critical mixture (K), if the relative amounts of A and B are altered in the direction xx', while the per cent of C is maintained constant, the system will become heterogeneous when the composition reaches the point y, and will remain heterogeneous with changing composition until the point y' is passed, when it will again become homogeneous. A consideration of the tie-lines involved will show that the quantity of the layer newly formed at y will increase, pass through a maximum and diminish to zero at y'.

The Influence of Temperature. As has already been said, a ternary system existing in three phases possesses two degrees of freedom; and the state of the system is therefore dependent not only on the relative concentration of the components, but also on the temperature. As the temperature changes, therefore, the boundary curve of the heterogeneous system will also alter; and in order to represent this alteration, use may be made of the right prism, in which the temperature is measured upwards. In this way the boundary curve (binodal curve), passes into a boundary surface (or binodal surface), as shown in Fig. 103. In this figure the curve *akb* is the isothermal for the ternary system; the curve *aKb* shows the change in the *binary* system AB with the temperature, with a critical point at K. This curve has the same meaning as those given in Chapter VI. The curve *k*K is a critical curve or plait point curve joining together the plait points of the different isothermals, In such a case as is shown in Fig. 103, there does not exist any real critical temperature for the ternary system, for as the temperature is raised, the amount of C in the "critical" solution becomes less and less, and at K only two components, A and B, are present. Such is the behaviour of the system aniline—acetone—water.[9] In the case, however, represented in Fig. 104, a real ternary critical point is found. In this figure *ak′b* is an isothermal, *ak″b* is the

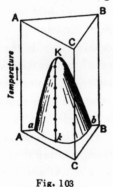

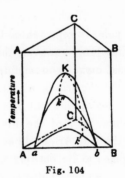

Fig. 103   Fig. 104

curve for the binary system AB and K is a ternary critical point. All points outside the helmet-shaped boundary surface represent homogeneous ternary solutions, while all points within the surface belong to heterogeneous systems. Above the temperature of the point K, the three components are miscible in all proportions. An example of a ternary system yielding such a boundary surface is that consisting of phenol, water, and acetone.[10] In this case the critical temperature K is 92°, and the composition at this ternary critical point is

Water, 59 per cent.
Acetone, 12 ”
Phenol, 29 ”

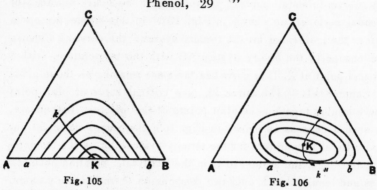

Fig. 105   Fig. 106

The difference between the two classes of systems just mentioned is seen very clearly by a glance at the Figs. 105 and 106, which show the projection of the isothermals on the base of the prism. In Fig. 105, the projections yield paraboloid curves, the two branches of which are cut by one side of the trian⌐˙ and the critical point is represented by a point on this side. In the second case (Fig. 106), however, the projections of the isothermals form ellipsoidal curves surrounding the supreme critical point which now lies *inside the triangle*. At lower temperatures these isothermal boundary curves are cut by a side of the triangle; at the critical temperature, k'', of the binary system AB, the boundary curve *touches* the side AB, while at still higher temperatures the boundary curve comes to lie entirely within the triangle. At any given temperature, therefore, between the critical point of the binary system (k''), and the supreme critical point of the ternary system (K), each pair of the three components is miscible in all proportions; for the region of heterogeneous systems is now bounded by a closed curve lying entirely within the triangle. Outside this curve only homogeneous systems are found. Binary mixtures, therefore, represented by any point on one of the sides of the triangle must be homogeneous, for they all lie outside the boundary curve for heterogeneous states.

II. *The three components can form two pairs of partially mis-*

cible liquids.

When two of three pairs of components are only partially miscible two binodal curves will be obtained in the triangular diagram, as shown in Fig. 107, and there will be two areas of heterogeneity, each with its own plait point, k_1 and k_2. On changing the temperature, the binodal curves will undergo alteration, in a manner similar to that just discussed. As the temperature falls, the two curves will spread out more and more into the centre of the triangle, and may at last meet one another; while at still lower temperatures we may imagine the curves still further expanding so that the two heterogeneous regions flow into each other and form a *band* on the triangular diagram (Fig. 108). The merging of the two areas of heterogeneity

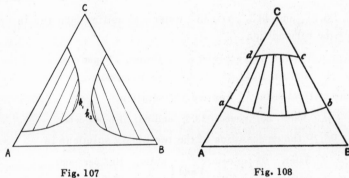

Fig. 107   Fig. 108

may occur in a variety of ways[11] but experimental data on the subject are meagre. It will depend, for instance, on whether k_1 and k_2 eventually coincide as the temperature is changed. If they do not coincide there will be an intermediate range of temperature over which three liquid phases will coexist, as, for example, in Fig. 109, *a*, *b* and *c*. A behaviour similar to this has been found for the system silver perchlorate-water-benzene.[12] Regardless of its manner of formation with change of temperature the existence of a band of heterogeneity is well-known, for example, in the case of the system ethyl acetate-water-*n*-butyl alcohol.[13] Likewise the system water—phenol—aniline[14,15] at temperatures above 67° behaves in this way, although in this case the band develops by the gradual expansion, with the lowering of temperature, of a *single* binodal curve.

Consider, for example, the system water—phenol—aniline, for which, in Fig. 110, are shown three isothermals, viz. those for

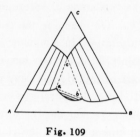

Fig. 109

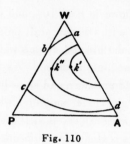

Fig. 110

148°, 96.7°, and 48°. At 148° water and aniline form two layers having the composition

Water,   83.5 per cent. ⎫
Aniline, 16.5   ,,   ⎬ and ⎰ water,   20 per cent.
                        ⎭   ⎱ aniline, 80   ,,

and the critical point k' has the composition

Water, 65;   phenol, 13.2;   aniline, 21.8 per cent.

At 96.7° the composition of the two binary solutions is

Water,   93 per cent. ⎫
Aniline, 7   ,,   ⎬ and ⎰ water,   10.5 per cent.
                     ⎭   ⎱ aniline, 89.5   ,,

while the point k'' has the composition

Water, 59.8;   phenol, 35.5;   aniline, 4.7 per cent.

At 48° the region of heterogeneous states now forms a band, and the two layers formed by water and aniline have the composition

Water,   95.9 percent. ⎫
Aniline, 4.1   ,,   ⎬ and ⎰ water,   6.2 per cent.
                      ⎭   ⎱ aniline, 93.8   ,,

while the two layers formed by water and phenol have the composition

Water,   87.6 per cent. ⎫
Phenol, 12.4   ,,   ⎬ and ⎰ water,   37 per cent.
                       ⎭   ⎱ phenol, 63   ,,

All mixtures of water, phenol, and aniline, therefore, the composition of which is represented by any point within the band *abcd*, will form two ternary solutions; while if the composition is represented by a point outside the band, only one homogeneous solution will be produced.

III. *The three components form three pairs of partially miscible liquids.*

The third chief case which can occur is that no two of the components are completely miscible with each other. In this case, therefore, three paraboloid binodal curves will be obtained, as shown in Fig. 111. If we imagine these three curves to expand in towards the centre of the triangle, as might happen, for example, by lowering the temperature, a point will be reached at which the curves partly overlap, and we shall have the appearance shown in Fig. 112.

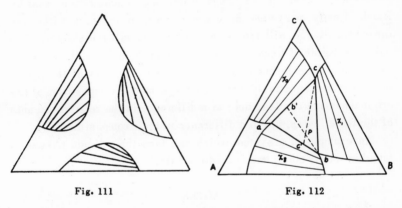

Fig. 111   Fig. 112

Here again there will be a variety of ways in which this merging can occur.

The points a, b, and c represent the points where the three curves cut, and the triangle abc is a region where the curves overlap. From this diagram we can see that any mixture having a composition represented by a point in one of the clear spaces at the corners of the larger triangle, will form a homogeneous solution; if the composition corresponds to any point lying in one of the quadrilateral regions x_1, x_2, or x_3, two ternary solutions will be formed; while, if the composition is represented by any point P in the inner triangle, separation into three layers, having the composition a, b and c respectively, will occur. If straight lines be drawn through any two corners of the inner triangle to pass through P the ratio of the intercepts on the sides of the triangle will be a measure of the relative amounts of the phases formed. Thus, if weight per cent has been plotted, the ratio of ac' to $c'b$ gives the ratio of the weight of phase b to that of phase a and the ratio of ab' to $b'c$ gives the ratio of the weight of phase c to that of phase a.

Since in the regions adjacent to the corners of the triangle ABC we have three components in two phases, liquid and vapour, the systems have three degrees of freedom. At constant temperature, therefore, the condition of the system is not defined until the concentrations of two of the components are fixed. A system belonging to one of the quadrilateral spaces has, as we have seen, two degrees of freedom; besides the temperature, one concentration must be fixed. Lastly, a system the composition of which falls within the inner triangle abc, will form three layers, and will therefore possess only one degree of freedom. If the temperature is fixed, the composition of the three layers is also determined, viz. that of the points a, b, and c respectively; and a change in the composition of the original mixture can lead only to a difference in the relative amounts of the three layers, not to a difference in their composition.

An example of a system which can form three liquid phases is found in water, ether, and succinic nitrile.[16]

NOTES

1. A summary of the literature covering such systems will be found in: J. C. Smith, *J. Ind. Eng. Chem.*, 1942, **34**, 234; 1949, **41**, 2932.

2. R. M. Woodman, *J. Physical Chem.*, 1926, **30**, 1283.

3. Because on this curve there are always two related values of the solubility, the curve is called a binodal curve, to distinguish it from an ordinary solubility curve.

4. The distribution coefficient will not remain constant because, apart from other reasons, the mutual solubility of toluene and water is altered by the addition of the acid. This increase in the mutual solubility of two liquids by the addition of a third substance is of great importance, both scientifically and industrially. See also Chap. VI.

5. C. R. A. Wright, *Proc. Roy. Soc.*, 1891, **49**, 174; 1892, **50**, 375.

6. A. N. Campbell, *J. Amer. Chem. Soc.*, 1945, **67**, 981.

7. See, for example, the system aluminium-lead-silver, Campbell, Yaffe Wallace and Ashley, *Can. J. Research*, 1941, B**19**, 212.

8. Bodländer, *Berg- und Hüttenmänn. Ztg.*, 1897, **56**, 331.

9. Campbell and Brown, *Trans. Faraday Soc.*, 1933, **29**, 835.

10. Schreinemakers, *Z. physikal. Chem.*, 1900, **33**, 78.

11. Roozeboom, *Die Heterogene Gleichgewichte*, Vol III (2), *Vieweg, Braunschweig*, 1913.

12. Hill, *J. Amer. Chem. Soc.*, 1922, **44**, 1163.

13. Beech and Glasstone, *J. Chem. Soc.*, 1938, **67**.

14. Schreinemakers, *Z. physikal. Chem.*, 1899, **29**, 577.

15. Campbell, *J. Amer. Chem. Soc.*, 1945, **67**, 981.

16. Schreinemakers, *Z. physikal. Chem.*, 1898, **25**, 543. See also Holmes, *J. Chem. Soc.*, 1918, **113**, 263.

CHAPTER XV

B. SYSTEMS CONSISTING OF LIQUID AND VAPOUR PHASES ONLY.

When systems of the type described in the previous chapter are subjected to reduced pressure or increased temperature vapour will form giving rise to liquid-vapour equilibria, and if more than one of the liquids is volatile a complete description of the phase relations will have to include the composition of the vapour. In addition to the liquid-vapour equilibria arising from the systems of the previous chapter there are simpler types which we shall discuss first, namely, those arising from three liquids which are miscible in all proportions—a type not considered previously because, of course, in the absence of vapour, there is no heterogeneous equilibrium.

In their relations with vapour the three binary systems which comprise the ternary system can belong to a number of types described in Chapter VII. This variety of binary types gives an even greater variety of ternary types[1,10] and we shall find it necessary to restrict our discussion to only a few of them. Furthermore, the number of systems which has been investigated experimentally both as to the vapour and liquid composition is not large so that only a limited number of useful illustrations is available.

We shall again use triangular coordinates for concentrations and measure temperature on the vertical axis, the pressure for any one solid model being constant. One should bear in mind, however, that the model will be different at different pressures.

I. Systems with only One Liquid Phase.

(a) Each of the three binary systems has neither a maximum nor a minimum boiling-point.

The three liquids of a system of this type must of necessity be similar chemically and the three binary systems will all belong to the type illustrated in Fig. 29 (p. 116). When liquid and vapour compositions are plotted against boiling-points the three vertical faces of the triangular prism will therefore have the appearance shown in Fig. 113 (an isobar), where t_A, t_B, and t_C are the respective boiling-points of the components at the pressure of the isobar $(t_A < t_B < t_C)$. Each of the liquid curves which represents the temperatures at which different binary liquids have a vapour pressure equal to that of the isobar will form, in the ternary system, the boundaries of a curved surface representing the same thing for all possible ternary liquids. Similarly the vapour or condensation curves of the binaries form the boundaries of a curved surface, above the other surface, representing the composition of the coexisting vapours. Thus every point on the lower surface is joined to a point on the upper by a tie-line in a plane parallel to the plane of the base. These tie-lines will not be parallel to each other, however, but will gradually change in direction across the model approaching parallel-

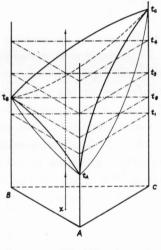

ism to one of its faces as the latter is approached. This will be made clearer by Fig. 114 which shows projections of isothermal sections of Fig. 113 taken at four different temperatures t_1, t_B, t_3 and t_4. (These isotherms actually overlap, but for the purpose of clarity they are not drawn in this way.) Each isothermal plane shows two lines the area between which is crossed by tie-lines joining the compositions of liquid and vapour at equilibrium at the temperature of the isothermal section. The lines showing liquid

Fig. 113

compositions are labeled l and the vapour compositions v. Returning to Fig. 113, any ternary mixture represented by a point between the two surfaces will yield a liquid in equilibrium with vapour; such a system, therefore, has a variance of two (at constant pressure). Likewise systems represented by points above the upper

surface yield only vapour and below the lower surface only liquid
(trivariant systems).

Suppose a liquid of composition x at some low temperature were
heated in a closed system kept at the constant pressure of the isobar
(Fig. 113). Vapour will begin to form when that temperature is
reached where the line drawn vertically through x strikes the lower
surface. Suppose this temperature to be t_1 (Fig. 114). The first

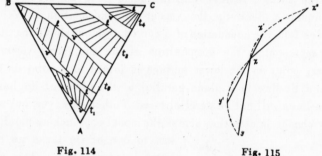

Fig. 114   **Fig. 115**

vapour which forms at this temperature will have the composition y
at the other end of the tie-line. As the temperature is raised the
amount of vapour will increase and that of the liquid will decrease,
but the composition of each will alter, for the system is entering
different isotherms in which the tie-lines have gradually altering
directions. Thus, in Fig. 115 which is an enlargement of the part
of Fig. 114 with which we are concerned, at a certain temperature
slightly higher than $|t_1$ the liquid composition will have moved to
x' and the vapour to y', $x'xy'$ being the tie-line at that temperature.
On raising the temperature still further the liquid reaches x'' while
the vapour has reached x the original liquid composition. At the
temperature corresponding to the tie-line xx'' the last drop of liquid
disappears and any further rise in temperature will cause no other
phase changes.

Let us examine the possibility of separating the liquids of such
a ternary system by fractional distillation by reference to the projection Fig. 116. Suppose that a liquid of composition L_O be subjected to isobaric distillation at the pressure of the isobar. The
liquid will begin to boil (assuming equilibrium to obtain between

liquid and vapour) at the temperature at which the vertical line from L_O strikes the lower curved surface in the solid model, and the first vapour formed will have the composition V_O, $V_O L_O$ being a tie-line at this temperature. If an infinitesimal amount of this vapour be removed from the system by condensation the composition of the residual liquid will move along the linear prolongation of $V_O L_O$ to L_1. The liquid L_1, however, boils at an infinitesimally higher temperature so that the boiling-point will have risen through the condensation of the small quantity V_O. At the same time L_1, being on a different tie-line $V_1 L_1$, will yield a vapour of composition V_1. Removal by condensation of vapour V_1 will cause the residual composition to move along the prolongation of $V_1 L_1$ to L_2. The liquid L_2 boils at a still higher temperature than L_1 and gives vapour V_2. Thus it can be seen that distillation of L_O yields residues $L_1, L_2,$ $L_3,$ etc., and vapours V_O, V_1, V_2, V_3, etc. accompanied by a rising boiling-point and that the loci of L and V are curves. Now if the distillation be stopped when the liquid composition reaches, say, •L_3 the overall distillate will be the sum of V_O, V_1, V_2, V_3, given by some point V (a kind of "centre of gravity" of V_O, V_1, V_2 and V_3), and the residue will be that of the last residue, L_3. Obviously V, L_O and L_3 must lie on a straight line for the original liquid L_O has, in effect, been divided into V and L_3. Suppose now that the overall distillate of composition V is distilled and the first vapours arising from it are condensed. By a repetition of the above reasoning we see that this second overall distillate will have a composition nearer to A, say V′, and by a continuation of this fractionation process the distillate will eventually be pure A. On the other hand, by continuing to boil away the original liquid L_O its composition will follow $L_1, L_2, L_3,$ etc., and ultimately reach that of pure C, the least volatile component, according to the trend of tie-lines. The trend of the tie-lines shows further that, no matter what be the original composition of the ternary liquid, fractionation of the vapour will eventually give pure A and boiling away of the residue pure C. It is thus theoretically impossible to isolate the component of intermediate volatility. In practice, however, it may be possible, with difficulty, to isolate even that component in a relatively pure condition as was found in the system consisting of methyl, ethyl and propyl acetates[2] which belongs to this type. The direction of movement of the composition of various residues can be shown by a series of "residue lines" indicated in Fig. 117. Obviously Fig. 117 repre-

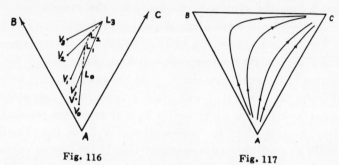

Fig. 116   Fig. 117

sents the loci of the liquid compositions of Fig. 116. It is seen that the residue composition may approach the composition of pure B but never actually reach it. A similar set of lines with arrows pointing in the opposite direction will likewise show the trend of the composition of the distillate with continued fractionation.

It is of some utility to examine the solid model for this type of system when the temperature is held constant and total pressure is measured on the vertical axis. As in the case of binary liquid-vapour equilibria such an isothermal model (Fig. 118) is very approx-

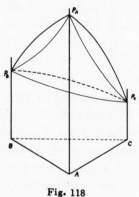

Fig. 118

imately a mirror image of the isobar, for the lowest boiling component A has the highest vapour pressure and the highest boiling component the lowest vapour pressure, *etc.* As in the isobar, the two resulting surfaces are joined by tie-lines the trend of which could be shown by projecting various isobaric sections on the base of the prism[3]. By means of these one could trace the course of distillate and residue in the isothermal distillation of various ternary liquids, bearing in mind that in any one step of such a process the total pressure in the system decreases as a result of the most volatile component vaporising the most rapidly. It could thus be shown that only the most volatile and least volatile components can be isolated from the ternary mixture by isothermal distillation, as is the case with isobaric distillation.

(b) One of the Three Binary Systems exhibits a Maximum Boiling-Point.

Examples are known in which one of the three binary systems shows a maximum boiling-point and examples are known in which one of the three binaries shows a minimum-boiling point, but for the sake of variety we have chosen to illustrate the former because cases involving minimum boiling-points, which are actually more common, are to be referred to frequently later. In the type to be considered here two of the three faces of the triangular prism will belong to the type of Fig. 29 (p. 116) but the third will be that of Fig. 28 (p. 115) The solid model (isobar), portrayed in Fig. 119 will again consist of two curved triangular surfaces, one below the other, in such a way that the boundaries correspond to the

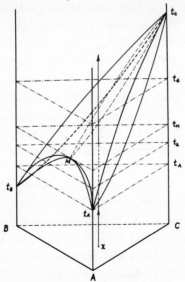

Fig. 119

liquid and vapour curves of the corresponding binaries. The temperatures t_A, t_B, t_C have their usual meanings and t_M is the boiling temperature of the azeotropic solution M. The occurrence of the maximum on one of the faces, however, will mean that the two surfaces now not only touch at their three corners, but also at a fourth point, M. This will give to both surfaces the shape of an inverted trough which gradually deepens in the direction of the binary with the maximum. As in the previous case, systems represented by points above the upper surface will consist entirely of vapour, and systems represented by points below the lower surface will consist entirely of a single liquid. Points lying between the two surfaces represent liquid-vapour equilibria.

In Fig. 120 four isothermal sections of the isobar at different temperatures t_A, t_2, t_M and t_4 are drawn schematically and, exactly as in Fig. 114 (p. 298), the members of each pair of curves at each temperature are joined by tie-lines, the vapour composition lines and liquid composition lines being indicated by the letters v and l respectively. It must always be true, of course, that as one approaches points of contact of the liquid and vapour surfaces (where the latter have identical composition) the tie-lines must diminish in length to zero. The isotherm at t_M illustrates this; for as the point M, where liquid and vapour have identical composition, is approached, the length of the tie-lines is seen to decrease.

It is unnecessary to describe the changes occurring when such a ternary liquid is heated in a closed system at constant pressure, as, in principle, the same changes occur as in the previous case (Fig. 115, p. 298). The isobaric distillation of this type, however, introduces certain differences by virtue of the presence of the azeotropic maximum.

Suppose that a liquid of composition x (Fig. 120) be distilled at the pressure of the isobar. It will begin to boil at t_2 and give a vapour of composition y. As boiling continues the composition of the residue will move away from A as will also the composition of the vapour, in accordance with the direction of movement of the tie-lines at gradually increasing temperatures above t_2. If the first portion of vapour which condenses be redistilled it will be seen that the composition of its vapour will be nearer to A than the first vapour. Obviously, it will be possible by continued fraction-

ation to obtain a vapour consisting of pure A. Continued boiling
of the residue, on the other hand, will cause the composition gradually to approach that of pure C, although in so doing it will also
temporarily increase in B content. The same scheme of changes
will apply to the fractionation and boiling away of any ternary
liquid whose composition x (Fig. 119) lies in the area AMC, that
is, far enough away from B that on raising its temperature to the
boiling point the vertical line through x intersects the portion of
the inverted trough sloping toward A. Similarly when a ternary
liquid, of composition such that its isoplethal line strikes the
other slope of the trough, is distilled, continued fractionation of
the vapour will give pure B and continued boiling of the residue
pure C. To summarise, it is possible to obtain pure A and pure C,

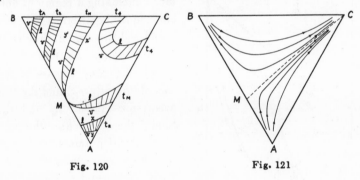

Fig. 120   Fig. 121

or pure B and pure C by distillation of ternary liquids of appropriate composition. This is further indicated by the series of residue
lines of Fig. 121 (*cf.* Fig. 117) showing the direction of movement
of the residues.

The system water-formic acid-acetic acid apparently belongs
to this type[4] where component A corresponds to formic acid, B to
water and C to acetic acid. The boiling-points at one atmosphere
are $100.5°$, $100.0°$ and $118.0°$ respectively, and the maximum in
the boiling-point curve for the first two liquids is at $107°$.

It should be pointed out that actually the example considered
above is only one of several possible sub-types of Case (b) for t_C
may lie between t_M and t_A, or between t_A and t_B, or below t_B, each
giving rise to a different disposition of the isotherms and tie-lines

of Fig. 120 and consequently altering the possibilities of isolating the various components by distillation. The student should examine such possibilities for himself and show, for instance, that if t_C lies below t_M it is no longer possible to isolate pure C by continued boiling of the residue, or even by fractional distillation unless t_C is below both t_A and t_B.

(c) Two of the Three Binary Systems exhibit Minimum Boiling-Points.

Two of the constituent binaries will here belong to the type of Fig. 27 (p. 114) and the third to the type of Fig. 29 (p. 116).

As in the two cases described above the solid model (Fig. 122)

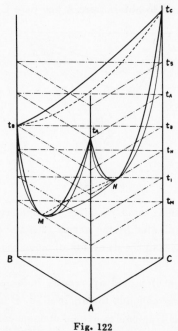

Fig. 122

has two triangular curved surfaces enclosing a region of heterogeneous equilibrium between liquid and vapour, but they meet in five points on the edges, namely the three corners of the triangle (t_A, t_B, t_C) and the two azeotropic minima t_M and t_N. Each, therefore, has the appearance of a trough the base of which runs from M to N. Five isothermal sections at gradually increasing temperatures (t_1, t_N, t_B, t_A, t_5) are given in Fig. 123 to indicate the arrangement of the tie-lines the meaning of which should be clear if the previous types have been understood. Fig. 124, which gives the corresponding residue lines follows immediately from Fig. 123 and one concludes that fractional distillation of any ternary liquid for such systems can eventually lead to a distillate of the azeotropic composition M. The composition of the residue can, however, be either pure A or pure C depending on whether the composition of the original liquid lies within the area AMN or BMNC.

An example of three liquids showing the above type of behaviour is the system ethyl alcohol (A)—carbon tetrachloride (B)—benzene (C)[5]. At one atmosphere pressure $t_A = 78.4°$, $t_B = 76.8°$ and $t_C = 80.1°$, and the temperatures of M and N are $65.1°$ and $68.1°$ respectively. The general direction of the residue lines of Fig. 124 and their consequences in the matter of separating the three components by distillation have been confirmed by experiment.

In conclusion, the student should be reminded that the type just described is really only one of many; for the magnitudes of t_A, t_B and t_C and of t_M and t_N can be such as to present a great variety of possibilities. We have here limited our treatment to the

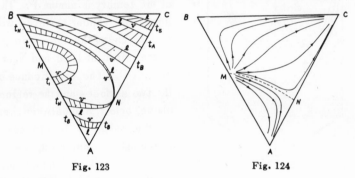

Fig. 123   Fig. 124

type where $t_M < t_N < t_B < t_A < t_C$.

(d) All Three Binary Systems and the Ternary System Exhibit Minimum Boiling-Points.

We have not as yet discussed a system in which there is a ternary azeotropic boiling-point, that is, a *ternary* liquid boiling to give a vapour of the same composition, but the latter is, in fact, of frequent occurrence when all three of the constituent binary systems exhibit azeotropism. There are no known cases where all three binaries have maximum boiling-points[6] but many where all three have minimum boiling-points either with or without a minimum ternary azeotropic boiling-point.

The new feature presented by the type to be described is

that both liquid and vapour surfaces have a minimum *within* the prism. According to the Gibbs-Konovalov theorem (loc. cit.) this must mean that at this minimum both liquid and vapour have identical composition so that in the solid model the two surfaces must touch at this point.

Figure 125 is a typical isobar of such a system, in which

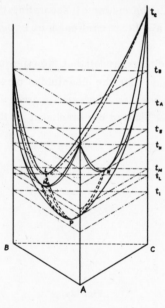

Fig. 125

$t_P < t_L < t_M < t_N < t_A < t_B < t_C$ where t_A, t_B, t_C, are the respective boiling-points of the components at the pressure of the isobar, t_L, t_M, t_N, the temperatures of the binary minima (L, M, N,) and t_P is the temperature of the ternary minimum P. The liquid and vapour surfaces will now touch at the three corners of the prism, at L, M and N, and also at P. The significance of the two surfaces and the regions above, below, and between them is the same as in the cases previously considered, as is also the meaning of the tie-lines on the corresponding isotherms of Fig. 126. At the point P, however, a ternary liquid is in equilibrium with a vapour of the same composition, and if such a liquid is distilled at the constant pressure of the isobar the distillate will have the same composition as the residue at all times, in other words it will distil as if it were a pure liquid. The Phase Rule tells us that both the composition and the boiling point of this azeotropic solution will alter with the pressure; for the system at this point is univariant. This can be shown as follows: There are two phases in equilibrium and three components present so that substitution in the Phase Rule gives a variance of three. From this, however, we must subtract two, because, by reason of the fact that two ternary phases become identical, two degrees of freedom are automatically lost, for the two independent concentration variables in the liquid and vapour have thereby become equal.

The residue lines of such a system are given in Fig. 127.

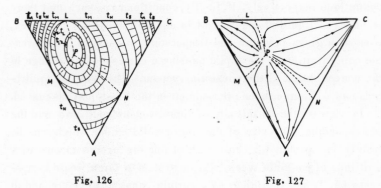

Fig. 126   Fig. 127

They show that any ternary liquid except one of the composition of P, when boiled away at the pressure of the isobar, will finally yield a residue of either pure A, B or C according as its original composition lies in the area AMPN, BLPM or CNPL respectively. Conversely, continued fractionation of the vapours of any ternary liquid in which only the most volatile fractions are redistilled will yield eventually a liquid of the composition of P.

As an illustration of three liquids which show this kind of behaviour we mention acetone (A), methyl alcohol (B) and isobutyl chloride (C)[7] for which at one atmosphere $t_A = 56.3°$, $t_B = 64.7°$; $t_C = 68.9°$, $t_L = 53.1°$, $t_M = 55.7°$, $t_N = 55.8°$ and $t_P = 52.0°$.

II. Systems with More than One Liquid Phase.

When more than one liquid phase is present in a liquid-vapour equilibrium the phase changes can become very complex. Systems of this kind can arise when conditions are such as to have a vapour phase appearing in systems of the type shown, for example, in Figures 101 (p. 283), 108 (p. 291) and 112 (p. 293).

The Phase Rule shows that *three* liquid phases in a ternary system can at a given pressure be in equilibrium with vapour only at one definite temperature, characteristic of the system. By similar reasoning it is seen that if, at constant pressure and a given tem-

perature, *two* liquid phases coexist with vapour the concentration
of each liquid phase and that of the vapour will be fixed. Such
equilibria therefore will be designated on any isothermal section
of an isobaric model by three points representing these three concentrations respectively. If, finally, conditions are such that there
is only *one* liquid phase present in equilibrium with vapour then,
even at a given pressure and temperature, it is possible to vary
the concentration of the liquid causing a corresponding change in
the concentration of the coexisting vapour. This type of equilibrium has, of course, been predominant in the types just discussed.

In view of the complexity of liquid-vapour equilibria and the
corresponding difficulty of drawing a solid model which can be
readily interpreted we shall restrict our discussion to one of a
multitude of possible types, viz., a system of three liquid components (A, B and C) which, at a certain constant pressure and at
a temperature just low enough to eliminate a vapour phase belongs
to the type shown in Fig. 108 (p. 291), A and B being the only
completely miscible pair of components. We shall assume further
that the binary system AB belongs to the type of Fig. 29 (p. 291).
and that both binary systems AC and BC belong to the type of Fig.
35 (p. 127), *i.e.*, exhibit a eutectic type of boiling-point diagram.
If t_M is the minimum boiling-point of the system AC and t_N that for
the system BC let us suppose that $t_M < t_A < t_N < t_C < t_B$, where
t_A, t_B, t_C have their usual meanings. In addition, let there be no
ternary maximum or minimum boiling-points within the system.

The temperature-concentration model (isobar) will, as a result
of these restrictions, belong to the type shown in Fig. 128 the
structure of which can best be studied by examining the various
isothermal sections shown in Figs. 129 to 133 at gradually increasing temperatures.

Fig. 129 is the isotherm for a temperature below that of t_M.
No vapour can form, for t_M is the lowest temperature at which
vapour appears in any of the binaries, and, as we have excluded
ternary minimum boiling-points, it must also be the lowest temperature at which vapour appears in the ternary. The diagram is
crossed by a two-liquid band separating two areas of single liq-

uid as in Fig. 108 (p. 291).

On raising the temperature to just above t_M, at which vapour begins to make its appearance in the binary AC, the isotherm has the form of Fig. 130. At this relatively low temperature only liquid mixtures near the edge AC can form vapour, the two-liquid system BC being the less volatile of the two two-liquid binaries ($t_N > t_M$). The point M of the binary AC (Fig. 128), which gives

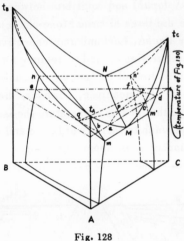

Fig. 128

the composition of the vapour in equilibrium with two liquid layers m and m' containing no B has now, in Fig. 130, moved inwards to

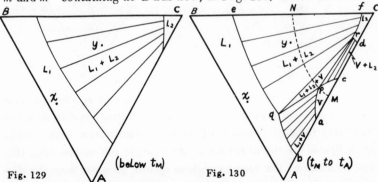

Fig. 129

Fig. 130

p as, at the higher temperature, it is now possible to have a vapour containing the less volatile component B. At the same time the two liquid layers which are in equilibrium with it have also moved away from AC as their B content has increased, and have the definite composition given by the points q and r. The triangle pqr is thus invariant at constant temperature and pressure, and total compositions taken within it at this temperature and pressure must yield these three phases. This invariant region must give rise to three univariant two-phase equilibria, crossed by tie-lines, viz., equilibria between L_1 and L_2 (the region $qrfe$), equilibria between L_1 and V ($qpab$) and equilibria between L_2 and V ($prdc$). Finally there are the three bivariant (one-phase) areas for L_1, L_2 and V denoted by BeqbA, Cdrf and apc respectively.

As the temperature rises p and therefore q and r must move still farther away from AC toward BC and the dimensions of the triangle pqr will alter. In the meantime, however, the boiling-point of $A(t_A)$ is passed so that at this temperature the isotherm (Fig. 131) must show the approach to identity of liquid and coexisting vapour as the composition of A is approached—in other words the tie-lines denoting L_1—V must have zero length at A. This is evident from the figure.

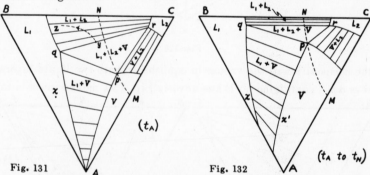

Fig. 131   Fig. 132

In Fig. 132, for temperatures between t_A and t_N, the temperature has become high enough for two coexisting liquids near the relatively involatile binary BC to be in equilibrium with vapour, as indicated by the nearness of the triangle pqr to the edge BC. The meaning of the various regions should be clear from the diagram. Notice that the area of vapour now covers a larger portion of the diagram and that the triangle pqr is beginning to "flatten out" for, in the approach of pqr to BC, the points p, q and r must all "reach" the edge at the same temperature (t_N), just as they all "left" the edge AC at the same temperature (t_M).

The locus of p in its progress from M to N is shown by a dotted line in Figs. 130 to 133.

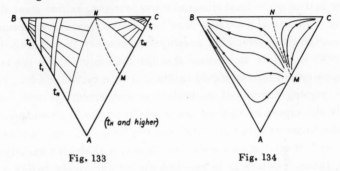

Fig. 133   Fig. 134

Fig. 133 shows the isotherms, drawn so as not to overlap, at the three different temperatures t_N, t_1, and t_2, where t_1 is between t_N and t_C and t_2 is between t_C and t_B. At t_N the points p, q and r of Fig. 132 have coincided with N, n and n' respectively of Fig. 128. As the temperature is raised still further the areas for L_1 and L_2 become smaller, L_2 disappears at t_C and L_1 at t_B.

We may now inquire as to the behaviour of the system during the distillation of various liquid mixtures. Suppose, for instance, that a liquid mixture of composition x (Fig. 129) is to be boiled at the pressure of these isotherms. It is evident that at the temperature of Fig. 129 there will be only one liquid phase and that as the temperature is raised the point x will not lie in an area of heterogeneity until the temperature of Fig. 132 is reached when it will boil to give a vapour x'. If the liquid is boiled away the tie-lines of Figs. 132 and 133 show that its composition will eventually be that of pure B. Suppose, however, that one heats a liquid mixture well within the two-liquid area such as that of the composition y (Fig. 129). This two-liquid system will not boil until that temperature is reached where x begins to be enclosed by the triangle pqr of Figs. 130 to 132. Suppose that pqr begins to enclose y at the temperature of Fig. 131. At this temperature, therefore, the two liquids, having of necessity the compositions

q and r will commence to boil to give a vapour p. As this vapour is removed by condensation the total composition y of the residue must alter directly away from p (and with it, of course, will alter the compositions of the two liquid layers). As y alters away from p the boiling-point must rise and the vapour composition must alter along the locus of p towards N as long as two liquid layers remain. By applying the principles developed in connection with Fig. 116 (p. 300) it will be understood that the path followed by the total composition of the two liquid layers will be a curved one (yz, Fig. 131) curving towards B as boiling is continued. Nevertheless, while the vapour being produced *at any instant* will be somewhere on the locus of p, the *accumulated* vapours, *i.e.*, the "centre of gravity" of all the vapours on the locus, will not lie exactly on this locus. Before B is reached one of the liquid layers will disappear and when this occurs the vapour composition will leave the locus of p and also move towards B. It will be realized that the residue in this example eventually becomes B only because the original liquid y lay within the area BNMA (Fig. 131). If it had lain within CNM similar reasoning shows that the final liquid would have been pure C. These results are summarised in the residue lines of Fig. 134.

As in the case of the distillation of homogeneous liquid mixtures one may at first sight think that the process of fractionating liquids such as y (Fig. 131), in such a way that the first vapours in each step are redistilled, would produce a sequence of changes approximately the reverse of the residue changes just described. Closer examination will reveal that this is not true; for the immediate vapour from y or, for that matter, any liquid mixture corresponding to heterogeneity will always lie on the locus of p, namely NM and condensation of vapour over a short temperature interval will give a two-layer distillate not differing greatly in total composition from some point on NM. (This total composition would be *on* NM if NM were a straight line.) This distillate will, in turn, when distilled, give an initial vapour again on NM *etc*. Thus fractionation in this way will yield a vapour which more or less follows NM giving, in the limit, a distillate of composition M. Throughout this fractionation the boiling-points will, of course, have become progressively lower.

A system approaching the type just described is that comprising benzene (A)—toluene (B)—water (C)[8], where $t_A = 80.3°$, $t_B = 110.6°$, $t_C = 100.0°$, $t_M = 69.3°$ and $t_N = 84.3°$. Here, however, A and C are almost immiscible, as are also B and C, so that the areas of homogeneous liquid, e.g., ABeqb and Cfrd of Fig. 130 are very small.

If the student wishes to study further the fascinating and very practical problem of liquid-vapour equilibria he is referred to the system ethyl alcohol-water-benzene[9] in which two of the component binaries show azeotropic minima, the third shows the eutectic type of heterogeneity, and in which there is a *ternary* minimum boiling-point. This particular system has merited much study because of the use of benzene in the dehydration of ethyl alcohol.

NOTES

1. A very comprehensive list of boiling-points of binary and ternary liquids is given in Lecat, *La Tension de Vapeur des Melanges de Liquides, L'Azeotropisme*, Vol. 1, Lamertin, Brussels, 1918.

2. Barrell, Thomas and Young, *Proc. Phys. Soc.*, 1893, **12**, 422.

3. Schreinemakers, *Z. physikal. Chem.*, 1901, **36**, 257 and 413.

4. Lecat, *loc. cit.*, p. 13.

5. Schreinemakers, *Z. physikal. Chem.*, 1904; **47**, 445 and **48**, 257; Campbell and Dulmage, *J. Amer. Chem. Soc.*, 1948; **70**, 1723.

6. Lecat, *loc. cit.*, p. 14.

7. Lecat, (*loc. cit.*), p. 184.

8. Barbaudy, *J. chim. phys.*, 1926, **23**, 307.

9. Barbaudy, *J. chim. phys.*, 1927, **24**, 1.

10. For a more recent compilation see Horsley, *Anal. Chem.*, 1947, **19**, 508; 1949, **21**, 831.

C. SYSTEMS CONSISTING OF SOLID AND LIQUID PHASES ONLY

The study of ternary solid-liquid equilibria covers a wide field. It may include, for example, systems of three elements, three oxides, two salts with a common ion and solvent, three salts with a common ion in the absence of solvent, and systems involving metathesis in the absence of solvent.[1] In this chapter we shall deal chiefly with the temperature variable and postpone isothermal studies to the next chapter. We shall, moreover, confine our discussion to those systems where only one liquid phase appears.[2]

I. The Solid Phases are the Pure Components.

Since it is necessary to take into account not only the changing composition of the liquid phase, but also the variation of the temperature, we shall again employ the right prism for the graphic representation of the systems, as shown in Fig. 135, where t_A, t_B and t_C denote the melting-points of the pure components. If we start with the component A at its melting-point, and add B, which is capable of dissolving in liquid A, the freezing-point of A will be lowered; and, similarly, the freezing-point of B by addition of A. In this way we get the freezing-point curve $t_A k_1 t_B$ for the binary system, k_1 being a eutectic point. This curve will, of course, lie in the plane formed by one face of the prism. In a similar manner we obtain the freezing-point curves $t_A k_2 t_C$ and $t_B k_3 t_C$. These curves give the composition of the binary liquid phases in equilibrium with one of the pure components, or, at the eutectic points, with a mixture of two solid components. If to the system represented say by the point k_1 a small quantity of the third component, C, is added, the temperature at which the two solid phases A and B can exist in equilibrium with the liquid phase is lowered; and this depression of the eutectic point is all the greater the larger the addition of C. In this way we obtain the curve k_1K, which slopes inwards and downwards, and indicates the varying composition of the ternary liquid phase with which a mixture of solid A and B are in equilibrium. Similarly, the curves k_2K and k_3K are the corresponding eutectic curves for A and C, and B and C in equilibrium with ternary solutions. At the point K, the three solid components are in equilibrium with the liquid phase; and this point, therefore, represents *the lowest temperature attainable with the three components given.* The point K is known as a ternary eutectic, the chief characteristics of which are that it is invariant and that on withdrawal of heat the phase reaction is $L \rightarrow S_1 + S_2 + S_3$. Each of the ternary eutectic curves, as they may be called, is produced by the intersection of two surfaces, while

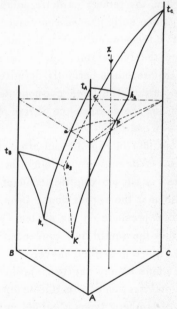

Fig. 135

at the ternary eutectic point, three surfaces, viz. $t_A k_1 K k_2$, $t_B k_1 K k_3$, and $t_C k_2 K k_3$, meet. Any point on one of these surfaces represents a ternary solution in equilibrium with only one component in the solid state; the lines or curves of intersection of these represent equilibria with two solid phases, while at the point K, the ternary eutectic point, there are three solid phases in equilibrium with a liquid. With vapour present the surfaces just mentioned represent bivariant systems. One component in the solid state can exist in equilibrium with a ternary liquid phase and vapour under varying conditions of temperature and concentration of the components in the solution; and before the state of the system is defined, these two variables, temperature and composition, must be fixed. On the other hand, the curves formed by the intersection of these planes represent univariant systems; at a given temperature two solid phases can exist in equilibrium with a ternary solution and vapour only when the latter have definite composition. Lastly, the ternary eutectic point, K, represents an invariant system; three solid phases can exist in equilibrium with a ternary solution and vapour only when the latter have fixed composition and when the temperature has a definite value. This eutectic point, therefore, has a perfectly definite position, depending only on the nature of the three components. Such an invariant point representing the coexistence of five phases in a ternary system is known as a *quintuple* point.

It is to be noted that in Fig. 135 no attempt is made to show vapour composition. Alternatively we may, as on previous occasions, if the system is not too volatile, conduct the investigations in open vessels so that the vapour phase is absent, provided we realize that the total pressure on the system is now fixed. This will affect negligibly the equilibrium concentrations and will have no effect on the variance described above.

The phase relations at any one temperature will evidently be shown by a horizontal section of Fig. 135 taken at the appropriate height. A series of isotherm types obtained in this way is shown in Fig. 136. (We have assumed that the melting-points of the components and the eutectic temperatures are such that $t_K < t_{k_1} < t_{k_3} < t_B < t_{k_2} < t_A < t_C$ ——other possibilities are treated similarly.) On these isotherms compositions of liquid in equilibrium with a single solid (represented by a surface in Fig. 135) are now designated by lines, compositions of liquid in equilibrium with two solids (represented by lines in Fig. 135) are now designated by points, and compositions of liquids in equilibrium with three solids—there is only one, point K—only appear in specific isotherms. This is equivalent, of course, to the loss of a degree of freedom as a result of keeping the temperature constant. Consider, for instance, the last isotherm of Fig. 136 for a certain temperature between t_B and t_{k_2} (cf. also Fig. 135). The line ap obviously gives the composition of solutions in equilibrium with solid A; the region aAp is therefore appropriately crossed by tie-lines intersecting at A. Similarly cp represents solutions in equilibrium with solid C. The lines ap and cp are thus (isothermal) solubility curves of A and C respectively. The point p is the composition of the only solution which, at the given temperature and pressure, is in equilibrium with both solid A and solid C. As such it is called an isothermally invariant point. The area $Bcpa$ is a one phase (liquid) area and represents solutions unsaturated with respect to A and C. Finally the triangle ApC encloses all total compositions which at equilibrium must give the solution p and the two solid phases A and C. A similar interpretation is attached to the other isotherms. At gradually increasing temperatures above the last isotherm of Fig. 136 it is obvious that first p will reach the edge AC, then the fan-shaped area converging on A will disappear, and finally that converging on C, to give a homogeneous liquid for all proportions of the three components, Of course at still higher temperatures the boiling-points of the system may be reached and the subject matter of the previous chapter becomes applicable—indeed it may well happen that the vapour pressure of one of the components or of a certain binary or ternary liquid becomes equal to the total pressure of the isobar before all solid phases have disappeared from the diagram. Such complications cannot be considered here; in any case they would merely involve an extension of the principles developed. Proceeding in the direction of lower temperature it is clear from the isotherms that the area of homogeneous liquid becomes smaller and the isothermally univariant fan-shaped areas enlarge until t_K is reached, the meaning of which has already been described. Below t_K there can only exist a mixture of the three component solids.

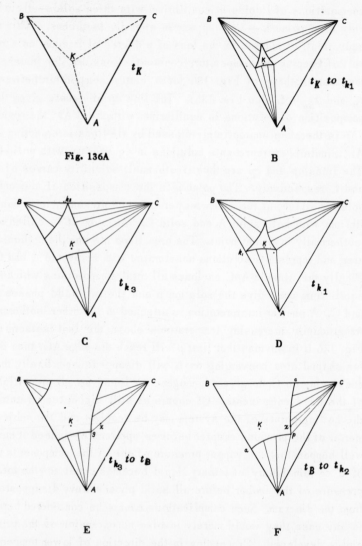

Fig. 136A

By sacrificing some of the information regarding the composition of the ternary solutions it is possible to secure a plane diagram which will give the temperature variations of the system.

Thus, by projecting perspectively the curves in Fig. 135 not on the base of the prism but on one of the faces, say the face BC of the prism,[3] a polythermal diagram is obtained which shows the *relative* proportions of the two components B and C in the different systems. The proportion of the component A in the different systems, however, will not be shown in this diagram; and the diagram will therefore not convey full information regarding the composition of the solutions.

We shall find it more instructive, however, to project Fig. 135 orthogonally on the base of the prism to give Fig. 137 which is

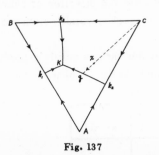

Fig. 137

lettered to correspond with Figs. 135 and 136. The line Kk_2 is, of course, the locus of p (Fig. 136). Suppose a melt of the composition x be cooled under equilibrium conditions. At the temperature at which the vertical line from x (Fig. 135) strikes one of the surfaces solid will begin to separate. In the present example this will occur at the temperature of the sixth isotherm of Fig. 136 and the solid appearing will be C, which in this case is called the *primary phase*, this being a term commonly used to denote the first solid to appear on cooling a liquid in an isoplethal process such as this. As cooling continues the composition of the residual liquid must move directly away from C and yet remain on the surface $t_C k_2 K k_3$ (Fig. 135), that is, it follows the linear extension of Cx towards q (Fig. 137). At a certain temperature (for example, that of the fifth isotherm of Fig. 136) x lies on the edge of the isothermally invariant triangle and in the meantime the composition of the liquid has moved to q (Fig. 137). By still further cooling solid A as well as solid C must now separate, for x becomes enclosed by the isothermally invariant triangle. At the same time, the liquid composition leaves q and alters its course in order to remain on $k_2 K$, a condition demanded by the presence of both solid A and C. Eventually the temperature of K is reached at which what liquid there is left solidifies completely to give the ternary eutectic mixture of A, B and C. While this occurs the temperature must, of course, remain constant for the system is invariant.

The cooling of any other ternary melt can be treated similarly. For instance if the prolongation of Cx in Fig. 137 had intersected k_3K instead of k_2K solid B would have been the second solid to appear. It can be seen that the final point of crystallisation will always be K even though the order of appearance of the various solids may differ. These facts are conveyed by the arrows in the figure; they are commonly used to denote the direction of change of composition of residual liquids in such crystallisation processes.

The calculation of the amounts of the various solids deposited in such a crystallisation can be illustrated by a simple example. Let the compositions of x, q and K be as follows:

	Wt. %A	Wt. %B	Wt. %C
x	25	15	60
q	33.3	20	46.7
K	30	50	20

Suppose that 100 g. of a melt of composition x be gradually cooled and that u be the weight of C deposited from x to q. Of the original 60 g. of C there is now left in solution $(60-u)$g. of C, but all of the original 15g. of B. Therefore, in the liquid at q, Wt. C : Wt. B : : $(60-u)$: 15 and this ratio equals 46.7 : 20 from the known composition of q. Solving gives $u = 25$ g. of C deposited by the time q is reached. The residual solution at q thus contains 25 g. of A, 15 g. of B and $(60-25 = 35)$g. of C. By similar reasoning, if, from q to K, an additional v g. of C and a quantity w g. of A are deposited we find v and w from the following equations which are valid at K:

$$\text{Wt. } C : \text{Wt. } B : : 20 : 50 : : (35 - v) : 15$$
and $$\text{Wt. } A : \text{Wt. } B : : 30 : 50 : : (25 - w) : 15$$

Solving gives $v = 29$ g. of C and $w = 16$ g. of A deposited. Therefore the residual solution consists of $(25-16 = 9)$g. of A, 15 g. of B and $(35-29 = 6)$g. of C, and, of course, these are the amounts of the solid components which K gives on complete solidification.

An example of the above type is the system[4] sodium nitrate (A)—lithium nitrate (B)—potassium nitrate (C), except that here $t_K < t_{k_3} < t_{k_1} < t_{k_2} < t_B < t_A < t_C$. In the field of metallurgy we may cite the system[5] lead—tin—bismuth as an approximate example. It may here be noted that metal systems usually involve complicated types of behaviour and are therefore rarely satisfactory for use as illustrations in a work of this kind.

II. A Congruently Melting Binary Compound Can Form.

In the example just discussed, the components crystallised out from solution in the pure state. If, however, combination can take place between two of the components to form a congruently melting compound the relationships will be somewhat different; the curves which are obtained in such a case may be as represented in Fig. 138. From the figure we see that the two components B and C form a compound of melting-point D, and the freezing point curve of the binary system has therefore the form shown in Fig. 38 (p. 135). Further, there are two *ternary* eutectic points, K_1 and K_2, the solid phases present being A, B, and compound, and A, C, and compound respectively. It is to be noted that D′ is the maximum temperature of the curve $K_1 D K_2$ just as D is the maximum of the curve $k_3 D k_4$, and furthermore that D, D′ and A are all in the same vertical plane. This may be shown qualitatively by regarding the system A-B-C as being comprised of the two "sub-systems" A-compound-B and A-compound-C by cutting the solid model in two by a vertical plane through both D and A. The point D′ is now the binary eutectic of compound and A, and, since the addition of either B or C to this latter system must lower this eutectic temperature, D′ is obviously at the maximum temperature in the curve $K_1 D′ K_2$.[6]

The salient features of such a system can be indicated by projecting Fig. 138 on the base of the prism to give Fig. 139 which is lettered to correspond. The arrows denote the direction of movement of the composition of residual liquid during crystallisation in

the cooling of a melt. There are now four possible primary phases.
The triangles ABD and ACD are called composition triangles, a
term applied in the study of ternary systems to the triangles formed
by the lines or "joins" connecting the points representing the
composition of any three primary phases whose liquidus surfaces
meet at a point.

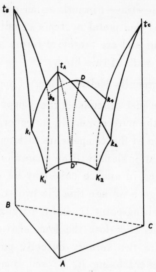

Fig. 138

To trace the path of crystallisation we apply the ideas developed above. For instance a melt of composition x will first throw
down solid C and the liquid composition will move to y at which
point both compound and C are thrown down simultaneously while
the liquid moves to K_2. At K_2 the residual liquid deposits all three
solids (compound, C and A) and itself remains constant in composition and temperature. Similarly a melt lying originally in BDA
will solidify to give a mixture of compound, B and A, and the last
liquid to solidify will have the composition K_1. There are thus
two "end points" to the liquid compositions, the composition of
the original melt determining which of the two is reached. An
example of this type is to be found in the system sodium chloride-

sodium sulphate-sodium fluoride[7] which forms the congruently melting compound Na_3SO_4F.

Consider, now, another possible type which will arise when, in Fig. 138, the imaginary plane through D and the edge of the prism at A cuts k_2K_2 and k_4K_2 instead of K_2K_1. Fig. 140 shows the corresponding projection. The line K_2K_1 now has no temperature maximum for reasons to be described later, and therefore in passing along the curves $k_2K_2K_1$ one is always moving in the direction of lower temperature. It follows that while K_1 is still a ternary eutectic, K_2 is now a *ternary peritectic*, the term given to an invariant point in a ternary system where the phase reaction is $L + S_1 \rightarrow S_2 + S_3$ on withdrawal of heat. In this case the general equation becomes $L + S_C \rightarrow S_A + S_D$. The point K_2 could not be a ternary eutectic because this would require a liquid of composition K_2 to produce, on cooling, a mixture of A, D and C (for it lies at the junction of the fields for these solids), and this, in turn, would require K_2 to lie within the composition triangle ADC, which is not the case. Finally, it should be pointed out that the system A-D is not a real binary system for the line AD cuts across the field for a substance foreign to A and D, namely C.

Let us now examine in detail the crystallisation of melts in

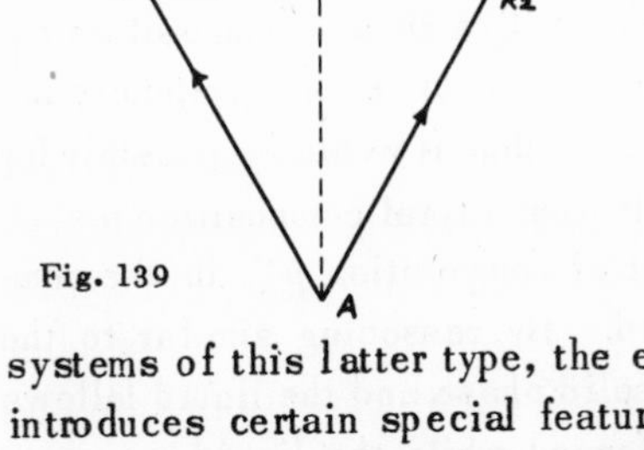

Fig. 139 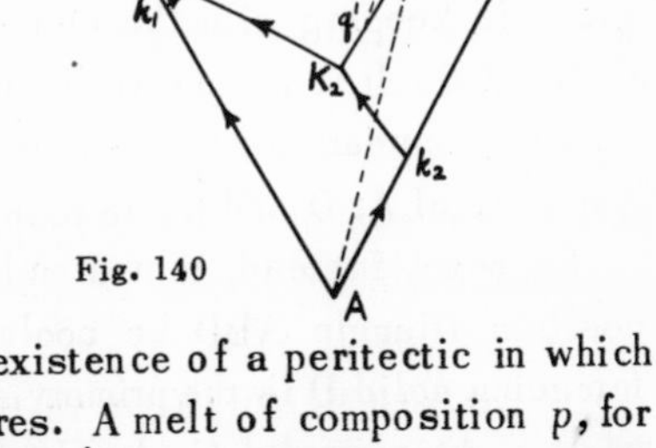   Fig. 140

systems of this latter type, the existence of a peritectic in which introduces certain special features. A melt of composition p, for instance, will first deposit solid C for p lies within the field for C. Deposition of C will leave the liquid poorer in C and the melt therefore moves away from C along the prolongation of Cp to q.

As q is on the line for liquids in equilibrium with solid D as well as C, solid D must begin to form at this point. The liquid composition therefore follows qK_2 while deposition of D and more C occurs. At any instant during the process the mean composition of the solid being formed from a given liquid can be found by drawing the tangent to k_4K_2 at the point representing the composition of that liquid; for example the liquid at n deposits a mixture of solids of composition x, the relative amounts of C and D in this mixture being given, of course by the ratio of Dx to xC. Similarly at any instant during the process the mean composition of the total solid deposited since the beginning of crystallisation can be found by joining the liquid composition to the total composition and producing the line. Thus by the time the liquid has reached n the mean composition of the total solid deposited thus far is given by y. Eventually the liquid composition reaches K_2 when solid A must appear. Solid A, C and D cannot form simultaneously at this point, however, for it is not an eutectic; the only alternative is for some of C to redissolve and react with the liquid to give A and D, the temperature remaining constant meanwhile. To check that this is at least possible mathematically we note that the straight line joining the resultant phases (A and D) crosses that joining the reactant phases (C and K_2). (Exercise: Show that if two phases are formed from two other phases it is a necessary condition that the straight lines joining the pairs of compositions cross[8].) It is to be noted that in this last stage the liquid will be used up before all of C has disappeared and we shall be left with a solid mixture of A, C and D in keeping with the fact that p lies in the composition triangle ACD. It is not possible for all of C to redissolve before the liquid disappears for that would mean that it would be possible for a mixture of A, D and K_2 to result from a total composition p.

Suppose, instead, that a melt of composition p', in the composition triangle ABD be cooled. By reasoning similar to the foregoing solid D is the primary solid phase and the liquid follows $p'q'$. At q' solid C also is formed while the liquid moves to K_2. At the peritectic K_2 C redissolves and reacts with liquid K_2 to form A and more D while the temperature remains constant. This time, however, C disappears before liquid K_2, for p' lies within the triangle ABD. When C has disappeared there are only three phases left so that the temperature is free to drop, the liquid following K_2K_1, meanwhile depositing more A and D. When K_1 is reached the temperature halts and the residual liquid solidifies to give the eutectic mixture of A, B and D.

III. A Congruently Melting Ternary Compound Can Form.

A compound formed from all three components is said to be congruently melting when it melts to give a liquid of the same composition as itself. The meaning is therefore analogous to that of a congruently melting binary compound (cf. page 144). The analogy can be carried further in that such a melting-point is always a maximum temperature for a given pressure, but the maximum is the maximum temperature of a surface rather than of a curve as it is in binary systems.

For systems of this type involving no additional complications the isobaric prism will consist of four surfaces, viz. the three of Fig. 135 (p. 315) with the addition of a dome-shaped surface lying entirely within the model giving the composition of liquids in equilibrium with the ternary compound. The temperature and composition of the maximum in this dome-shaped surface correspond respectively to the melting-point and composition of the compound. As the melting-point is at the maximum temperature on this surface addition of any of the three components to the molten compound will lower its freezing-point. The intersection of the dome-shaped surface with the other three surfaces forms curves giving liquids in equilibrium with two solids, and these curves in turn intersect at points, signifying liquid compositions in equilibrium with three solids.

Fig.141 is a projection of such a prism where D is the composition of the ternary compound, k_1, k_2, k_3 are binary eutectics and K_1, K_2, K_3 are ternary eutectics. The three solid phases coexisting with liquid at any of the ternary eutectics are, of course, those of the adjacent fields; for example, liquid of composition K_1 is in equilibrium with the solids A, B and compound. The lines for compound and component, viz. K_1K_2, K_1K_3 and K_3K_2 must all pass through a maximum temperature and these maximum temperatures must be at their intersections with the straight lines joining D to A, B and C respectively. Thus A ′, the intersection of K_1K_2 and AD is the maximum temperature on K_1K_2, C is the maximum temperature on K_2K_3 *etc.* This is readily seen when it is realized that the points A′, B′ and C′ are, in fact, binary eutectics in the respective sub-systems A-compound, B-compound, C-compound, and since addition of a third substance to the solution must lower the temperature of such eutectics the latter must be at temperature maxima. The arrows of the figure have the significance described previously, and it is seen that there are three possible end points in the solidification of ternary melts, viz., K_1, K_2 and K_3.

IV. An Incongruently Melting Binary Compound Can Form.

If two of the three components form an incongruently melting compound one of the faces of the ternary prism will be of the type shown in Fig. 42 (p. 149). The solid model will consist of four surfaces as in Fig. 138 with the important difference that k_3k_4 will not pass through a (stable) maximum temperature. If, for example, k_4 is the melting-point of the incongruently melting compound of B and C (a binary peritectic), k_3 will be the eutectic for this compound with component B, and will therefore always lie at a lower temperature than k_4. Addition of A to the binary system B-C will lower both the transition point k_4 and the eutectic point k_3 to K_2 and K_1 respectively.

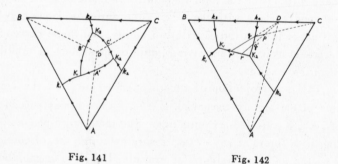

Fig. 141   Fig. 142

Consider two cases illustrated by projecting such a solid model onto the base in the usual way. In the one we have Fig. 142, where the line joining D, the composition of the incongruently melting compound, to A does not intersect K_1K_2 and in the other, Fig. 143, where it not only intersects K_1K_2 but also intersects k_4K_2. The arrows, as usual, point to lower temperatures. In Fig. 142 K_1 is a ternary eutectic but K_2 is a ternary peritectic. In Fig. 143 both K_1 and K_2 are ternary eutectics and D′ is at a maximum temperature for the line K_1K_2. We may show this qualitatively by imagining that a melt of composition m be cooled. As m is on the line separating the fields for compound and A it must yield these two solids. Now if the temperature of D be lower than that of K_2 (that is, if the arrow head between D and K be reversed so that D′ be not a maximum temperature) the liquid composition on cooling would pass in the direction of D′, say to some point n. In other words liquid m would have yielded n and two solids of composition D and A. Inasmuch as m lies outside the triangle DAn this is impossible (see p. 280). This and similar conclusions can be reached with the aid of the useful rule enunciated by Roozeboom[9], and sometimes referred to as the theorem of Alkemade, which enables one to predict readily whether a given univariant line, corresponding to equilibrium between a liquid and two solids in any such projection of a ternary liquid-solid system moves toward higher or lower temperatures in a given direction. According to this rule, for such univariant lines the temperature rises in the direction of the straight line which joins the points expressing the compositions of the solid phases belonging to that univariant line.

The crystallisation of melts of such systems should cause no real difficulty if the discussion of the previous types is thoroughly understood, but we shall use Fig. 142 to refer to another possible type of crystallisation. If the original melt has the composition p, solid, C will separate while the liquid moves from p to q. Then C will dissolve and D separate while the liquid follows qK_2, but the latter can never reach K_2 for that would mean the impossible situation of a total composition p giving the compositions K_2, C and D. The liquid composition will therefore follow

qK_2 only as far as q', the extension of Dp, during which time all of the solid C which separated initially returns to solution and some solid D separates. At q , therefore, we now have the liquid q' and solid D. As there is only one solid present the liquid need not now follow $q'K_2$; it will follow $q'r$, the extension of Dq', meanwhile depositing more D. At r solid A forms as well as D and the liquid must now follow rK_1. At K_1 the usual temperature halt is observed while the remaining liquid solidifies completely in depositing B, more A and more D.

Still other complications can arise when ,for instance, k_4K_2 in Fig. 142 is so strongly curved that tangents to it intersect CD instead of BD. This can give rise to the phenomenon of "recurrent crystallisation" in which a solid phase begins to separate, re-dissolves, and then separates again.[10]

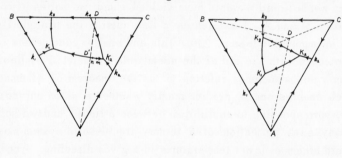

Fig. 143   Fig. 144

It must be emphasised that all the above discussion is applicable only when the total composition of the system remains constant during a given crystallisation. If, as is often the case in actual practice, certain solids are removed, either actually or effectively, from contact with the system as soon as they are formed, the phase changes are considerably altered. This is a matter of no small importance in considering, for instance, the crystallisation of magmas where gravitational and deformative forces are at work[11]. Suppose, for example, that, in the crystallisation of the melt p, Fig. 142, all of the solid C which had formed while the liquid moved to q was at this point removed from the liquid. This leaves a total composition q, so that further cooling will cause only separation of D while the liquid follows qr', the extension of Dq.[12]

V. An Incongruently Melting Ternary Compound Can Form.

When the incongruently melting compound comprises all three components the projection is typified by Fig. 144 where D is the composition of the compound and k_1, k_2, k_3 are binary eutectics. Here the point D must lie outside the field for liquids saturated with D, that is, outside of $K_1K_2K_3$. It is therefore evident that solid D can never be in stable equilibrium with a melt of the same composition——this is, of course, why it is designated as an incongruently melting compound. The direction of the arrows can readily be ascertained by applying the rule of Roozeboom (loc. cit.), and the course of crystallisation of various melts is treated in the same way as that described above.

VI. Binary Solid Solutions Can Form.

The formation of solid solutions has been excluded from all the above discussion, but in actual practice, particularly with metal systems, solid solution formation is of common occurrence. No discussion of solid-liquid equilibria would therefore be complete without at least a brief reference to it. As for ternary liquid systems a variety of types is found depending on how many pairs of the three components form solid solutions, whether such solid solutions comprise a complete or an incomplete series, and whether they show a minimum in the freezing-point curve. Of course, there may be compounds formed as well as solid solutions, but it is impossible to include all these types in the present work. We shall present only two types, the first of which is a system in which one pair of components forms a complete series of solid solutions the melting-points of which lie between those of the two components forming them.

Suppose that A, B and C are three components, that A and B, and A and C are not soluble in the solid state, but that B and C form a complete series of solid solutions the melting-points of which all lie between the melting-point of B and that of C. The systems A-B and A-C will therefore belong to the simple eutec-

tic type as illustrated in Fig. 38 (p. 135) and the system B-C will
belong to the type of Fig. 45 (I) (p. 159). A typical series of isothermal sections of the corresponding prism is shown in Figs. 145
to 148 in which k_1, k_2 are the two eutectics. Let us suppose,
also, that $t_{k_2} < t_C < t_{k_1} < t_A < t_B$. At temperatures below the lowest
temperature at which liquid can form we have Fig. 145 where all
proportions of the three components yield two solid phases, namely
A and a solid solution of B in C. In Fig. 146, slightly above t_{k_2},
the temperature of the lower of the two eutectics (k_2), a liquid
phase is possible giving two sets of isothermally univariant liquid-
solid equilibria (at constant pressure), namely, liquids on ap saturated with A and liquids on bp saturated with solid solutions of

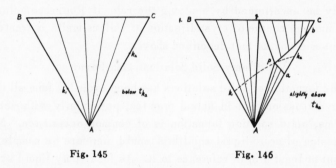

Fig. 145   Fig. 146

B in C (as far as q) as shown by the tie-lines. At the same time
the intersection of ap and bp at p gives a liquid which can exist
in contact with both solid A and solid solution q. The triangle
pqA is therefore isothermally invariant. Furthermore the area for
two solids has become reduced in size to ABq. When the temperature is raised to just above the melting-point of C (t_C) we
have Fig. 147. The point p is moving along k_2k_1 toward k_1, q
toward B and a toward A. At the same time the triangle pqA is
enlarging. Notice that solid solutions from q to s are in equilibrium with liquids p to l so that sl is actually a tie-line (corresponding, say, to dc of Fig. 46, p. 159). With rising temperature Fig.
148, corresponding to the temperature of k_1 is ultimately reached.
In the meantime the tie-line ls has lengthened (and, perhaps,

passed through a maximum length and begun to shorten again), Aq has become coincident with AB and (simultaneously) p has reached k_1. The line k_2k_1 is thus the locus of p, representing liquids saturated with A and solid solution. As the temperature is raised above t_{k_1} the univariant regions will diminish and eventually disappear, the lines lk_1 and ak_1 will no longer be coterminous and the tie-line ls will diminish to zero at the melting-point of B.

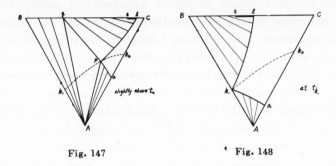

Fig. 147   ⁚ Fig. 148

The solid model of which Figs. 145 to 148 are the sections may now be visualised in part as two curved surfaces forming a trough along k_1k_2. We should, in fact, realise that there is considerable resemblance between this system and ternary liquid-vapour systems when two of the three liquid components are immiscible. This resemblance should be apparent by comparing the system under discussion with Fig. 128 (p. 309) and its isothermal sections (Figs. 129 to 133) modified to illustrate the case where C is *completely* immiscible in both B and A. For example, in Fig. 129 the bivariant areas marked L_1 and L_2 would be reduced to zero so that the two-liquid region would cover the entire triangle — corresponding modifications being made in Figs. 130 to 133.

Fig. 149 shows the projection of the solid model of which Figs. 145 to 148 are the isotherms. The crystallisation of melts in such systems introduces certain new aspects which have not arisen in the foregoing discussion. We shall illustrate by examining the crystallisation of a melt L_1, chosen to be within the area BCk_2k_1, under conditions such that equilibrium always obtains throughout the system. Solid will first appear when the temperature is lowered to that of the point where the vertical line dropped from L_1 in the solid model first strikes the surface for liquid saturated with solid solutions; in other words, to that of the isotherm in which L_1 lies on the curve for liquids in equilibrium with solid solutions of B in C. The solid will have some composition S_1. As the system is further cooled L_1 will fall within the univariant region for liquids saturated with solid solution and, according to the gradually altering direction of the tie-lines, the composition of the liquid will follow a curved path (initially directly away from S_1) toward L_2 while the solid will follow S_1S_2 to S_2, L_2S_2 being the tie-line at the new temperature. Notice that the path followed by the liquid during the crystallisation of the primary phase when the latter is a solid solution is not a straight line as it is when only a pure solid crystallises. At all times the line joining the two conjugate phases must, of course, pass through L_1, the total composition of the system. It must be understood that at any instant during this stage *all* of the solid phase has a

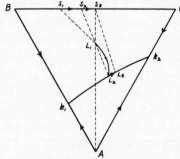

Fig. 149

single composition on S_1S_2. When the liquid has reached L_2 (and the solid has reached S_2) solid A must begin to form for L_2 is on k_1k_2 which denotes liquids saturated with respect to A as well as to solid solution. The liquid composition now follows k_1k_2 to k_2 with continued temperature lowering, de-

positing solid A and more solid solution of gradually altering composition along BC toward C. One might, at first sight, suppose that the liquid composition moves all the way to k_2, but a moment's consideration will show that this is not possible. By joining A to L_1 and producing the line to cut AB in S_3 it becomes apparent that when the total composition L_1 is completely solidified to a mixture of A and solid solution, the composition of the latter can be no richer in C than that represented by the point S_3. This, therefore, must be the last solid solution to be formed, and the liquid L_3, on the tie-line L_3S_3, must be the last liquid. In other words, the last drop of melt must have the composition L_3 and at that point crystallisation is complete. It is clear that the composition of the last liquid will depend on the original total composition—a fact which, as shown previously, is not always true when solid solutions are absent. An example of the type just described is the silicate system diopside (A)—anorthite (B)—albite (C)[13], in which, however, the eutectic in the system diopside-albite practically coincides with pure albite.

VII. Ternary Solid Solutions Can Form.

Just as two solids may under certain circumstances form a binary solid solution so also may three solids form a ternary solid solution—a homogeneous solid in which the concentration of all three components can be varied, often only within definite limits. They are thus completely analogous to ternary liquid solutions.

In considering ternary solid solutions we can again abbreviate our treatment by referring to the parallel which exists between the systems of this section and the ternary liquid-vapour equilibria of Chapter XV. Indeed much of the material there discussed can be transcribed to solid-liquid equilibria merely by replacing the words 'liquid' by 'solid', 'vapour' by 'liquid' and 'boiling-point' by 'melting-point' wherever they occur. This parallel results in an analogy between the phase changes occurring in a closed liquid-vapour system when the temperature is altered (as, for example, in the isoplethal changes described on p. 298) and those occurring in a solid-liquid system during melting or freezing. In practice, however, the slower attainment of equilibrium in solid-liquid systems gives rise to some differences. The student should be reminded, too, that whereas a binary maximum azeotropic boiling-point in liquid-vapour systems is of common occurrence the analogous maximum in solid-liquid systems is very rare (see p. 161).

To illustrate the parallel we observe that Fig. 113 (p. 297) represents essentially the phase relationships between solid and liquid when all three components are soluble in the solid (and liquid) state in all proportions. The temperatures t_A, t_B and t_C are thus the melting-points instead of the boiling-points of the respective components under the pressure of the diagram. (We have assumed also that none of the three component binaries exhibits a minimum in the melting curve).

In the same way Fig. 122 (p. 304) typifies a system of three solids (A, B, C) which are completely mutually soluble but in which there is a minimum in the melting-point curves for both of the component binaries A - B and A - C but not in the binary B - C. Such is the case in the system p-dichlorobenzene (A) — p-dibromobenzene (B) — p-chlorobromobenzene (C)[14].

VIII. Complex Types.

Many systems of great practical importance to the ceramist, glass technologist, geologist and metallographer show a phase behaviour which represents a combination of many of the foregoing types and the phase relations are often found to be most complex.[15] We shall now describe such a system.

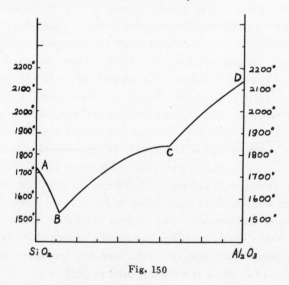

Fig. 150

The system CaO—Al_2O_3—SiO_2: The well-known product Portland cement, while containing appreciable quantities of the oxides of iron and magnesium, *etc.* can be considered as essentially comprising the oxides of calcium, aluminium and silicon. The importance of the study of the system CaO—Al_2O_3—SiO_2 will therefore be apparent, and it has received considerable attention.[16]

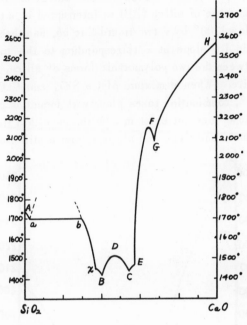

Fig. 151

The three components, calcium oxide, aluminium oxide, and silica, (the stable form of which at the melting-point is cristobalite), melt at 2570°, 2050°, and 1710° respectively. These components do not give rise to any solid solutions but form a number of binary and ternary compounds.

The freezing-point curves for the binary systems are shown in Figs. 150, 151 and 152. From Fig. 150 it will be seen that silica and alumina form only one compound, $Al_6Si_2O_{13}$ the incongruent melting-point of which, C, lies at 1810°. The eutectic B occurs at 1545°. The binary system silica—lime is more complex, there being formed at the temperature of the fusion curve (Fig. 151) three compounds $CaSiO_3$ (curve BDC), $Ca_3Si_2O_7$ (curve CE), and

Ca_2SiO_4[17] (curve EFG). The melting-point of $CaSiO_3$ (D) lies at 1540°, and that of Ca_2SiO_4 (F) at 2130° The compound $Ca_3Si_2O_7$ undergoes transition to Ca_2SiO_4 at 1475° (E). The eutectics B, C, and G lie at 1436°, 1455° and 2065° respectively. The melting curve of silica (AB) is interrupted at a temperature slightly below 1700° by a two-liquid line *ab*, and there is a discontinuity in its slope at x corresponding to the transition, at 1470°, between the two polymorphic forms of silica, cristobalite and tridymite. When a mixture of Ca_2SiO_4 and CaO is cooled below 1900°, combination takes place with formation of Ca_3SiO_5. This compound does not exist in equilibrium with a liquid phase. The two components lime and alumina form a still more complex

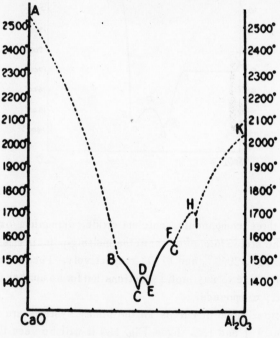

Fig. 152

system and give rise to four compounds stable in contact with a liquid phase. These compounds are $Ca_3Al_2O_6$, $Ca_5Al_6O_{14}$[18], $CaAl_2O_4$, and $Ca_3Al_{10}O_{18}$[19]. The first compound undergoes decom-

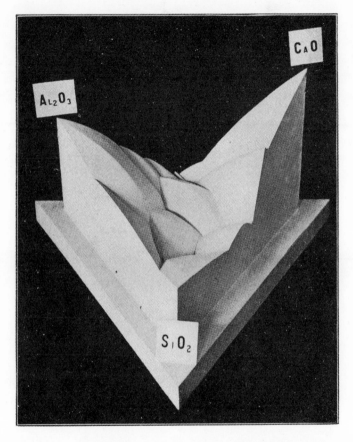

Fig. 153—Model of systems of CaO—Al_2O_3—SiO_2.

[*To face page* **336**.

position at 1535° (B, Fig. 152), a temperature below its melting-point. The compound $Ca_5Al_6O_{14}$ (D) melts at 1455°, the compound $CaAl_2O_4$ (F) at 1600°, and the compound $Ca_3Al_{10}O_{18}$ (H) at 1720°. The eutectics C, E, G and I lie at 1395°, 1400°, 1590° and 1700° respectively.

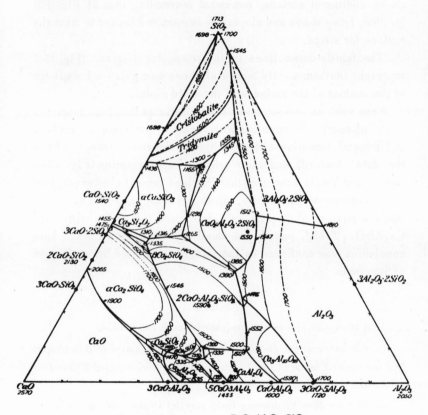

Fig. 154 — The system $CaO-Al_2O_x-SiO_2$.

For the representation of the ternary equilibria use may be made of the solid prismatic model, Fig. 153, and of the projection of the ternary curves on the base of the prism, Fig. 154[20]. Two ternary compounds have been obtained, both stable at the melting-point, and there are therefore two areas lying entirely within the prism or triangle. The stable ternary compounds are $CaAl_2Si_2O_8$ (anorthite), melting at $1550°$, and $Ca_2Al_2SiO_7$, melting at $1590°$. A third ternary compound, $Ca_3Al_2SiO_8$, is unstable at the melting-point and is not represented in the diagram or model. There is a small region of two liquids near the silica apex of Fig. 154, not shown in Fig. 153.[21] In the solid model this would appear as an additional surface, somewhat resembling that of Fig. 103 (p. 289), lying above and sloping downward and inward to meet the surface for silica.

The faintly-drawn lines in the triangular diagram (Fig. 154) represent isotherms. By means of these one gains a knowledge of the contour of the surfaces of the solid model.

From such an investigation of equilibria as that just described much information is obtained with regard to problems in petrology and mineral formation and the origin of igneous rocks.[22] From the data obtained, and their graphic representation (Fig. 154), Rankin and Wright concluded that Portland cement clinker prepared in the ordinary way from lime, silica and alumina, would be essentially a mixture of Ca_3SiO_5, Ca_2SiO_4, and $Ca_3Al_2O_6$ with some $Ca_5Al_6O_{14}$[23] and, possibly, a small amount of free CaO. This conclusion was confirmed by the work of the United States Bureau of Standards.

NOTES

1. A triangular plot is not adequate for such metathesis.

2. For an excellent discussion of the subject matter of this chapter see the special issue of the *J. Amer. Ceramic Soc.* entitled Phase Diagrams for Ceramists, November 1, 1947, Part II.

3. This is done by drawing lines parallel to the base of the prism, from the edge $t_A A$ to the face BC, and passing through the points on the different ternary curves.

4. Carveth, *J. Physical Chem.*, 1898, **2**, 209.

5. Mazzotto, *Z. Metallkde*, 1913, **4**, 273.

6. For a more extensive treatment of this and similar topics see, for example, Roozeboom, *Z. physikal. Chem.*, 1893, **12**, 359.

7. Wolters, *Neues Jahrb. f. Min. Geol. u. Pal. Beil.-Bd.*, 1910, **30**, 55.

8. This may be stated in another way: It is a necessary condition that the quadrilateral formed by joining the compositions of the four phases have no re-entrant angles.

9. Roozeboom, *Z. physikal. Chem.*, 1893, **12**, 359.

10. See Geer, *J. Phys. Chem.*, 1904, **8**, 257.

11. See Bowen, *The Evolution of Igneous Rocks*, Princeton University Press, 1928.

12. Geer, *loc. cit.*

13. Bowen, *Am. J. Sci.*, 4th Series, 1915, **40**, 161. See also Sahmen and von Vegesack, *Z. physikal. Chem.*, 1907, **59**, 257 for a description of other types of systems with solid solution.

14. Campbell and Prodan, *J. Amer. Chem. Soc.*, 1948, **70**, 553.

15. See, for instance, Jänecke, *Kurzgefasstes Handbuch Aller Legierungen*, Leipzig, 1937, and the special issue of the *J. Amer. Ceramic Soc.*, Nov. 1947, Part II.

16. Rankin and Wright, *Amer. J. Sci.*, 1915 (4), **39**, 1; Bowen and Greig, *J. Amer. Ceramic Soc.*, 1924, **7**, 238; Greig, *Amer. J. Sci.*, 1927 (5), **13**, 1; Bogue, *The Chemistry of Portland Cement*, Reinhold, 1947.

17. The compound Ca_2SiO_4 occurs in three polymorphic forms, α, β, and γ. The form stable at the melting-point is α.

18. The compound $Ca_5Al_6O_{14}$ may have the composition $Ca_{12}Al_{14}O_{33}$ (see Bussem and Eitel, *Z. Krist.*, 1936, **A 95**, 175 and Thorvaldson and Schneider, *Can. J. Res.*, 1941, **B 19**, 109).

19. The compound $Ca_3Al_{10}O_{18}$ may really be two compounds $(CaAl_4O_7$ and $Ca_3Al_{32}O_{51})$. See Lagerqvist, Wallmark and Westgren, *Z. anorg. allgem. Chem.*, 1937, **234**, 1.

20. J. W. Greig, *Amer. J. Sci.*, 1927 [5], **13**, 41.

21. The existence of two liquids in this system places it, strictly speaking, outside of the subject matter of this chapter (see p. 314).

22. Bowen, *J. Geol.*, 1915, **23**, Supplement; *ibid.*, 1917, **25**, 209.

23. See, however, the work of Bussen and Eitel (*loc. cit.*) and that of Thorvaldson and Schneider (*loc. cit.*).

CHAPTER XVII

AQUEOUS SYSTEMS

We are now to consider a special but very common case of the ternary solid-liquid equilibria described in the preceding chapter. This arises when one of the three components has a melting-point considerably below that of the other two, so that at ordinary temperatures it is molten and can therefore be regarded as solvent for the other two which are solids. Usually the molten component is water and the solid components are salts with a common ion.[1] We shall confine ourselves largely to such systems in this chapter.[2] It need hardly be said that the study of the relations of salts and water is a matter of not only theoretical but great practical importance.

As in the preceding chapter we shall require two dimensions in which to express the two independent concentration variables. The two dimensional diagram may have the form of an equilateral triangle, or it may be based on rectangular coordinates. Examples of both kinds will be found in the sequel. The pressure variable is usually ignored, for a change in pressure has a negligible effect on liquid-solid equilibria. If it is required to show the effect of change of temperature then a third axis is added at right angles to the plane of the concentration axes. Furthermore, as the salts are ordinarily involatile it is not necessary to show vapour compositions as all vapours will, of course, be pure water.

The equilateral triangle method of expressing concentrations has already been described in Chapter XIII. It suffices, therefore, to describe the method based on rectangular coordinates. A common way is to plot grams or moles of one salt in a fixed amount of water along the horizontal axis and grams or moles of the other salt in the same fixed amount of water along the vertical axis. The

340

fixed amount of water is often 100 grams or 1000 grams. A real weakness of this method of plotting is its inability to express any composition which does not contain water; for example, there is no point on the diagram which represents the composition of either of the pure anhydrous salts for these would be at an infinite distance from the origin along the rectangular axes. In other words such a plot has no limits, but for many purposes (see Chapter XVIII) it is quite adequate, and, indeed, to be preferred for purposes of certain calculations. In order to produce a plot which has finite boundaries one may, alternatively, plot grams of one salt in a fixed total weight of mixture against grams of the other salt in the same fixed total weight of mixture to give a right-angled isosceles triangle, but this procedure, suggested by Roozeboom,[3] is not widely used.

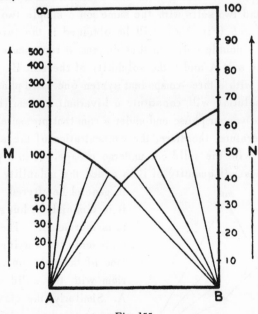

Fig. 155

Another method of representing the isothermal relations in a ternary system is to make use of the rectangular diagram due to Jänecke[4] (Fig. 155). In constructing this diagram the total salt is put equal to 100, and the amounts of the two salts, xA and

(100 -x) B, are measured off along the side AB of the rectangle.
The amount M of water in the solution associated with 100 parts
of total salt is measured upwards along the side of the rectangle.
Since, according to this method, M would become infinite for pure
water, it is better to represent the amount of water in the solution
by a number N the value of which is given by $N = 100M/100 + M$.
For pure water ($M = \infty$), N becomes equal to 100. It is possible,
by modifying this type of plot, to form a plane diagram which gives
a good general picture of the effect of change of temperature on
the system. This is accomplished by plotting temperature instead
of the amount of water on the vertical axis. Such a diagram will
not, of course, convey any information regarding water content.

I. The Anhydrous Salts are the Only Solids.

Where we are dealing with the equilibria between aqueous
solutions and two salts with the same ion a simple two branched
curve, *e.g. acb* (Fig. 156), will be obtained if the two salts do
not form any double salt. In this diagram *a* represents the solubility of the salt A and *b* the solubility of the salt B. Since we
are dealing with a three-component system one solid phase in contact with solution will constitute a bivariant system (in the absence of the vapour phase and under a constant pressure). At any
given temperature, therefore, the concentration of the solution in
equilibrium with the solid can undergo change. If to a pure solution of A a small quantity of B is added the solubility of A will

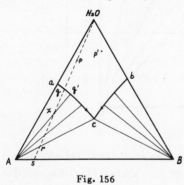

Fig. 156

in general be altered; as a rule
it is diminished, but sometimes
it is increased.[5] The curve *ac*
represents the varying composition of the solution in equilibrium with the solid component
A. Similarly, the curve *bc* represents the composition of the
solutions in contact with pure
B as solid phase.[6] At the point
c, where these two curves inter-
sect, there are two solid phases, viz. pure A and pure B, in equi-

librium with solution, and the system becomes isothermally (and isobarically) invariant. At this point the solution is saturated with respect to both A and B, and at a given temperature must have a perfectly definite composition.

A mixture of the three components having a total composition represented by a point x within the triangular area aAc will give rise to the heterogeneous system consisting of solid A and a saturated solution represented by the point on the saturation curve ac where the tie-line Ax cuts the curve ac. Similarly, mixtures having a total composition represented by a point in the area bBc will give rise to solid B and a saturated solution represented by a point on the curve bc. From this diagram, also, the relative amounts of solid phase and saturated solution formed can be obtained. Thus, in the case of the mixture x, the amount of saturated solution formed will be represented by the distance Ax, and the amount of solid phase deposited will be represented by the distance of x from the curve ac.

An equilibrium diagram of the type shown in Fig. 156 is given by the system $NaCl—KCl—H_2O$.[7]

The isothermal solubility curves are of great importance for obtaining an insight into the behaviour of a solution when subjected to isothermal evaporation. Suppose, for example, a solution of A and B of composition p is evaporated at the temperature of the isotherm under conditions such that equilibrium is maintained throughout the process. Loss of water by evaporation must cause the total composition to leave p and follow the prolongation of the line joining the water apex to p, namely $pqxrs$. When evaporation has been sufficient for the total composition to reach q the liquid is now saturated with respect to A and further evaporation causes solid A to separate. By the time the total composition has reached, say, x, the liquid composition will have moved to q', on the end of the tie-line through A and x. Similarly when the total composition has reached r the liquid composition has reached c, solid A always continuing to separate. Further evaporation causes the total composition to enter the isothermally invariant triangle AcB which means •that the liquid c will deposit B and more A simultaneously but must itself maintain constant composition. This state of affairs must obtain throughout the remainder of the evaporation, that is, until the total composition has reached s where all the water has evaporated. The last drop of liquid will therefore still have the composition c. In a similar manner the iso-thermal evaporation of a liquid p' would first deposit B and then both B and A when the liquid reaches c. The point c represents, therefore, the composition of the last drop of liquid before the system completely dries up. It is referred to as the *"drying up"* point. One need hardly say that even though c represents a solu-tion in equilibrium with two solids it is very far from being a eutectic point in spite of its slight resemblance to the eutectic of Fig. 38 (p. 135).

Let us now examine the effect of change of temperature on the general aspect of Fig. 156. Usually a drop in temperature will decrease the solubility of both A and B in water so that both a and b will move nearer to the water apex. The position of c will also alter accordingly. Indeed, this will become clear if the reader will refer to the last two isotherms shown in Fig. 136 (p. 318) and realise that we are at present dealing merely with a special case of the general type there shown; namely, that in which B (Fig. 136) corresponds to water and A and C to the two salts. The fifth isotherm of Fig. 136 would thus be at a temperature below the freezing-point of water so that the fan-shaped area at B denotes liquids in equilibrium with ice.

The familiar operation of purification of solids by recrystallisa-tion can often be interpreted in the light of Fig. 156. We shall assume that the solid to be obtained is denoted by A, that water is the solvent to be used, that the (one and only) soluble impurity to be removed is denoted by B and that the phase relations between A, B and solvent are of the type shown in Fig. 156. Let the orig-inal mixture of A contaminated with B be denoted by s. Solvent (water) is added to bring the total composition to x. The tempera-ture is now raised to the point where a, b and c have altered their positions so as to leave x in the bivariant, unsaturated liquid area. In other words, at this higher temperature the original solid has dissolved, except for any insoluble impurities. The latter are now filtered off and the solution is cooled, say to the original temperature represented by Fig. 156. From the location of x it is obvious that only solid A will separate, all of the original B being retained in the mother liquor q. Finally, by filtering, the required pure A is obtained. The small amount of mother liquor adhering to the solid, and which contains an even smaller amount of the impurity B, may then be removed by blotting or centrifuging. It might be pointed out that *theoretically* purification could have been effected merely by thorough stirring of the original mixture x without raising the temperature if insoluble impurities had not been present. In practice, however, one cannot be sure that thorough stirring of the complex x will result in all of the impurity B being retained by the liquid phase q. One should also remember that if A forms a compound or solid solution with the impurity purification may not be nearly so simple a process.

II. Binary or Ternary Compounds are Formed.

If either A or B or both A and B form compounds (hydrates) with the solvent the general character of the isotherm is not greatly different from Fig. 156. Thus, in Fig. 157, A forms a hydrate of composition D, and ac is the (isothermal) solubility curve of D, bc that of B. In Fig. 158 both A and B form the hydrates D and

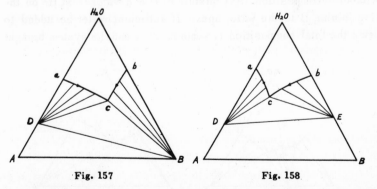

Fig. 157   Fig. 158

E respectively, of which ac and bc are the respective solubility curves. The triangles DcB in Fig. 157 and DcE in Fig. 158 denote isothermally invariant, three-phase equilibria (liquid c in equilibrium with two solids). The system $NaCl-Na_2SO_4-H_2O$ at $15°$[8] is of the type shown in Fig. 157, there being a hydrate of the composition $Na_2SO_4 \cdot 10H_2O$; the system $CaCl_2-MgCl_2-H_2O$ at $0°$[9] is of the type shown in Fig. 158 where the hydrates are $CaCl_2 \cdot 6H_2O$ and $MgCl_2 \cdot 6H_2O$.

When the two components, A and B, can form a compound, the isothermal diagram will exhibit three curves, such as $ac, cc', c'b$ (Fig. 159), c and c' representing solutions which are in equilibrium with pure A and double salt, and pure B and double salt respectively. The composition of the anhydrous double salt is represented by the point D on the side of the triangle AB.[10]

If the line joining the point D with the angle of the triangle representing pure water cuts the curve cc' for the double salt (as in Fig. 159), then the double salt will be stable and will dissolve in water without undergoing decomposition (see *infra*, p. 347); the compound D is then said to be "congruently saturating".[11] But if the line joining D with the opposite angle of the triangle cuts the curve for one of the single salts, then the double salt on being brought into contact with water will undergo decomposition with deposition of the single salt; the compound is then said to be "incongruently saturating",

Returning to Fig. 159 we can see why D will dissolve in water without decomposition. Any mixture of D and water must lie on the line joining D to the water apex. If sufficient water be added to bring the total composition to some point x and the system brought

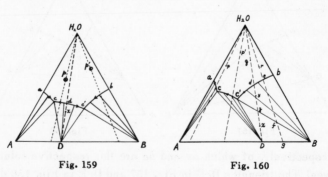

Fig. 159   Fig. 160

to equilibrium, it is obvious that since we are within the area for liquids saturated with D some of the D will remain undissolved and there will be *no other solid phase* present. In other words the D that has dissolved has done so without decomposition, at least without decomposing to form a new solid phase. It will always be possible to do this if, as stated above, the line joining D to the water apex cuts cc'. The point of intersection d is, in fact, the (stable) solubility of D in water.

It is seen from the foregoing that the system $D-H_2O$ is a stable one, and we can regard the system $A-B-H_2O$ as comprised of the two sub-systems $A-D-H_2O$ and $B-D-H_2O$. In this way one can predict the results of the isothermal evaporation of various solutions by applying the discussion on p. 343 for the isothermal evaporation of systems of the type shown in Fig. 156 to both sub-systems. Thus evaporation of the liquid p, Fig. 159, will first deposit D and then dry up at c in depositing both D and A. Similarly evaporation of the liquid p' will give B then both B and D while drying up at c' There are, therefore, two drying up points, c and c', for the entire system at the temperature of the isotherm.

Consider, on the other hand, Fig. 160. Clearly, addition of water to D can never give a complex lying within the area for liquids saturated only with D. If only enough water is added to give a total composition x, some of D must not merely dissolve but must decompose to form some solid B, and liquid saturated with these two solids must have the composition c', for x lies within the isothermally invariant triangle $Dc'B$. If enough water is added to bring the complex to y then all of the original D must dissolve and the only solid present will be B. Obviously, then, if not too great a quantity of water is added to D (not enough to produce an unsaturated solution by bringing the complex into the area $acc'\, b\overline{H_2O}$) solid B will always be formed by decomposition of D. Hence the term "incongruently saturating" used to describe D.

We are now in a position to describe the isothermal evaporation of liquids in systems of this type. Evaporation of solution p will first deposit A and then both A and D when the solution composition reaches c. Similarly evaporation of the solution p' will deposit D and then both D and A. Certain complexities arise, however, when we begin with a liquid such as q. The phase changes will be the reverse of those described in the preceding paragraph: B will separate when the composition reaches d and will increase in amount while the liquid composition follows the solubility curve to c'. At this point the quantities of liquid and B will be in the ratio of zB to $c'z$. Continued evaporation, bringing the complex, say, to x causes the quantity of liquid to diminish, but its concentration to remain constant at c', while D separates and B gradually dissolves. By the time B has disappeared the total composition has reached D and the last drop of liquid, still of composition c', has dried up. The point c' is, of course, not a peritectic point or a transition point in spite of the fact that it may involve, as just described, a disappearance of one, and the appearance of another, solid. (We can check the feasibility of this latter process by the fact that the line joining the compositions of the reactant phases (Bc') crosses that joining the compositions of the phases produced $(D-\overline{H_2O})$, the water lost by evaporation being regarded as a separate phase, $cf.$ p. 324.)

If we evaporate isothermally a liquid of composition r the above description requires modification. When the total composition reaches e solid B begins to form and continues to do so while the liquid moves to c'. As the complex passes from f to g some of B redissolves and D separates leaving at g a solid mixture of D and B as the last drop of liquid c' dries up. (Check: Bc' intersects $g-\overline{H_2O}$).

It is evident from the foregoing that systems of the type of Figs. 159 and 160 have two "drying up points" depending on the composition of the original liquid.

We have used the terms "congruently" and "incongruently saturating" above in connection with solids, but one commonly speaks somewhat analogously of "congruently" and "incongruently saturated solutions". These terms were first introduced by Meyerhoffer[12]. A "congruently saturated solution"[13] is one from which the solid phases are continuously deposited during isothermal evaporation to dryness. This means that such solutions can be prepared by mixing, in appropriate proportions, solvent and the solid phase or phases with which the solution is in equilibrium. Thus solutions *a, c, d, c'* and *b* in Fig. 159, and solutions *a, c* and *b* in Fig. 160, are congruently saturated. An "incongruently saturated solution", on the other hand, is a solution during the isothermal evaporation of which (in the presence of the solid phases with which it is in equilibrium), at least one of the solids disappears. Solution *c'* of Fig. 160 is thus incongruently saturated. We may here point out that an incongruently saturated solution, as here defined, is not, as one might expect, the exact converse of a congruently saturated one, for this would require the former to mean solely a solution which cannot be prepared by mixing solvent and the solid phases with which it is in equilibrium. While this is a necessary condition for an incongruently saturated solution it is not a sufficient one — if it were a sufficient one all solutions along *ac, cc'* or *bc'* in Fig. 159, except solutions *a, c, d, c'* and *b*, would be incongruently saturated, but the term is not ordinarily employed in this sense. Further it may be noted that whereas the idea of evaporation to dryness is inherent in the definition of congruently saturated solution it is not in incongruently saturated solution, for an incongruently saturated solution, such as *c'* in Fig. 160, may or may not remain incongruently saturated as evaporation is continued to dryness, depending on the total composition of the original system.

It should be borne in mind that in all of the evaporation processes so far described only water is assumed to be removed from the system. If, however, one of the salts, say the first one deposited, be removed from the system as soon as formed, the subsequent phase changes may be quite different. (Exercise: In the evaporation of the liquid *r* (Fig. 160) what would be the effect of filtering off all the solid B which had been deposited up to the time the complex had reached *f*, and continuing the evaporation of the filtrate?)

The system $NH_4NO_3 - AgNO_3 - H_2O$ at $30°$[14] is of the type shown in Fig. 159 for the double salt $NH_4NO_3 \cdot AgNO_3$ is formed and it is congruently saturating. On the other hand in the system

KNO_3—$AgNO_3$—H_2O at $30°$[15] there is the double salt $KAg(NO_3)_2$ which is incongruently saturating, and the system follows the type of Fig. 160.

Sometimes, as in the system Na_2SO_4—$(NH_4)_2SO_4$—H_2O[16] at $35°$, the double salt is a ternary compound, *i.e.*, it is hydrated, while the component salts remain anhydrous, but more commonly at least one of the component salts is hydrated when the double salt is hydrated. Such a type is shown in the isotherm Fig. 161 where not only does one of the component salts form a stable hydrate (D) at the given temperature (as in Fig. 157) but also a ternary compound of composition E (hydrated double salt) is formed. Again it is seen that the three saturating solid phases have their own solubility curves. As before the compound D is congruently saturating when the line joining its composition to the water apex cuts its solubility curve cc'. Total compositions within the triangles DcE and $Ec'B$ give liquid c, solids D and E, and liquid c', solids E and B respectively. The triangles DEB and ADB represent three-solid mixtures. An example of this type is the system Tl_2SO_4—$Al_2(SO_4)_3$—H_2O at $25°$[17] where $Al_2(SO_4)_3$ forms the hydrate $Al_2(SO_4)_3 \cdot 17H_2O$ and there is a hydrated double salt (alum) $TlAl(SO_4)_2 \cdot 12H_2O$.

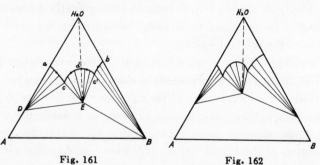

Fig. 161   Fig. 162

Fig. 162 shows another common type in which are found hydrates of both component salts as well as of the double salt, each with its own solubility curve. The system $FeSO_4$—$Al_2(SO_4)_3$—H_2O at $25°$[18] is of this type.

Finally, it should be stated that frequently several compounds, both binary and ternary, are found. Opportunity for examining such types will be found later in this chapter.

III. Transition Point and Transition Interval.

As is very well known, there exist a number of hydrated salts which, on being heated, undergo apparent partial fusion; and in Chapter VIII the behaviour of such hydrates was more fully studied in the light of the Phase Rule. Glauber's salt, or sodium sulphate decahydrate, for example, on being heated to a temperature of about 32.5°, partially liquefies, owing to the fact that the water of crystallisation is split off and anhydrous sodium sulphate formed, as shown by the equation

$$Na_2SO_4, 10H_2O \rightleftharpoons Na_2SO_4 + 10H_2O;$$

the water on the right then dissolving some of the sodium sulphate to form a saturated solution. The temperature of 32.5°, it was learned, constitutes a *transition point* for the decahydrate and anhydrous salt plus water; decomposition of the hydrated salt occurring above this temperature, combination of the anhydrous salt and water below it.

Analogous phenomena are met with in systems constituted of two salts and water in which the formation of double salts can take place. Thus, for example, if *d*-sodium potassium tartrate is heated to above 55°, apparent partial fusion occurs, and the two single salts, *d*-sodium tartrate and *d*-potassium tartrate, are deposited, the change which occurs being represented by the equation

$$4NaKC_4O_6H_4, 4H_2O \rightleftharpoons 2Na_2C_4O_6H_4, 2H_2O + 2K_2C_4O_6H_4, \frac{1}{2}H_2O$$
$$+ 11H_2O,$$

where, again, the water produced forms a solution. We can generalise this phase reaction, as we did in the analogous two-component case (p. 151), by the equation

$$S_{12} \rightleftharpoons S_1 + S_2 + L,$$

where S_1 and S_2 stand for the salts which form the double salt S_{12}, and L is the resulting saturated solution. On the other hand, if sodium and potassium tartrates are mixed with water in the proportions shown on the right side of the equation, the system will remain partially liquid so long as the temperature is main-

tained above 55° (in a closed vessel to prevent loss of water),
but on allowing the temperature to fall below this point, complete solidification will ensue, owing to the formation of the hydrated double salt. Below 55°, therefore, the hydrated double
salt is the stable system, while above this temperature the two
single salts plus saturated solution are stable.[19] The decomposition of sodium potassium tartrate differs from that of Glauber's
salt in that *two* new solid phases are formed.

In the example of double-salt decomposition just mentioned
sufficient water was yielded to cause a partial liquefaction; but
other cases are known where this is not so. Thus, when copper
calcium acetate is heated to a temperature of 75°, although decomposition of the double salt into the two single salts occurs as
represented by the equation[20]

$$CuCa(C_2H_3O_2)_4, 8H_2O \rightleftharpoons Cu(C_2H_3O_2)_2, H_2O + Ca(C_2H_3O_2)_2, H_2O$$
$$+ 6H_2O,$$

that is, $S_{12} \rightleftharpoons S_1 + S_2 + L$ as before, the amount of water split off
is insufficient to give the appearance of partial fusion, and, there-
fore, only a change in the crystals is observed.

The preceding examples, in which decomposition of the double
salt was effected by a rise of temperature, were chosen for first
consideration as being more analogous to the case of Glauber's
salt; but not a few examples are known where the reverse change
takes place, formation of the double salt occurring *above* the transition point, and decomposition into the constituent salts below it.
Instances of this behaviour are found in the case of the formation
of astracanite from sodium and magnesium sulphates, and of sodium
ammonium racemate from the two sodium ammonium tartrates, to
which reference will be made later. Between these various systems, however, there is no essential difference; and whether decomposition or formation of the double salt occurs at temperatures
above the transition point will of course depend on the heat of
change at that point. For, in accordance with the principle of
LeChatelier (p. 22), that change will take place at the higher
temperature which is accompanied by an absorption of heat. If,
therefore, the formation of the double salt from the single salts

is accompanied by an absorption of heat, the double salt will be formed from the single salts on raising the temperature; but if the reverse is the case, then the double salt on being heated will decompose into the constituent salts.[21]

In those cases where the change at the transition point is accompanied by the taking up or the splitting off of water *the general rule can be given that if the water of crystallisation of the two constituent salts together is greater than that of the double salt the latter will be produced from the former on raising the temperature (e.g.* astracanite from sodium and magnesium sulphates); *but if the double salt contains more water of crystallisation than the two single salts raising the temperature will effect the decomposition of the double salt.* When we seek for the connection between this rule and the principle of LeChatelier, it is found in the fact that the heat effect involved in the hydration or dehydration of the salts is much greater than that of the other changes which occur, and determines, therefore, the sign of the total heat effect.

The preceding account may now be interpreted by means of triangular diagrams. Let us suppose, as with the double tartrate and double acetate cited above, that the double salt (D) which undergoes the transition, and the salts (E and F) into which it decomposes are all hydrated, that the double salt exists in equilibrium with solution below but not above the transition temperature, and that the composition of D can be expressed in terms of water and the two hydrates formed by its decomposition. In other words let us consider the type where the transition is of such a nature that the phase reaction is

$$S_{12} \rightleftharpoons S_1 + S_2 + L - \text{heat.}$$

At a temperature just above the transition temperature the isotherm may be as shown in Fig. 163 (*cf.* Fig. 158, p. 345). Notice that D lies within the triangle $EF\overline{H_2O}$, for we have assumed that D can be expressed in terms of E, F and H_2O. The solution c, saturated with respect to both E and F always lies, except by sheer coincidence[22] to one side of the line joining D to the water apex. At this temperature, according to our assumption that D cannot exist as a stable solid in contact with solution, a complex of the composition D, when brought to this temperature, must give solids E and F and liquid c. Let us now lower the temperature to just below the transition temperature to give, say, Fig. 164. It is now

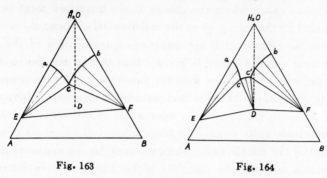

Fig. 163   Fig. 164

possible for D to exist in contact with solution and D will therefore have its own solubility curve cc'. In passing through the transition point, therefore, the three phases E, F and c, of total composition D, just referred to, will have combined to form solid D in accordance with the equation ·given above, or rather the reverse of it, for we are here considering a temperature change such as will form, not decompose, the double salt. It will be observed that D is now incongruently saturating, and that D can coexist with solid E and liquid c, or with solid F and liquid c'. At some still lower temperature it is now possible for the disposition of the solubility curves to alter so as to make D congruently saturating. This will occur when c' moves so as eventually to lie on D-$\overline{\text{H}_2\text{O}}$ as in Fig. 165. Continuing to lower the temperature will give an isotherm of the type of Fig. 162 (p. 350). *The range of temperature between that at which double salt can begin to be formed (the transition point) and that at which it ceases to be decomposed by water is called the transition interval.*[23]

In this example the transition interval extends downwards from the transition temperature; but many cases are known, such as those referred to on p. 352, where the transition interval extends upwards from the transition temperature. Indeed we shall later describe the system $(NH_4)_2SO_4$—Na_2SO_4—H_2O where there is found a double salt with both an upper *and* a lower transition interval.

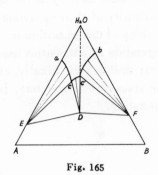

Fig. 165

One special case may here be noted: If the components A and B are optical antipodes and D represents a racemate then, inasmuch as A and B or their hydrates have identical solubilities, the isotherm corresponding to Fig. 163 will be symmetrical with respect to the line D-H$_2$O and *c* will lie *on* the latter. At the transition point where the racemate comes into existence the isotherm will still be symmetrical and therefore the solubility curve of D (*cc'*, Fig. 164) will be intersected symmetrically by D-H$_2$O. The racemate, therefore, will be congruently saturating as soon as it comes into existence and there will be *no* transition interval.

There is, however, another type of transition where the double salt, in decomposing, requires water to yield the two single salts. This is so for astracanite, Na$_2$Mg(SO$_4$)$_2$·4H$_2$O, which cannot yield its single salts Na$_2$SO$_4$·10H$_2$O and MgSO$_4$·7H$_2$O without acquiring water, according to the equation

Na$_2$Mg(SO$_4$)$_2$·4H$_2$O + 13H$_2$O $\rightleftharpoons$ Na$_2$SO$_4$·10H$_2$O + MgSO$_4$·7H$_2$O.

In general terms, then, the phase reaction at this transition point is

$$L + S_{12} \rightleftharpoons S_1 + S_2.$$

Graphically, such a situation arises when, in Fig. 163, the point D lies outside of the triangle E*c*F as in Fig. 166. This is for a temperature on the side of the transition point where E and F are stable and D unstable in contact with solution. It is to be noted that while D is unstable in contact with solution it can exist in the absence of liquid. Let us alter the temperature in the direction of the transition point. When the latter is reached all four phases, D, E, F and liquid can coexist. On the other side of the transition temperature we have Fig. 167 where D is now stable in contact with liquid but, as yet, it is incongruently saturating. Clearly, D can exist on both sides of the transition temperature but on only one side of it in contact with liquid. We shall have occasion to refer to this later. In view of the possibility of D being stable, under appropriate conditions, on both sides of the transition temperature, it is better to regard this temperature as a transition temperature of the system rather than of the double salt. Finally, at temperatures further removed from the transition temperature, D may, of course, become congruently saturating.

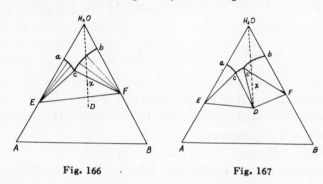

Fig. 166   Fig. 167

Solubility Curves at the Transition Point. At the transition point, as has already been shown, the double salt and the two constituent salts can exist in equilibrium with the same solution. The transition point, therefore, must be the point of intersection of two solubility curves:[24] the solubility curve of the double salt and the solubility curve of the mixtures of the two constituent salts. It should be noted here that we are not dealing with the solubility curves of the single salts separately, for since the systems are composed of three components, a single solid phase can, at a given temperature, be in equilibrium with solutions of different composition, and two solid phases in contact with solution (and vapour) are therefore necessary to give a univariant system. The same applies, of course, to the solubility of the double salt; for a double salt also constitutes a single phase, and can therefore exist in equilibrium with solutions of varying composition. If, however, we make the restriction (which we do for the present) that the double salt is not decomposed by water, then the solution will contain the constituent salts in the same relative proportions as they are contained in the double salt, and the system may therefore be regarded as one of *two* components, viz. double salt and water. In this case one solid phase is sufficient, with solution and vapour, to give a univariant system; and at a given temperature, therefore, the solubility will have a perfectly definite value.

Since in almost all cases the solubility is determined in open vessels, we shall in the following discussion consider that the vapour phase is absent, and that the system is under a constant pressure, that of the atmosphere. With this restriction, therefore, four phases will constitute an invariant system, three phases a univariant, and two phases a bivariant system.

It has already been learned that for sodium sulphate and water, the solubility curve of the salt undergoes a sudden change in direction at the transition point, and that this is accompanied by a change in the solid phase in equilibrium with the solution. The same behaviour is also found with double salts. To illustrate this, we shall briefly discuss the solubility relations of a few double salts, beginning with one of the simplest examples, that of the formation of rubidium racemate from rubidium *d*- and *l*-tartrates. The solubilities are represented diagrammatically in Fig. 168, the the numerical data being contained in the following table, in which the solubility is expressed as the number of gram-molecules $Rb_2C_4H_4O_6$ in 100 gm.-molecules of water:[25]

Temperature.	Solubility of tartrate mixture.	Solubility of racemate.
25°	13·03	10·91
35°	—	12·63
40·4°	—	13·48
40·7°	13·46	—
54°	13·83	—

In Fig. 168 the curve AB represents the solubility of the racemate, while A′BC represents the solubility of the mixed tartrates. The line AB represents, in fact, the variation with temperature of the concentration of a solution such as d (Fig. 161) and A´BC corresponds to the variation with temperature of the solution c (Fig. 163), it being remembered that for optical isomers c lies on D-H_2O and the isotherm is symmetrical.[26] Below the transi-

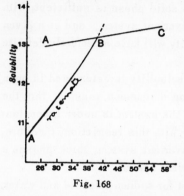

Fig. 168

tion point, therefore, the solubility of the racemate is less than that of the mixed tartrates. The solution, saturated with respect to the latter, will be supersaturated with respect to the racemate; and if a nucleus of this is present, racemate will be deposited, and the mixed tartrates, if present in equimolecular amounts, will ultimately entirely disappear, and only racemate will be left as solid phase. The solution will then have the composition represented by a point on the curve AB. Conversely, above the transition point, the saturated solution of the racemate would be supersaturated with respect to the two tartrates, and transformation into the latter would ensue. If, therefore, a solution of equimolecular proportions of rubidium d- and l-tartrates is allowed to evaporate at a temperature above 40° a mixture of the two tartrates will be deposited,[27] while at temperatures below 40° the racemate will separate out.

Similar relationships are met with in the case of sodium ammonium d- and l-tartrate and sodium ammonium racemate; but here the racemate is the stable form in contact with solution above the transition point (27°).[28] In the examples just described the solubility relationships at the transition point are of a simpler character than for most double salts as a consequence of the identical solubility of the two tartrates and the resulting zero transition interval. Very different, however, is the behaviour of, say, astracanite, or of the majority of double salts; for the solubility of the constituent salts is now no longer the same. If, for example, excess of a mixture of sodium sulphate and magnesium sulphate, in equimolecular proportions, is brought in contact with water below the transition point (22°), more magnesium sulphate than sodium sulphate will dissolve, but a solution saturated with both solids will result. This will be made clearer by referring to Figs. 166 and 167, where A may be taken as representing $MgSO_4$, B as Na_2SO_4, E as $MgSO_4 \cdot 7H_2O$, F as $Na_2SO_4 \cdot 10H_2O$, and D as astracanite $(Na_2Mg(SO_4)_2 \cdot 4H_2O)$. The total composition of the mixture just described corresponds to some point x in these diagrams. The composition of the resulting solution is given by the following figures, which express number of gm.-molecules of the salt in 100 gm.-molecules of water:[29]

COMPOSITION OF SOLUTIONS SATURATED WITH RESPECT TO
$Na_2SO_4, 10H_2O$ AND $MgSO_4, 7H_2O$ (point c, Fig. 166).

Temperature.	Na_2SO_4.	$MgSO_4$.
18·5°	2·16	4·57
24·5°	3·43	4·68

At the transition point, then, it is evident that the solution contains more magnesium sulphate than sodium sulphate; and this must still be the case when astracanite, which contains sodium sulphate and magnesium sulphate in equimolecular proportions, separates out. If, therefore, the temperature is raised slightly above the transition point, magnesium sulphate and sodium sulphate will pass into solution, the former, however, in larger quantities than the latter, and astracanite will be deposited; and this process will go on until all the magnesium sulphate has disappeared, and a mixture of astracanite and sodium sulphate decahydrate is left as solid phases. Since there are now three phases present, the system is univariant (by reason of the restriction previously made that the pressure is constant and the vapour phase is absent), and at a given temperature the solution will have a definite composition, as given in the following table, (p. 360).

From these figures, therefore, it will be seen that at a temperature just above the transition point a solution in contact with the two solid phases, astracanite and Glauber's salt, contains a relatively smaller amount of sodium sulphate than a pure solution of

COMPOSITION OF SOLUTION SATURATED WITH RESPECT TO
$Na_2Mg(SO_4)_2,4H_2O$ AND $Na_2SO_4,10H_2O$ (point c', Fig. 167).

Temperature.	Na_2SO_4.	$MgSO_4$.
22°	2·95	4·70
24·5°	3·45	3·62

astracanite would; for in this case there would be equal molecular
amounts of Na_2SO_4 and $MgSO_4$. A solution which is saturated
with respect to astracanite alone, will contain more sodium sulphate than the solution saturated with respect to astracanite plus
Glauber's salt, and the latter will therefore be deposited. From

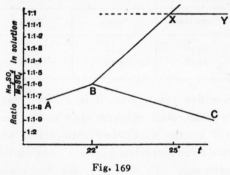

Fig. 169

this, therefore, it is clear that if excess of astracanite is brought
in contact with water at about the transition point, it will undergo decomposition with separation of Glauber's salt (supersaturation being excluded).

This will perhaps be made clearer by considering Fig. 169.
In this diagram the ordinates represent the ratio of sodium sulphate to magnesium sulphate in the solutions, and the abcissae
represent the temperatures. The line AB represents solutions
saturated with respect to a mixture of the single salts (p. 359);
BC refers to solutions in equilibrium with astracanite and magnesium sulphate; while BX represents the composition of solutions in contact with the solid phases astracanite and Glauber's
salt. The values of the solubility are contained in the following

table, and in that on p. 360, and are, as before, expressed in gm.-molecules of salt in 100 gm.-molecules of water:[30]

Temperature.	Astracanite + sodium sulphate.		Astracanite + magnesium sulphate.	
	Na_2SO_4.	$MgSO_4$.	Na_2SO_4.	$MgSO_4$.
18·5°	—	—	3·41	4·27
22°	2·95	4·70	2·85	4·63
24·5°	3·45	3·62	2·68	4·76
30°	4·58	2·91	2·30	5·31
35°	4·30	2·76	1·73	5·88

At the transition point the ratio of sodium sulphate to magnesium sulphate is approximately 1:1.6. In the case of solutions saturated with respect to both astracanite and Glauber's salt, the relative amount of sodium sulphate increases as the temperature rises, while in the solutions saturated for astracanite and magnesium sulphate, the ratio of sodium sulphate to magnesium sulphate decreases.

If we consider only the temperatures above the transition point we see from the figure that solutions represented by points above the line BX contain relatively more sodium sulphate than solutions in contact with astracanite and Glauber's salt; and solutions lying below the line BC contain relatively more magnesium sulphate than solutions saturated with this salt and astracanite. These solutions will therefore not be stable, but will deposit on the one hand, astracanite and Glauber's salt, and on the other hand, astracanite and magnesium sulphate, until a point on BX or BC is reached. All solutions, however, lying to the right of CBX, will be *unsaturated* with respect to these two pairs of salts, and only the solutions represented by the line XY (and which contain equimolecular amounts of sodium and magnesium sulphates) will be saturated with respect to the pure double salt.

IV. Presence of Vapour.

With Glauber's salt we saw that at a certain temperature the vapour pressure curve of the hydrated salt cuts that of the saturated solution of anhydrous sodium sulphate. That point, it will be remembered, is a quadruple point at which the four phases sodium sulphate decahydrate, anhydrous sodium sulphate, solution, and vapour, can coexist; and is also the point of intersection of the curves for four univariant systems. In the formation of double salts, similar relationships are met with; and also certain differences, for we are now dealing with systems of three components. Two examples will be chosen here for brief description, one in which formation, the other in which decomposition of the double salt occurs with rise of temperature.

On heating a mixture of sodium sulphate decahydrate and magnesium sulphate heptahydrate it is found that at 22° partial liquefaction occurs with formation of astracanite. At this temperature, therefore, there can coexist the five phases

$$Na_2SO_4,10H_2O; \quad MgSO_4,7H_2O; \quad Na_2Mg(SO_4)_2,4H_2O;$$
$$\text{solution; vapour.}$$

This constitutes, therefore, a *quintuple point*, which term we have had occasion to use before (p. 316) in connection with ternary eutectics. Since there are three components present in five phases the system is invariant. This point, also, will be the point of intersection of curves for five univariant systems, which must each be composed of four phases. These systems are:

I. $Na_2SO_4,10H_2O; \quad MgSO_4,7H_2O; \quad Na_2Mg(SO_4)_2,4H_2O; \quad$ vapour.

II. $Na_2SO_4,10H_2O; \quad MgSO_4,7H_2O; \quad$ solution; vapour.

III. $MgSO_4,7H_2O; \quad Na_2Mg(SO_4)_2,4H_2O; \quad$ solution; vapour.

IV. $Na_2SO_4,10H_2O; \quad Na_2Mg(SO_4)_2,4H_2O; \quad$ solution; vapour.

V. $Na_2SO_4,10H_2O; \quad MgSO_4,7H_2O; \quad Na_2Mg(SO_4)_2,4H_2O; \quad$ solution.

On representing the vapour pressures of these different systems graphically, a diagram is obtained such as is shown in Fig. 170,[31] the curves being numbered in accordance with the above list. When the system I is heated, the vapour pressure increases until at the quintuple point the liquid phase (solution) is formed, and it will then depend on the relative amounts of the different phases whether, on further heating, there is formed system III, IV, or V. If either of the first two is produced, we shall obtain the vapour pressure of the solutions saturated with respect to both double salt and one of the single salts; while if the vapour phase disappears, there will be obtained the pressure of the condensed system formed of double salt, two single salts and solution. This curve, therefore, indicates the *change of the transition point with pressure;* and since, in the ordinary determinations of the transition point in open vessels, we are in reality dealing with condensed systems under the pressure of 1 atm., it will be evident that the transition point does not accurately coincide with the quintuple point (at which the system is under the pressure of its own vapour). As with other condensed systems, however, pressure has only a relatively slight influence on the temperature of the transition point. Whether or not pressure raises or lowers the transition point will depend on whether transformation is accompanied by an increase or diminution of volume (principle of Le Chatelier, p. 22). In the formation of astracanite expansion occurs, and the transition point will therefore be raised by in-

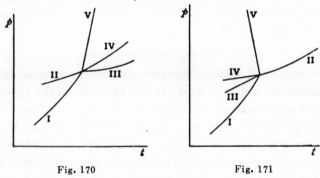

Fig. 170   Fig. 171

crease of pressure. Although measurements have not been made for this system the existence of such a curve has been experimentally verified for copper and calcium acetates and water (v. *infra*).[32]

The vapour pressure diagram for copper calcium acetate and water (Fig. 171), is almost the reverse of that already discussed, Here, the double salt decomposes on heating, and the decomposition is accompanied by a contraction. Curve I is the vapour pressure curve for double salt, two single salts (p. 352), and vapour; curves III and IV give the vapour pressures of solutions saturated with respect to double salt and one of the single salts; curve

II is the curve of pressures for the solutions saturated with respect to the two single salts; while curve V again represents the change of the transition point with pressure. On examining this diagram it is seen that whereas astracanite could exist both above and below the quintuple point, copper calcium acetate can exist only *below* the quintuple point. This behaviour is found only when the double salt is decomposed by rise of temperature, and where the decomposition is accompanied by a diminution of volume. [33]

As already mentioned, the decomposition of copper calcium acetate into the single salts and saturated solution is accompanied by a contraction, and it was therefore to be expected that increase of pressure would *lower* the transition point. This expectation of theory was confirmed by experiment, for van't Hoff and Spring found that although the transition point under atmospheric pressure is about 75°, decomposition of the double salt apparently took place even at the ordinary temperature when the pressure was increased to 6000 atm. [34]

V.   Rectangular Coordinates.

The method of plotting concentrations on rectangular coordinates described earlier (p. 340) may now be illustrated by considering types of isotherms for systems such as those used previously to illustrate the transition interval, *etc.*. We have already learned in the preceding chapter that if the temperature is outside[35] the transition interval, it is possible to prepare a pure saturated solution of the double salt. If we suppose the double salt to contain the two constituent salts in equimolecular proportions, its saturated solution must be represented by a point lying on the line which bisects the angle AOB, *e.g.* point D, Fig. 172. But a double salt constitutes only a single phase, and can exist, therefore, in contact with solutions of varying concentration, as represented by EDF.

Let us compare, now, the relations between the solubility curve for the double salt, and those for the two constituent salts. We shall suppose that the double salt is formed from the single salts when the temperature is raised above a certain point (as in the formation of astracanite). At a temperature below the transition point, as we have already seen, the solubility of the double salt is greater than that of a mixture of the single salts. The curve EDF, therefore, must lie above the point C, in the region representing solutions supersaturated with respect to the single salts (Fig. 173). Such a solution, however, would be metastable, and on being brought in contact with the single salts would deposit these and yield a solution represented by the point C. At this particular temperature, therefore, the isothermal solubility curve will consist of only two branches.

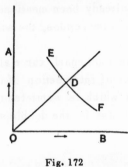

Fig. 172   Fig. 173

Suppose, now, that the temperature is that of the transition point. At this point, the double salt can exist together with the single salts in contact with solution. The solubility curve of the double salt must, therefore, pass through the point C, as shown in Fig. 174.

From this figure it is seen that a solution saturated with respect to double salt alone (point D), is supersaturated with respect to the component A. If, then, at the temperature of the transition point, excess of the double salt is brought in contact with water,[36] and if supersaturation is excluded, *the double salt will undergo decomposition and the component A will be deposited.* The relative concentration of the component B in the solution will, therefore, increase, and the composition of the solution will be thereby altered in the direction DC. When the solution has the composition of C, the single salt ceases to be deposited, for at this point the solution is saturated for both double and single salt; and the system becomes isothermally invariant.

This diagram explains very clearly the phenomenon of the decomposition of a double salt at the transition point. As is evident, this decomposition will occur when the solution which is saturated at the temperature of the transition point with respect to the two single salts (point C), does not contain these salts in the same ratio in which they are present in the double salt. If point C lay on the dotted line bisecting the right angle, then the pure saturated solution of the double salt would not be supersaturated with respect to either of the single salts, and the double salt would, therefore, not be decomposed by water. As has already been mentioned, this behaviour is found for optically active isomerides, the solubilities of which are identical.

At the transition point, therefore, the isothermal curve also consists of two branches; but the point of intersection of the two branches now represents a solution which is saturated not only with respect to the single salts, but also for the double salt in presence of the single salts.

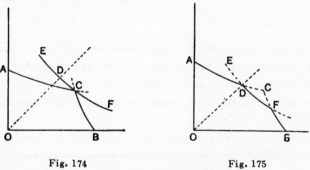

Fig. 174   Fig. 175

We have just seen that by a change of temperature the two solubility curves, that for the two single salts and that for the double salt, were made to approach each other (*cf.* Figs. 173 and 174). In the previous section, however, we found that on passing the transition point to the region of stability for the double salt, the solution which is saturated for a mixture of the two constituent salts is supersaturated for the double salt. Point C must lie, therefore, above the solubility curve of the pure double salt (Fig. 175), and a solution of the composition C, if brought in contact with double salt, will deposit the latter. If the single salts were also present, then as the double salt separated out, the single salts would pass into solution, because so long as the two single salts are present, the composition of the solution must remain unaltered. If one of the single salts disappear before the other, there will be left double salt plus A, or double salt plus B, according to which was in excess; and the composition of the solution will be either that represented by D (saturated for double salt plus A), or that of the point F (saturated for double salt plus B).

In connection with the isotherm represented in Fig. 175, it should be noted that at this particular temperature a solution saturated with respect to the pure double salt is no longer supersaturated for one of the single salts (point D); so that at the temperature of this isotherm the double salt is not decomposed by water. At this temperature, further, the boundary curve consists of three branches—AD, DF, and FB—which give the composition of the solutions in equilibrium with pure A, double salt, and pure B respectively; while the points D and F represent solutions saturated for double salt plus A and double salt plus B.

On continuing to alter the temperature in the same direction as before, the relative shifting of the solubility curves becomes more marked, as shown in Fig. 176. At the temperature of this isotherm the solution saturated for the double salt now lies in a region of distinct unsaturation with respect to the single salts, and the double salt can now exist as solid phase in contact with solutions containing both relatively more of A

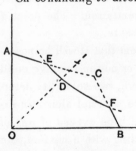

Fig. 176

(curve ED), and relatively more of B (curve DF), than is contained in the double salt itself.

From what has been said and from examination of the isothermal diagrams of Figs. 173 to 176 it will be seen that the transition interval is the temperature range between the temperature for Fig.

174 and that for Fig. 175.

Application to the Characterisation of Racemates. The form of the isothermal solubility curves is also of great value for determining whether an inactive substance is a racemate or a conglomerate of equal proportions of the optical antipodes.[37]

The formation of racemates from the two enantiomorphous isomerides is analogous to the formation of double salts. In Fig. 177 are given diagrammatically two isothermal solubility curves for

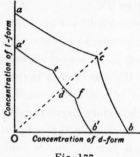

Fig. 177

optically active substances. The upper isotherm *acb* represents the solubility relations when the formation of a racemate is excluded, as, *e.g.* in the case of rubidium *d-* and *l-*tartrates above the transition point (p. 357). The solution at the point *c* is, of course, inactive, and *is unaffected by addition of either the* d- *or* l-*form.* The lower isotherm, on the other hand, would be obtained at a temperature at which the racemate could be formed. The curve *a'e* is the solubility curve for the *l*-form; *b'f*, that for the *d*-form; and *edf*, that for the racemate in presence of solutions of varying concentration. The point *d* corresponds to saturation for the pure racemate.

From these curves, now, it will be evident that it will be possible, in any given case, to decide whether or not an inactive solid is a mixture or a racemate. For this purpose, two solubility determinations are made, first with the inactive material alone (in excess), and then with the inactive material plus excess of one of the optically active forms. If we are dealing with a mixture, the two solutions thus obtained will be identical, both will have the composition corresponding to the point *c*, and will be inactive. if, however, the inactive material is a racemate, then two different solutions will be obtained; namely, an inactive solution corresponding to the point *d* (Fig. 177), and an *active* solution corresponding either to *e* or *f*, according to which enantiomorphous form was added.

The Solid Model. When a series of isothermal diagrams is assembled so that temperature is plotted along a third axis at right angles to the plane of the other two a rectangular solid model is obtained. For our first illustration we have chosen the system sodium sulphate-ammonium sulphate-water at one atmosphere[38] over a temperature range from about -20° to 100°(Fig. 178). Concentrations are plotted in moles of salt per fixed amount of water. The stable solid phases found are ice, anhydrous ammonium sulphate, anhydrous sodium sulphate, sodium sulphate decahydrate and the double salt $NaNH_4SO_4 \cdot 2H_2O$, for each of which there is a surface of saturation in the model. These surfaces intersect at lines (univariant equilibria) and the latter intersect at points (invariant equilibria). The equilibria of the component binary sys-

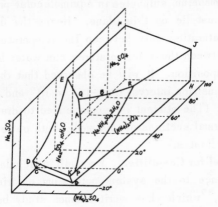

Fig. 178

tems Na_2SO_4-H_2O and $(NH_4)_2SO_4$-H_2O are given, as one would expect, by the corresponding faces of the model: thus CDEF is really a portion of Fig. 79 (p. 243) and CGH a simple eutectic type of diagram such as given in Fig. 38 (p. 135). DK and GK are ternary eutectic curves and K is a ternary eutectic point. The double salt comes into existence as an incongruently saturating salt at -16° (point P). Between 18° and 38° (the temperature of A and B respectively) it is congruently saturating and at the latter temperature it again becomes incongruently saturating. Finally at 59.3° (point R) it disappears from the diagram altogether. The temperatures of the points on the diagram are as follows:

Point	°C	Point	°C
A	18	G	-18.3
B	38	K	-19.5
C	0	P	-16.0
D	-1.1	Q	26.5
E	32.4	R	59.3

The line AB is drawn to show where a plane which bisects the right angle between the concentration axes would intersect the saturation surface for the double salt. As the latter contains sodium and ammonium sulphates in equimolecular proportions its composition must lie on this plane. Hence the double salt is congruently saturating only between the temperatures of A and B, for only between those temperatures can water be added to it without decomposition. It will be observed that the double salt has a lower transition interval from -16° to 18° and an upper from 38° to 59.3°. (The student is recommended to draw for himself various isothermal sections of this model both on rectangular and triangular coordinates.)

Space Model for Carnallite. We shall conclude this section with a reference to the system potassium chloride-magnesium chloride-water,[39] which has merited much study because of its relation to the famous Stassfurt salt deposits where large quantities of carnallite ($KMgCl_3 \cdot 6H_2O$) are found.

Fig. 179 is a diagrammatic sketch of the model for carnallite. Along the X-axis is measured the concentration of magnesium chloride in the solution; along the Y-axis, the concentration of potassium chloride; while along the T-axis is measured the temperature. The various saturation surfaces are labelled according to the solid phases present and given in the accompanying table (page 371). Most of the features should be evident from the diagram. The point F_1 is at a maximum temperature in the melting curve BF_1G_1 of $MgCl_2 \cdot 12H_2O$. Similarly F is a maximum temperature on EFG and M is a maximum temperature on EMK. Carnallite

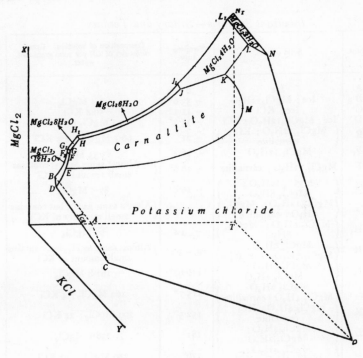

Fig. 179

is at all temperatures incongruently saturating because all points on its surface of saturation have a ratio of $MgCl_2$ to KCl greater than that in the double salt.

Bivariant Systems

Solid phase.	Area of existence.
Ice	ABDC
KCl	CDEMKLNO
Carnallite	EFGHJKM
$MgCl_2, 12H_2O$	BF_1G_1GFED
$MgCl_2, 8H_2O$	G_1H_1HG
$MgCl_2, 6H_2O$	H_1J_1JH
$MgCl_2, 4H_2O$	J_1L_1LKJ
$MgCl_2, 2H_2O$	L_1N_1NL

The data from which the model is constructed are given in the following table:

Invariant Systems—Binary and Ternary

Point.	Solid phases.	Temperature.	Composition of solution. Gram-molecules of salt per 1000 gram-mol. water.
A	Ice	$0°$	—
B	Ice ; $MgCl_2 12H_2O$	$-33.6°$	49.2 $MgCl_2$
C	Ice ; KCl	$-11.1°$	59.4 KCl
D	Ice ; $MgCl_2, 12H_2O$; KCl	$-34.3°$	43 $MgCl_2$; 3KCl
E	$MgCl_2, 12H_2O$; KCl ; carnallite	$-21°$	66.1 $MgCl_2$; 4.9 KCl
F_1	$MgCl_2, 12H_2O$	$-16.4°$	83.33 $MgCl_2$
F	$MgCl_2, 12H_2O$; carnallite	$-16.6°$	Almost same as F_1; contains small amount of KCl
G_1	$MgCl_2, 12H_2O$; $MgCl_2, 8H_2O$	$-16.8°$	87.5 $MgCl_2$
G	$MgCl_2, 12H_2O$; $MgCl_2, 8H_2O$; carnallite	$-16.9°$	Almost same as G_1, but contains small quantity of KCl
H_1	$MgCl_2, 8H_2O$; $MgCl_2, 6H_2O$	$-3.4°$	99 $MgCl_2$
H	$MgCl_2, 8H_2O$; $MgCl_2, 6H_2O$; carnallite	ca. $-3.4°$	Almost same as H_1, but contains small amount of KCl
J_1	$MgCl_2, 6H_2O$; $MgCl_2, 4H_2O$	$116.67°$	161.8 $MgCl_2$
J	$MgCl_2, 6H_2O$; $MgCl_2, 4H_2O$; carnallite	$115.7°$	162 $MgCl_2$; 4 KCl
K	$MgCl_2, 4H_2O$; KCl ; carnallite	$152.5°$	200 $MgCl_2$; 24 KCl
L_1	$MgCl_2, 4H_2O$; $MgCl_2, 2H_2O$	$181°$	238.1 $MgCl_2$
L	$MgCl_2, 4H_2O$; $MgCl_2, 2H_2O$; KCl	$176°$	240 $MgCl_2$; 41 KCl
M	Carnallite ; KCl	$167.5°$	166.7 $MgCl_2$; 41.7 KCl
N_1	$MgCl_2 . 2H_2O$	$186°$	ca. 241 $MgCl_2$
N	$MgCl_2, 2H_2O$; KCl	$186°$	240 $MgCl_2$; 63 KCl
O	KCl	$186°$	195.6 KCl

VI. Formation of Solid Solutions or Mix-Crystals.[40]

We have so far excluded from our discussion in this chapter the possibility of formation of solid solutions, although we have referred to them in Chapter XVI. If two salts with a common ion do not crystallise pure from solution but crystallise together as a single phase (solid solution), the composition of the latter, even at a fixed temperature, can be altered by altering the composition of the liquid from which it crystallises. We shall now examine the isotherms when solids of this kind are formed.

Two possibilities immediately arise: either the two salts at the given temperature form an unbroken series of solid solutions or they form an incomplete series (*cf.* Chapter VIII).

In the first of these it is evident that in the ternary system consisting of the two salts and water an isothermally invariant system cannot be produced for there can never be more than one solid phase and we are assuming that there is only one liquid phase possible. The isothermal solubility curve will therefore be continuous, joining the solubilities of the component salts, the liquid solutions of varying composition being in equilibrium with solid solutions, also of varying composition. This is illustrated in Fig. 180 where *ab* is the solubility curve just referred to, while the coexisting solids lying, of course, on AB, are joined by tie-lines to the corresponding points on the solubility curve (*cf.* Fig. 146 p. 330). The area A*ab*B is thus isothermally univariant and the area $ab\overline{H_2O}$ bivariant (unsaturated solutions). The system $(NH_4)_2SO_4$—K_2SO_4—H_2O[41] at 25° may be cited as an example of this kind.

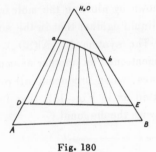

Fig. 180

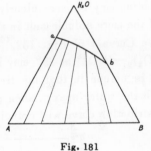

Fig. 181

The salts which comprise the solid solution need not be anhydrous—one may be anhydrous and the other hydrated, as in the system NH_4Cl—$FeCl_2$—H_2O[42] at 70° in which NH_4Cl and $FeCl_2$ $2H_2O$ form a series of solid solutions, although, admittedly, it is an incomplete series. More commonly both salts are hydrated as in the system $NH_4Cr(SO_4)_2$—$NH_4Fe(SO_4)_2$—H_2O[43] at 25°. A typical isotherm for the latter case is given in Fig. 181 where D and E are the hydrated salts. In a survey of the subject Blasdale (*loc. cit.*) concludes that, in ternary systems of two salts and water where solid solution is found, the water is always associated with either or both of the salts in a simple stoichiometric ratio. At the same time, when *both* salts are hydrated, they are not found to be hydrated differently.

The slope of the tie lines in these isotherms, which, of course, is determined by the distribution of the salts between liquid and solid solutions, is of some significance.[44] Roozeboom,[45] in a classification of types of distribution in ternary systems,[46] distinguished five types, three of which refer to complete series of solid solutions of the kind we are now considering. In Type I the concentration of one of the salts in the liquid (concentrations being reckoned as mole fraction of dissolved salts only) is always greater than the concentration of the same salt in the coexisting solid solution. This will mean that all the tie-lines on being produced in the direction of the water apex will pass the latter on the same side. Such is found to be the case in the system $NH_4Cr(SO_4)_2$—$NH_4Fe(SO_4)_2$—H_2O at $25°$ referred to above. This distribution may be more clearly shown by plotting the mole fraction of the more soluble salt in the liquid against that in the solid to give Curve I of Fig. 182.[47] The system $NH_4Al(SO_4)_2$—$KAl(SO_4)_2$—H_2O[48] at $25°$ may be mentioned as another example, but it is unique in that the tie lines, when produced, all pass through the water apex; when plotted as in Fig. 182, therefore, the distribution curve will coincide with the diagonal.

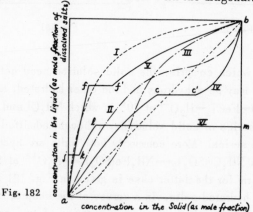

Fig. 182

In Type II the concentration of one of the salts in the liquid (expressed as mole fraction of dissolved salts) is greater than that of the same salt in the coexisting solid solution for lower total concentrations of that salt, but becomes less for higher total concentrations. This situation gives rise to Curve II in Fig. 182 and, on the triangular diagram, appears as a tendency for the tie lines to converge to a point on the liquid curve. This, in turn, suggests a tendency toward a break in the series of solid solutions (*v. infra*). As an example we cite the system $Mg(NH_4)_2(SO_4)_2$ — $Mg(NH_4)_2(SeO_4)_2$—H_2O[49] at 25° where, again, the components are hydrated.

In Type III the concentration of one of the salts in the liquid is less than that of the same salt in the coexisting solid solution for lower concentrations of that salt but becomes greater for higher concentrations (Curve III, Fig. 182). This means that on the triangular diagram the tie-lines tend to converge on the solid solution line, or a tendency toward compound formation. The system $PbBr_2$—$PbCl_2$—H_2O[50] shows this behaviour.

In all three types isothermal evaporation of solutions produces different results, and the composition of the last drop of solution will, at the same time, depend upon the original total composition of the liquid being evaporated. Moreover, in each of Types II and III there will be a "congruent solution", corresponding to the intersection of Curves II and III respectively with the diagonal (Fig. 182). Evaporation of a solution of concentration corresponding to this point of intersection will cause no change in the composition either of the liquid or of the solid being deposited; evaporation of any other solution will cause a change in the liquid and therefore in the solid composition either toward (Type II) or away from (Type III) this congruent solution. (The student will do well to test these conclusions for himself from an examination of the disposition of the tie-lines for each type).

We have now to consider the possibility of an incomplete, or broken, or interrupted, series of solid solutions. Usually this will mean that there are two series of solid solutions, less commonly it will mean that there is only one series of solid solutions which is nevertheless an incomplete series. There will, however, always be a break in the solubility curve at the point where two solid phases are present in equilibrium with the liquid, whether the two solids are the limiting solid solutions or one is a solid solution and the other a compound.

An illustration of an incomplete series is found in the system $KCl—KI—H_2O^{51}$ at $25°$ which is shown diagrammatically in Fig. 183. The points a and b have the usual meaning. Solid B is soluble in solid A up to the concentration of d, and B in A up to the concentration of e. The solubility curve shows a break at c (an isothermally invariant solution) at which the liquid is in equilibrium with the two limiting solid solutions d and e. The regions Aacd and Bbce are isothermally univariant and crossed by tie lines.

In Fig. 183 the solids are anhydrous, but they are commonly hydrated and sometimes even hydrated differently. In the system $MnCl_2 —CoCl_2—H_2O^{52}$ at $15-20°$, for instance, there are two series of solid solutions, one a solution of $MnCl_2 \cdot 4H_2O$ in $CoCl_2 \cdot 4H_2O$ and the other a solution of $MnCl_2 \cdot 6H_2O$ in $CoCl_2 \cdot 6H_2O$.

Roozeboom (loc. cit.) has included in his classification such cases of incomplete solid solution and described two possible types (Types IV and V) on the basis of the direction of the tie-lines. In Type IV one of the two solid solutions contains a larger concentration of one of the salts than the coexisting liquid and the other solid solution contains a smaller concentration of that salt than in the coexisting liquid. Fig. 183 illustrates this situation, for the tie-lines for one of the series, when produced, all pass on one side of the water apex whereas those for the other series all pass on the other side of it. On Fig. 182 this appears as Curve IV ($acc'b$), ac being on one side and $c'b$ on the other side of the diagonal.

Type V (Curve V, $aff'b$) describes the rather rare occurrence of an incomplete series where the concentration of one of the salts is always greater in the liquid than in the coexisting solid. Here the entire curve is on the one side of the diagonal. While not belonging properly to the present chapter on aqueous systems, we give the system $HgBr_2—HgI_2—acetone^{53}$ at $25°$ as an example. On the triangular diagram both sets of tie-lines will, when produced, pass on the same side of the solvent apex.

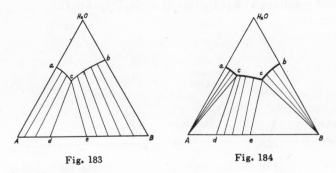

Fig. 183   Fig. 184

To the above five types should be added at least a sixth to which attention was first drawn by Ricci[54] (*cf.* p. 169). Several systems are known where there is incomplete miscibility in the solid state but in which there is only one series of solid solutions. It is therefore necessary to admit the existence of a limiting solid solution in equilibrium with a pure substance. This situation may give rise to Fig. 184 where the isothermally invariant liquids *c* and *c'* are in equilibrium with mixtures of A and limiting solution *d*, and B and limiting solution *e* respectively. This corresponds in Fig. 182 to Curve VI (*ajklmb*), the relation of which to Fig. 184 should now be clear. The system Na_2SO_4—$KBrO_3$—H_2O[55] at 45° is typical of such behaviour.

The study of the isothermal evaporation of solutions from systems of Types IV, V and VI is left to the student.

Finally, the reader is reminded that a system which belongs to one of the above types at one temperature may well belong to another at a different temperature. Furthermore, many actual systems involve a combination of the above types at a single temperature; there may, for example, be both compound formation and solid solution formation, and there may be more than two portions of an interrupted series of solid solutions. Illustrations of such multiple types can be readily found in the literature.[56] Fig. 185, for the system K_2CO_3—Na_2CO_3—H_2O at 30°[57], is given to show that isotherms can attain a considerable degree of complexity.

The solid phases are $2K_2CO_3 \cdot 3H_2O$, $KNaCO_3$, the mono-, hepta- and decahydrates of sodium carbonate, and an incomplete series of solid solutions of $K_2CO_3 \cdot 6H_2O$ in $Na_2CO_3 \cdot 6H_2O$.

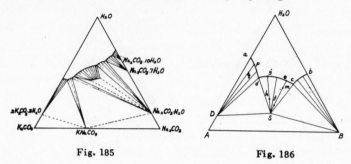

Fig. 185   Fig. 186

VII. Indirect Identification of Solid Phases.

It will be shown later (p. 472) how the composition of the solid phase in a system of two components can be determined without analysis, but we shall now describe how this can be done in a system of three components.[58]

We shall assume that we are dealing with the aqueous solution of two salts which can give rise to a double salt, in which case we can represent the solubility relations in a system of triangular co-ordinates. We should then obtain the isotherm *adcb* (Fig. 186).

Let us suppose that the double salt is in equilibrium with the solution at a definite temperature and that the composition of the solution is represented by the point *e.* The greater part of the solution is now separated from the solid phase, and the latter, *together with the adhering mother liquor*, is analysed. The composition will be represented by a point (*e.g. f*) on the line *eS*, where S represents the composition of the double salt. That this is so will be evident when one considers that the composition of the whole mass must lie on the line joining the composition of the solution to that of the double salt, no matter what may be the relative amounts of the solid phase and the mother liquor.

If, in a similar manner, we analyse a solution of a different composition in equilibrium with the same double salt (not necessarily at the same temperature as before), and also the mixture of solid phase and solution, we shall obtain two other points, as, for example, g and h, and the line joining these must likewise pass through S. The method of finding the composition of an unknown double salt consists, therefore, in finding, in the manner just des-scribed, the position of two lines such as ef and gh. The point of intersection of these lines then gives the composition of the double salt. [70]

One.can, however, determine this point of intersection alge-braically with greater accuracy. Suppose, for example, that the point e has the composition 10%A, 25%B and that f has the com-position 29%A, 36%B. Similarly suppose that point g is 20%A, 10%B and that h is 30%A, 30%B. Let the point of intersection of the corresponding tie-lines through ef and gh be x%A, y%B. By the geometry of the figure, for each of these lines the change in percent of A will be directly proportional to the change in the percent of B. For ef, therefore, $(29-10)/(36-25) = (x-10)/(y-25)$ and for gh, $(30-20)/(30-10) = (x-20)/(y-10)$. Solving these two simultaneous equations gives $x = 34.6$%A and $y = 39.2$%B.

The same result is arrived at by means of the rectangular meth-od of representation.

If it is known, for example, that the solid is anhydrous, this information is equivalent to knowing the position of one of the tie-lines, so that, at least in theory, only one tie-line must be determined experimentally, and only one equation in one unknown need be solved if the algebraic method is used. Thus if S is known to be anhydrous it is located on the base AB and it suffices to produce either ef or gh till it intersects AB. Similarly if it is known that the solid phase is a hydrated component and therefore that its composition lies on one of the sides of the triangle, only the point of intersection of one tie-line with the appropriate side of the triangle is required. It may be noted that instead of analys-ing the wet solid as described above it is frequently more accu-rate to determine the total composition of the system at the outset of the solubility measurement by using known quantities of the initial components. This will give a point that must still be on the tie-line when the system has come to equilibrium. Thus an original complex m will give the solution e saturated with solid S, and the extrapolation can be made as above using the points e and m instead of e and f. It is true that m, being farther removed from S, gives a greater error to the extrapolation, if the accuracy with which m is known is no greater than that with which f is known, but experimentally it is often possible to determine m with such high accuracy that the extrapolation is actually improved.[59]

The indirect determination of the composition of a solid phase is commonly resorted to when it is difficult to isolate the solid or maintain it in its pure condition while it is being analysed. Thus, in Fig. 186, if such were the case with the hydrate D, the points p and q could be determined by finding the solubility of D in the presence of a small amount of B, and by extrapolation, the point D could be located. In this way it was found,[60] for instance, that the composition of hydrated aluminium sulphate in equilibrium with its saturated aqueous solution at $25°$ was $Al_2(SO_4)_3 \cdot 17H_2O$ and not $Al_2(SO_4)_3 \cdot 18H_2O$ as hitherto supposed.

VIII. Hydrolysis.

It is well known that many salts, when dissolved in water, hydrolyse sufficiently to deposit a second solid phase. Such systems are no longer binary, for the composition of every phase cannot be expressed in terms of two concentration variables; they are, in fact, ternary systems. Consider, for instance, a hypothetical sulphate of a bivalent metal M, which, when dissolved in not too large a quantity of water forms a basic salt[61] of composition $M_2(OH)_2SO_4$ according to the equation

$$2MSO_4 + 2HOH \rightleftharpoons M_2(OH)_2SO_4 \downarrow + H_2SO_4.$$

There are thus three phases (if we exclude vapour), viz., the two solids, MSO_4 and $M_2(OH)_2SO_4$, and the liquid saturated with respect to both. In order to express the composition of all of these phases at least three concentration variables are required. If we choose MO, SO_3, HOH the two solids have the composition $MSO_4 = MO + SO_3 + 0HOH$ and $M_2(OH)_2SO_4 = 2MO + SO_3 + HOH$. (The liquid can be expressed in similar terms). If we prefer to choose $M(OH)_2$, H_2SO_4, HOH for variables we have $MSO_4 = M(OH)_2 +$

H_2SO_4-2HOH and $M_2(OH)_2SO_4 = 2M(OH)_2 + H_2SO_4-2HOH$. Obviously a large number of choices is available, but for convenience it is customary to use the first-mentioned, thereby avoiding negative coefficients.

When such basic salts are formed it is often impossible, by the ordinary methods of analysis, to decide whether one is dealing with a definite chemical individual or with a mixture, and it is here that the Phase Rule has performed exceptional service. If we are dealing with a condition of equilibrium at constant temperature between liquid and solid phases, three cases can be distinguished,[62] viz.:

1. The solutions in different experiments have the same composition, but the composition of the precipitate alters. In this case there must be two solid phases.

2. The solutions in different experiments can have varying composition, while the composition of the precipitate remains unchanged. In this case only one solid phase exists, a definite compound.

3. The composition both of the solution and of the precipitate varies. In this case the solid phase is a solid solution or a mix-crystal. (*cf.* Fig. 182, p. 374).

In order, therefore, to decide what is the nature of a precipitate produced by the hydrolysis of a normal salt it is only necessary to ascertain whether and how the composition of the precipitate alters with alteration in the composition of the solution.

We shall take for our illustration the basic salts formed at 25° by the hydrolysis of mercurous nitrate; *i.e.*, the system $Hg_2O-N_2O_5-H_2O$,[63] and interpret the results in terms of the triangular diagram shown in Fig. 187 (schematic). Only a portion of the complete isotherm has been investigated so that the diagram is incomplete. The solid phases found are the hydrated normal salt $Hg_2O \cdot N_2O_5 \cdot 2H_2O$ (point D in the Figure), which exists in an α- and a β- modification, and three basic salts $2Hg_2O \cdot N_2O_5 \cdot H_2O$ (point A), $5Hg_2O \cdot 3N_2O_5 \cdot 3H_2O$ (point B) and $4Hg_2O \cdot 3N_2O_5 \cdot H_2O$ (point C). The curve *de* is the stable portion of the solubility curve of the α- form of D and *ef* that of the β- form. The remainder of the diagram should require no further explanation.

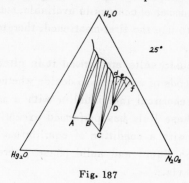

Fig. 187

IX. Two-Liquid Systems.

With one exception[64] we have not yet referred to any system in which are found, at any one temperature, more than one liquid phase as well as solid phases. Such a behaviour is common, however, particularly in connection with the phenomenon known as "salting out", and we shall now refer to it briefly.[65]

When a salt is added to, say, a solution of an organic liquid such as alcohol or acetone in water, within a certain range of concentration, it frequently happens that two liquid layers are formed, one containing a high proportion of the organic liquid and the other a high proportion of water. If sufficient salt is added then this, too, appears as a third (solid) phase. By this means it is possible to effect at least a partial separation of the organic liquid from the water——hence the term "salting out" of the organic liquid. Conversely it is often feasible to separate a salt from its aqueous solution by the addition of an organic liquid.

Fig. 188 shows a typical isotherm for the system salt—— alcohol—water.[66] (We shall assume that the salt is anhydrous). The solubility of the salt in water is given, of course, by point a and that of the salt in alcohol by b, the relatively low solubility in alcohol being indicated by the nearness of b to the alcohol corner of the triangle. The aqueous solubility of the salt is altered along ac by the presence of the alcohol and the solubility of the salt in alcohol altered along bd by the presence of the water. Solutions c and d, however, are immiscible and form the ends of the binodal curve ckd enclosing a univariant area of two liquids crossed by tie-lines joining the conjugate liquids on ck and dk respectively. The point k is thus a plait point. The liquids c and d at the same time are both saturated with respect to salt and we therefore have the isothermally invariant triangle salt-c-d, any total composition within which must yield salt and the two liquid layers c and d. Finally the region bounded by $ackdb$ and the water and alcohol corners is one of single liquid phases.

Suppose an alcohol-water solution of composition p is to be "salted out". Addition of salt will bring the total composition to q, say, forming the two liquids x and y. Liquid layer y can now be separated and it has the desired high alcohol content.

Soap Systems. A part of the process for the manufacture of soap can be regarded for many purposes as a salting out phenomenon in a ternary system, and it is appropriate to describe it at this point, although it is, of course, beyond the scope of this work to describe such a complex process in detail.

The question of whether a colloidal dispersion such as a soap solution can be regarded as a one- or a two-phase system has been the subject of much discussion[67] and McBain[68] prefers to regard a soap solution as a single phase. It is a reversible colloid whose external properties are determined solely and completely by temperature, pressure and composition: the Phase Rule, therefore, in its usual form, is applicable to soap systems.

One may divide the manufacture of soap into three general steps: saponification of fats or oils to give soap and glycerol, separation or salting out of the soap by the addition of sodium chloride, and purification *etc.* of the product. We are here dealing primarily with the second and, to some extent, with the third of these. While numerous glycerides and electrolytes are involved in commercial manufacture it has been found convenient to consider the process as one involving merely the three components soap, water and electrolyte; and whether the soap is, say, potassium oleate or sodium palmitate, or whether the electrolyte is sodium chloride or potassium chloride, makes little difference as far as the qualitative nature of the phase diagram is concerned. The isotherm for such a system in the neighbourhood of 100° is shown schematically in Fig. 189. The phase C is a ternary crystalline

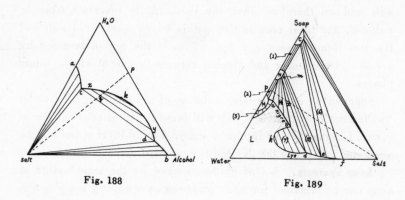

Fig. 188   Fig. 189

solid ("curd fibres"), which may be a solid solution, and N and M are anisotropic liquid crystals ("neat soap" and "middle soap" respectively).[69] The area L is one of isotropic liquid, part of which is bounded by a binodal curve enclosing an area of two-liquid equilibria bkd. Solutions along abk are called "nigre" and solutions along $kdef$ "lye". In practice the line def almost coincides with the base of the triangle and the isothermally invariant triangle bdm is narrower than shown. The solubility of the salt in water is, of course, given by f. There are seven areas denoting two-phase equilibria in which both phases are of varying composition; viz., (1) solid C and neat soap, (2) neat soap and middle soap, (3) middle soap and isotropic liquid, (4) neat soap and nigre, (5) neat soap and lye, (6) solid C and lye, and (7) nigre and lye already referred to. The remainder of the diagram should be self-explanatory. It will be apparent that if sufficient salt be added to a soap solution of composition p, say, to bring the total composition of the soap kettle to some point x three layers, one of neat soap, and one of nigre and one of lye will form.

After carefully conducting several operations of this general nature the glycerol and other impurities such as alkali are removed as constituents of the nigre and lye (hence the term "salting out") and the neat soap is further treated to give the final product.

NOTES

1. If the two salts have no ion in common metathesis is possible and the system becomes one of higher order. The restriction is also imposed that neither of the salts shall hydrolyse sufficiently to form another solid.

2. In connection with this chapter see, more especially, van't Hoff. *Bildung und Spaltung von Doppelsalzen*, pp. 3 ff.; Roozeboom, *Z. physikal. Chem.*, 1892, 10, 158; Bancroft, *Phase Rule*, pp. 201, 209.

3. Roozeboom, *Z. physikal. Chem.*, 1893, 12, 369.

4. *Z. anorgan. Chem.*, 1906, 51, 132.

5. Several factors are involved here. When A is a difficultly soluble salt and A and B have an ion in common the solubility of A may be lowered by the presence of B according to the common ion effect. On the other hand, the operation of the 'salt effect' or the formation of complex ions may cause an increase in the solubility of A.

6. See Pozner, *J. Phys. Chem.* (U.S.S.R.), 1947, 21, 377, 389 for relationships between the concentrations in these systems.

7. Precht and Wittjen, *Ber.*, 1881, 14, 1670; Blasdale, *J. Ind. Eng. Chem.*, 1918, 10, 344.

8. Chretien, *Caliche*, 1926, 8, 390.

9. Prutton and Tower, *J. Amer. Chem. Soc.*, 1932, 54, 3040.

10. See Pozner, *J. Phys. Chem.* (U.S.S.R.), 1947, 21, 1471 for relationships between the concentrations in such a system.

11. See p. 348.

12. Meyerhoffer, *Ber.*, 1897, 30, 1809.

13. Also called a congruent solution or congruent point.

14. Schreinemakers and de Baat, *Chem. Weekblad.*, 1910, 7, 259.

15. Schreinemakers, *Z. physikal. Chem.*, 1909, 65, 553.

16. Dawson, *J. Chem. Soc.*, 1918, 113, 675; Rivett, *J. Chem. Soc.*, 1922, 121, 379.

17. Hill, Smith and Ricci, *J. Amer. Chem. Soc.*, 1940, **62**, 858; Smith, *ibid.*, 1942, **64**, 41.

18. Occleshaw, *J. Chem. Soc.*, 1925, **127**, 2598.

19. Van Leeuwen, *Z. physikal. Chem.*, 1897, **23**, 33.

20. Reicher, *Z. physikal. Chem.*, 1887, **1**, 221.

21. For other examples of the formation and decomposition of double salts at a transition point, see Roozeboom-Schreinemakers, *Die. Heterogenen Gleichgewichte*, III., Part I.

22. See, however, systems involving the formation of racemates, p. 355.

23. Meyerhoffer, *Z. physikal. Chem.*, 1890, **5**, 109. On the importance of the transition interval for optically active substances, see Meyerhoffer, *Ber.*, 1904, **37**, 2604.

24. By 'solubility curves' is here meant the curves denoting variation of solubility with temperature, not isothermal solubility curves.

25. Van't Hoff and Müller, *Ber.*, 1898, 31, 2206.

26. There is also the difference that neither of the component tartrates is hydrated.

27. Traube, *Jahrb. Min. Beil. Bd.*, **10**, 795.

28. Van't Hoff and van Deventer, *Z. physikal. Chem.*, 1887, **1**, 165.

29. Meyerhoffer, *Z. physikal. Chem.*, 1890, **5**, 121. See, also, Blasdale and Robson, *J. Amer. Chem., Soc.*, 1928, **50**, 35.

30. Roozeboom, *Z. physikal. Chem.*, 1888, **2**, 518.

31. Roozeboom, *Z. physikal. Chem.*, 1888, **2**, 514.

32. The influence of pressure on the transition point of tachydrite has been determined by van't Hoff, Kenrick, and Dawson (*Z. physikal. Chem.*, 1901, **39**, 27, 34; van't Hoff, *Zur Bildung der ozeanischen Salzablagerungen*, I., p. 66 Vieweg, 1905). This salt is formed from magnesium chloride and calcium chloride at $22°$, in accordance with the equation

$$2MgCl_2 \cdot 6H_2O + CaCl_2 \cdot 6H_2O \rightleftharpoons Mg_2CaCl_6 \cdot 12H_2O + 6H_2O.$$

Increase of pressure raises the transition point, because the formation of tachydrite is accompanied by increase of volume, the elevation being $0.016°$ for an increase of pressure of 1 atm. The number calculated from the Clausius-Clapeyron equation (p. 23) is $0.013°$ for 1 atm.

If one calculates the influence of the pressure of sea-water on the temperature of formation of tachydrite (which is of interest on account of the natural occurrence of this salt), it is found that a depth of water of 1500 metres, exerting a pressure of 180 atm., would alter the temperature of formation of tachydrite by only $3°$. The effect is, therefore, comparatively unimportant.

33. Roozeboom, *Z. physikal. Chem.*, 1888, **2**, 517.

34. *Z. physikal. Chem.*, 1887, **1**, 227.

35. It must, of course, be understood that the temperature is on that side of the transition point on which the double salt is stable.

36. Excess of the double salt must be taken, because otherwise an unsaturated solution might be formed, and this would, of course, not deposit any salt.

37. Roozeboom, *Z. physikal. Chem.*, 1899, **28**, 494; *Ber.*, 1899, **32**, 537.

38. Matignon and Meyer, *Compt. rend.*, 1918, **166**, 115 and *Ann. chim.*, 1918, **9**, 251; Dawson, *J. Chem. Soc.*, 1918, **113**, 675. See also Blasdale, *Equilibria in Saturated Salt Solutions*, The Chemical Catalog Co., New York, 1927, p. 78.

39. Van't Hoff and Meyerhoffer, *Z. physikal. Chem.*, 1898, **27**, 75; 1899, **30**, 86; Fig. 179 is taken from the latter paper. See also Igelsrud and Thompson, *J. Amer. Chem. Soc.*, 1936, **58**, 318; d'Ans and Sypiena, *Kali*, 1942, **36**, 89; Lightfoot and Prutton, *J. Amer. Chem. Soc.*, 1946, **68**, 1001. To facilitate the understanding of the space models, the reader is referred to Kremann's *Leitfaden der graphischen Chemie* (Borntraeger), which gives instructions and materials for making cardboard models of different systems.

40. Bancroft, *Phase Rule*, p. 203; Roozeboom, *Z. physikal. Chem.*, 1891, **8**, 504, 531; Stortenbeker, *ibid.*, 1895, **17**, 643; 1897, **22**, 60; 1900, **34**, 108. See also experimental investigations by Allmand, *Z. anorgan. Chem.*, 1909, **61**, 202; Clendinnen and Rivett, *J. Chem. Soc.*, 1921, **119**, 1329; 1923, **123**, 1344, 1634; Perman and Howells, *ibid.*, 1923, **123**, 2128. See also the monograph by Blasdale, *Equilibria in Saturated Salt Solutions* (Chemical Catalog Co.), where the subject is

fully discussed.

41. Weston, *J. Chem. Soc.*, 1922, **121**, 1223; Hill and Loucks, *J. Amer. Chem. Soc.*, 1937, **59**, 2094, and others.

42. Clendinnin, *J. Chem. Soc.*, 1922, **121**, 802.

43. Smith and Lennox, *J. Amer. Chem. Soc.*, 1948, **70**, 1793.

44. A thermodynamic treatment of the distribution in these systems is given by Hill, Durham and Ricci, *J. Amer. Chem. Soc.*, 1940, **62**, 2723. See also Pozner, *J. Phys. Chem.* (U.S.S.R.), 1947, **21**, 1471, 1481.

45. *Z. physikal. Chem.*, 1891, **8**, 521.

46. This classification is not to be confused with his classification of solid solution types in binary systems, p. 157.

47. There are reasons for believing that a true Type I distribution always gives a symmetrical curve (see Hill, Durham and Ricci, *loc. cit.*).

48. Hill and Kaplan, *J. Amer. Chem. Soc.*, 1938, **60**, 550.

49. Hill, Soth and Ricci, *J. Amer. Chem. Soc.*, 1940, **62**, 2717.

50. Meyer, *Rec. Trav. Chim.*, 1923, **42**, 301 (temperature not given).

51. Amadori and Pampini, *Atta. accad. Linc.*, 1911, **20**, II, 473.

52. Stortenbecker, *Z. physikal. Chem.*, 1895, **16**, 250.

53. Reinders, *Z. physikal. Chem.*, 1900, **32**, 494.

54. Ricci, *J. Amer. Chem. Soc.*, 1935, **57**, 805.

55. Ricci. *loc. cit.*

56. See also International Critical Tables, Vol. IV.

57. Hill and Miller, *J. Amer. Chem. Soc.*, 1927, **49**, 669.

58. Schreinemakers, *Z. physikal. Chem.*, 1893, **11**, 76; Bancroft, *J. Physical Chem.*, 1902, 6, 179. *Z. anorgan. Chem.*, 1904, **40**, 148. See also Sahmen and von Vegesack, *Z. physikal. Chem.*, 1907, **59**, 257; Jänecke, *ibid.*, 697.

59. Hill and Ricci, *J. Amer. Chem. Soc.*, 1931, **53**, 4305.

60. Smith, *J. Amer. Chem. Soc.*, 1942, **64**, 41.

61. For a study of equilibria in the case of acid salts see Koppel and Blumenthal, *Z. anorgan. Chem.*, 1907, **53**, 228.

62. Lash Miller and Kenrick, *J. Physical Chem.*, 1903, 7, 259; Allan,

Amer. Chem. J., 1901, **25**, 307.

63. Denham and Fife, *J. Chem. Soc.*, 1933, 1416 (*cf.* Cox, *Z. anorgan. Chem.*, 1904, **40**, 146).

64. See p. 334.

65. For a reference table of such systems see J. C. Smith, *Ind. Eng. Chem.*, 1949, **41**, 2932.

66. For systems with alcohol see Frankforter and Frary, *J. Phys. Chem.*, 1913, **17**, 402; for systems with acetone see Frankforter and Bell, *J. Amer. Chem. Soc.*, 1914, **36**, 1103.

67. E. Buckner, "Colloids as One-Phase Systems", in Alexander's *Colloid Chemistry*, Vol. I, 1926, Chap. 4.

68. McBain *et al.*, *J. Am. Chem. Soc.*, 1938, **60**, 1866; *J. Soc. Chem. Ind.*, 1940, **59**, 243. See also Chap. 5 by McBain in Alexander's *Colloid Chemistry (loc. cit.)*.

69. A description of these phases will be found in Doscher and Vold, *J. Phys. Coll. Chem.*, 1948, 52, 97. Other forms of soap appear at elevated temperatures; see McBain and Lee, *Ind. Eng. Chem.*, 1943, **35**, 917.

70. In the interest of the accurate location of S it is, of course, desirable to have the points *h* and *f* as near as possible to S; this means, experimentally, that the wet solids should be freed as far as possible from adhering mother liquor before being analyzed.

CHAPTER XVIII

PRACTICAL APPLICATIONS OF EQUILIBRIUM DIAGRAMS.

Having discussed qualitatively the application of the Phase Rule to three-component systems formed by water and two salts with a common ion, one may now consider how the equilibrium diagrams, constructed on the basis of experimental data, can be employed in the quantitative study of the behaviour of such systems, and can be used to guide the practical operations of the winning of salts by crystallisation from solution.[1]

The System Sodium Chloride—Potassium Chloride—Water. This may be taken as an illustration of a simple system in which there is no double-salt formation, and in which, at all temperatures above 0°, the salts crystallise anhydrous from solution.

On determining the composition of the solutions in equilibrium with each of the single salts alone and with a mixture of the two salts (see p. 342), the values on p. 391 are obtained.[2]

These values may be plotted either in rectangular co-ordinates (p. 340) or in a triangular diagram (p. 278).[3] When the numbers are plotted in rectangular co-ordinates, curves such as AC, BC (Fig. 190), are obtained. Curve AC gives the composition of solutions, expressed in grams of anhydrous salt per 100 grams of water, in equilibrium with sodium chloride as solid phase; and the curve BC, similarly, represents solutions in equilibrium with potassium chloride. Point C gives the composition of the solution in equilibrium with both salts as solid phases.

As we have already learned a point in area I represents the total composition of a mixture which is composed of solid sodium chloride and saturated solution represented by a point on the curve AC, a point in area II a mixture of the two solid salts plus solution of composition C, and a point in area III, a mixture of solid potassium chloride and saturated solution represented by a point on the curve BC. Mixtures having a composition represented by a point in the area ACBO are unsaturated solutions.

Tempera-ture.	Solid phase.	Composition of solution.			
		In grams of salt per 100 grams of water.		In grams of salt per 100 grams of solution.	
		NaCl.	KCl.	NaCl.	KCl.
0°	NaCl	34·95	—	25·90	—
	KCl	—	28·20	—	22·0
	NaCl + KCl	31·53	10·55	22·19	7·43
25°	NaCl	35·63	—	26·28	—
	KCl	—	36·96	—	26·98
	NaCl + KCl	29·88	16·28	20·44	11·14
50°	NaCl	36·50	–	26·74	—
	KCl	—	43·12	—	30·14
	NaCl + KCl	29·09	22·03	19·25	14·58
75°	NaCl	37·75	—	27·39	—
	KCl	—	49·70	—	33·20
	NaCl + KCl	27·87	29·06	17·76	18·52
100°	NaCl	39·40	—	28·27	—
	KCl	—	56·20	—	35·97
	NaCl + KCl	27·39	35·16	16·85	21·62

The equilibrium (solubility) diagram, having been plotted to scale, may now be used for the purpose of giving information regarding the quantitative behaviour of mixtures of sodium chloride, potassium chloride and water of any given composition, at the temperature of the isotherm. Thus: What will be the result of shaking together, at 25°, 20 grams of sodium chloride, 30 grams of potassium chloride and 100 grams of water? From the solubility diagram it is found that a mixture of this composition is represented by a point x (Fig. 190) lying in the area III. The mixture, therefore, must yield a saturated solution represented by a point on the curve BC, together with solid potassium chloride. To find the composition of the saturated solution, a line xx' is drawn parallel with the horizontal axis, and the point x', where this line cuts the solubility curve, gives the composition of the saturated solution. From the curve, x' is found to represent a

solution composed of 20 grams of sodium chloride and 23.1 grams
of potassium chloride per 100 grams of water. The original mixture, therefore, gives 6.9 grams of solid potassium chloride and
143.1 grams of saturated solution of the composition just given.

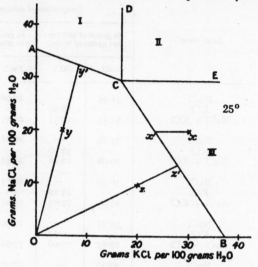

Fig. 190

A mixture of the composition 20 grams of sodium chloride, 5
grams of potassium chloride and 100 grams of water, is represented
by the point y (Fig. 190). At 25°, therefore, this mixture forms
an unsaturated solution. On evaporating this solution at 25°[4]
the composition will change as shown by the line yy' (see p. 343),
and when the composition reaches the point y' further evaporation
will lead to the deposition of solid sodium chloride. The composition of the solution will then change in the direction $y'C$, and at
C solid potassium chloride will also begin to separate out.

How much water must be evaporated off before sodium chloride
begins to be deposited, and how much pure sodium chloride can
be obtained by isothermal evaporation of the solution at 25°?

From the solubility curve it is found that y' has the composition 32.8 grams of sodium chloride and 8.2 grams of potassium
chloride per 100 grams of water. Since in the original solution,

the ratio of sodium chloride to water was $20:100$, and, in the solution y', the ratio is $32.8:100$, an amount of water x must have been lost by the original 125 grams of solution sufficient to bring the ratio of salt to water up to the value $32.8:100$. That is, $20:(100-x) = 32.8:100$. From this, $x = 39.0$ grams. When evaporation has been carried out to the point y', therefore, the original 125 grams of solution will have diminished to 86 grams, consisting of 20 grams of sodium chloride, 5 grams of potassium chloride and 61 grams of water.

Further evaporation leads to the point C, which has the composition 29.88 grams of sodium chloride and 16.28 grams of potassium chloride to 100 grams of water. Since, at the point y', the solution contains only 8.2 grams of potassium chloride to 100 grams of water, 141 grams of solution of composition y' must lose x' grams of water to give a solution of the composition C. To obtain the value of x', we have $8.2:(100-x') = 16.28:100$. Hence $x' = 49.6$ grams. The amount of water lost by 86 grams of solution y' would therefore be 30.3 grams.

The amount of sodium chloride deposited during evaporation of the solution from the point y' to the point C can be obtained as follows. For a constant amount of water the ratio of sodium chloride to potassium chloride diminishes from $32.8/8.2$ at y' to $29.88/16.28$ at C. The amount of sodium chloride, w, therefore, which must separate out is given by the expression $32.8-w:8.2 = 29.88:16.28$, from which one calculates $w = 17.75$. This is the weight of sodium chloride in grams which will separate when 141 grams of solution y' is evaporated at $25°$ until the point C is reached. From 86 grams of solution y', therefore, composed of 20 grams of sodium chloride, 5 grams of potassium chloride and 61 grams of water, 10.83 grams of sodium chloride would be deposited; and since, as we have seen, 30.3 grams of water would also evaporate away, the original 125 grams of unsaturated solution, when evaporated at $25°$ until the point C is reached, will have diminished to 44.97 grams of solution consisting of $(20-10.83) = 9.27$ grams of sodium chloride, 5 grams of potassium chloride and $(100-39-30.3) = 30.7$ grams of water.

In the same way, one can calculate the amount of water which will have to be evaporated off and the weight of potassium chloride which will be deposited when the unsaturated solution z, consisting of 20 grams of potassium chloride, 10 grams of sodium chloride and 100 grams of water is evaporated at 25°, until the point C is reached.

Separation of Salts by a Temperature–cycle Process. For the practical separation of two salts with a common ion, advantage may be taken, when possible, of the variation of the solubility of salts with the temperature, and by alternate evaporation at a higher temperature and cooling to a lower temperature an efficient separation of the salts may be effected. Such a cyclic process can be illustrated by means of the system sodium chloride—potassium chloride—water.[5]

In Fig. 191 the curves ac, cb represent the isotherm for 0°, and the curves $a'c'$, $c'b'$ the isotherm for 100°. If the original unsaturated solution, x, representing a mixture of 20 grams of sodium chloride, 14 grams of potassium chloride and 100 grams of water is evaporated at a temperature of 100°, the composition of the solution alters along the line xx'. On continued evaporation the solution then changes in the direction c'. At this point the sodium chloride which has been deposited is separated from the solution, which is then cooled down to 0°. During this process the composition of the solution alters in the direction $c'y$, for, at temperatures below 100° y lies in the area for potassium chloride and represents solutions which are supersaturated for potassium chloride. This salt, therefore, will be deposited, until, at 0°, the solution attains the composition represented by y. At this point the solid potassium chloride is separated from the solution. If the solution y is now evaporated at 100° deposition of sodium chloride takes place at the composition y', and the deposition continues until the point c' is again reached. The salt is separated and the solution cooled as before. This cycle of operations, which yields first sodium chloride and then potassium chloride, can be continued until all the solution is used up, or fresh solution can be introduced into the system at each evaporation.

From what has already been said in the preceding section, it will be easy to calculate, from the solubility data and the solubility diagram, the amount of water which must be evaporated off at each cycle and the amount of solid salt which will be deposited, and

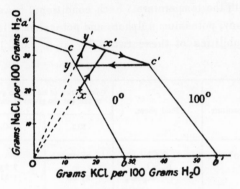

Fig. 191

so the process can be controlled. The following numbers, given by Blasdale, will serve as illustration:

	Composition of the solution.			Substances eliminated.
	NaCl.	KCl.	H₂O.	
At the outset .	20	14	100	—
At the point x' .	20	14	62·78	37·22 grams H_2O
,, ,, c' .	10·91	14	39·72	{ 9·09 ,, NaCl { 23·1 ,, H_2O
,, ,, y .	10·91	5·14	39·72	8·86 grams KCl
,, ,, y' .	10·91	5·14	31·83	7·89 ,, H_2O

Although the above cycle of operations has been carried out between the temperatures of 0° and 100°, it may also be carried out between any other two temperatures, *e.g.* 15° or 25° and 100°.[6] By means of quantitative calculations carried out in the manner already discussed, the conditions under which the cycle of operations may be most economically conducted may readily be decided in any given case.

Potassium Chloride–Potassium Sulphate–Water. The ease with which separation of mixtures of potassium chloride and sodium chloride into the pure salts can be effected is due to the fact that the solubility of potassium chloride varies considerably, whereas the solubility of sodium chloride varies but little with the temperature. That is, the ratio of KCl:NaCl in the solution saturated for the two salts (points c and c' in Fig. 190) varies markedly with the temperature. Such conditions, however, do not exist with, say, potassium sulphate and potassium chloride.

The solubilities of these two salts at $0°$ and $100°$ are as follows.[7]

Temperature.	Solid phase.	Composition of solution in grams of salt per 100 grams of water.	
		KCl.	K_2SO_4.
$0°$	KCl	28·20	—
	K_2SO_4	—	7·23
	KCl + K_2SO_4	27·88	1·21
$100°$	KCl	56·20	—
	K_2SO_4	—	23·44
	KCl + K_2SO_4	54·43	2·83

On plotting these numbers. the diagram shown in Fig. 192 is obtained, the curve acb being the isotherm for $0°$ and the curve $a'c'b'$ the isotherm for $100°$.

When a solution of the composition x is evaporated at $100°$

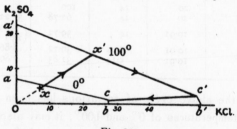

Fig. 192

potassium sulphate separates out at x' and continues to be deposited until the solution reaches the composition c'. At this point the potassium sulphate may be separated from the solution. Solution c', as will be seen, lies in what corresponds with area II in Fig. 190 (p. 392), and, consequently, when the solution is cooled down, separation of both potassium chloride and potassium sulphate takes place until the solution attains the composition c. Since the line joining O and c, when produced, cuts the curve $b'c'$, it follows that on evaporating the solution c at $100°$ potassium chloride will be deposited. The point of intersection, however, lies very near to the point c', so that only a small amount of potassium chloride, too small for industrial success, is deposited before the point c' is reached. In such a case as this, therefore, separation of the pure salts is not feasible, and one would have to be content with a separation into the potassium sulphate deposited in the first stage of the process and a mixture of the two salts containing about 5 per cent. of potassium sulphate.

In general, it can be said that when the ratio of the two salts in solutions saturated with respect to both salts at any two temperatures, t_1 and t_2, is the same, then separation of the two salts is impossible; and even when the ratio is not the same separation will be economically successful only when there is a sufficiently large variation of the ratio with temperature. With potassium sulphate and potassium chloride we find that the ratio $KCl : K_2SO_4$ is 23.04 at $0°$, and 19.23 at $100°$. The difference is too slight to make the separation feasible from an industrial point of view.

Ammonium Perchlorate–Ammonium Sulphate–Water. An interesting example of a multiple cycle process has been worked out by Freeth[8] for the separation of a mixture of equal weights of ammonium perchlorate and ammonium sulphate. The solubility data on which the process was based are as follows:

Temperature.	Solid phase.	Composition of solution per cent.		
		NH_4ClO_4.	$(NH_4)_2SO_4$.	H_2O.
25°	NH_4ClO_4	20·02	—	79·98
	$NH_4ClO_4 + (NH_4)_2SO_4$	3·0	41·70	55·30
	$(NH_4)_2SO_4$	—	43·5	56·5
60°	NH_4ClO_4	33·6	—	66·4
	$NH_4ClO_4 + (NH_4)_2SO_4$	8·2	40·9	50·9
	$(NH_4)_2SO_4$	—	46·8	53·2

For the process of separation the following flow-sheet was constructed. From 9823 grams of a mixture, having the composition 39.6 per cent. $(NH_4)_2SO_4$, 7.9 per cent. NH_4ClO_4 and 52.5 per cent. H_2O, there were deposited, at $25°$, 500 grams of perchlorate, and a mother liquor (9323 grams) was left having the composition 41.7 per cent. $(NH_4)_2SO_4$, 3.0 per cent. NH_4ClO_4, and 55.3 per cent. H_2O. This solution was evaporated at $60°$ until 318 grams of water had passed off, the concentrated solution (9005 grams) having the composition 43.2 per cent. $(NH_4)_2SO_4$, 3.1 per cent. NH_4ClO_4 and 53.7 per cent. H_2O. To this solution, at $60°$, there was added a mixture of 500 grams of $(NH_4)_2SO_4$ and 500 grams of NH_4ClO_4, giving 10,005| grams of a mixture of the composition 43.9 per cent. $(NH_4)_2SO_4$, 7.8 per cent. NH_4ClO_4 and 48.3 per cent. H_2O. From this mixture 500 grams of ammonium sulphate separated at $60°$, yielding a mother liquor (9505 grams) of the composition 40.9 per cent. $(NH_4)_2SO_4$, 8.2 per cent. NH_4ClO_4 and 50.9 per cent. H_2O. To this solution 318 grams of water were added, and the temperature lowered to $25°$, causing 500 grams of $(NH_4)ClO_4$ to separate. This completes the cycle, the mixture now being the same as the original one. This cyclic process can be repeated time after time, and at each cycle there is obtained, from the quantities taken, 500 grams of pure ammonium perchlorate and 500 grams of pure ammonium sulphate.[9]

By means of similar cyclic processes a separation can be effected with the salts potassium sulphate and potassium nitrate, potassium nitrate and sodium nitrate, sodium sulphate and sodium nitrate.[10]

When the two salts give rise to a double salt a more complicated procedure may be necessary for the separation of the single salts. A good example of this is given by the system ammonium sulphate——sodium sulphate——water, studied by Matignon and Meyer[11] Dawson,[12] Freeth[13] and others, and described below.[14]

Ammonium Sulphate–Sodium Sulphate–Water. This system differs markedly from those discussed in the preceding pages in the fact that a double salt, $(NH_4)_2SO_4$, Na_2SO_4, $4H_2O$, is formed, which decomposes into the single salts at $59.3°$. One of the component salts, also, crystallises from solution in the hydrated form, namely, $Na_2SO_4, 10H_2O$, at temperatures below $32°$. At $60°$ only the anhydrous single salts are stable.

The solubility values at $25°$ and at $60°$ are given in the following table:[15]

Temperature.	Solid phase.	Composition of solution per cent.		
		$(NH_4)_2SO_4$.	Na_2SO_4.	H_2O.
$25°$	$(NH_4)_2SO_4$	$43·4$	—	$56·6$
	$(NH_4)_2SO_4 + (NH_4)_2SO_4,$ $Na_2SO_4, 4H_2O$	$38·7$	$8·2$	$53·1$
	$(NH_4)_2SO_4, Na_2SO_4, 4H_2O$ $+ Na_2SO_4, 10H_2O$	$14·10$	$25·76$	$60·14$
	$Na_2SO_4, 10H_2O$	—	$21·71$	$78·29$
$60°$	$(NH_4)_2SO_4$	$46·80$	—	$53·20$
	$(NH_4)_2SO_4 + Na_2SO_4$	$36·91$	$16·33$	$46·76$
	Na_2SO_4	—	$31·20$	$68·80$

These values are represented graphically in Fig. 193, the triangular diagram being employed here. In this diagram the isotherm for $25°$ is represented by the curves AB, BC, CD, and the isotherm for $60°$ by the curves GH, HK. The lightly drawn lines delimit the areas of heterogeneous mixtures, as explained on page 342. Point E represents the composition of the hydrated double salt, and F the composition of sodium sulphate decahydrate.

Before passing to the description of the process by which a mixture of ammonium sulphate and sodium sulphate can be separated into the single salts, attention may be drawn to the fact that point H, which represents the composition of a solution saturated for both sodium sulphate and ammonium sulphate at $60°$, falls within the area for heterogeneous mixtures of double salt and solution at $25°$. A mixture, therefore, which has the composition H will, at $25°$, separate into solid double salt and a saturated solution, the composition of which will be given by joining EH and producing the line to meet the curve BC at x. Moreover, the relative weights of saturated solution and of solid double salt are given by the lengths of the lines EH and Hx.

The triangle GHY is the area of heterogeneous mixtures of

solid ammonium sulphate and saturated solution at 60°, and the triangle KHZ, similarly, is the area of heterogeneous mixtures of

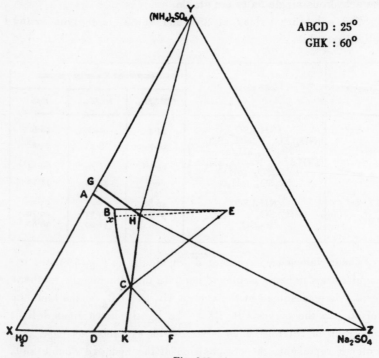

Fig. 193

anhydrous sodium sulphate and saturated solutions at 60°.

Based on the solubility data given above, the following process for the separation of a mixture of equal amounts of sodium sulphate and ammonium sulphate has been worked out by Freeth, the cycle of operations being indicated in Fig. 194, which represents portions of the two isotherms in the neighbourhood of the points B and H in Fig. 193.

Starting at 60° with 2632 grams of a liquor of composition represented by the point E in Fig. 194, namely, 24.5 per cent. $(NH_4)_2SO_4$, 10.8 per cent. Na_2SO_4, and 64.7 per cent. H_2O, 917 grams of the double salt are added (which give a mixture of composition F), and then 1000 grams of a fifty-fifty mixture of the two salts. In this way 4549 grams of a mixture (point D) having the composition, 32.8 per cent. $(NH_4)_2SO_4$, 25.5 per cent. Na_2SO_4, and 41.7 per cent. H_2O are obtained. Since D corresponds to a point on the line HZ in Fig. 193, the mixture deposits anhydrous

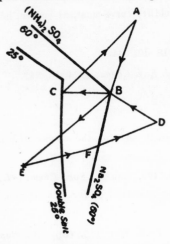

Fig. 194

sodium sulphate (500 grams) and gives 4049 grams of solution of composition B (Fig. 194). This solution, which corresponds to point H in Fig. 193, and has the composition 36.9 per cent. $(NH_4)_2SO_4$, 16.3 per cent. Na_2SO_4 and 46.8 per cent. H_2O, is cooled to 25°, and is allowed to deposit 917 grams of the double salt, the amount required for adding to the diluted liquor at E (see above). The mother liquor, C (3132 grams), is concentrated at 60° until it has the composition represented by point A,[16] namely, 51.0 per cent. $(NH_4)_2SO_4$, 12.6 per cent. Na_2SO_4 and 36.4 per cent. H_2O, the amount of water evaporated off being 887 grams. Point A corresponds to a point on the line HY in Fig. 193, and so deposits solid ammonium sulphate (500 grams) and gives 1745 grams of solution B, the composition of which has already been given. The solution B is then diluted by the addition of 887 grams of water to give 2632 grams of un-saturated solution of composition E. The cycle has thus been completed, and in its course the 1000 grams of mixture have been separated into 500 grams of each of the single salts.

NOTES

1. See Blasdale, *J. Ind. Eng. Chem.*, 1918, **10**, 344; Hildebrand, *ibid.*, 1918, **10**, 96; Reinders, *Z. anorgan. Chem.*, 1915, **93**, 202; Freeth, *Rec. trav. Chim.*, 1924, **43**, 475; *Thesis*, Leiden, 1924; Hamid, *J. Soc. Chem. Ind.*, 1926, **45**, 315 T; Schloesing, *Compt. rend.*, 1920, **171**, 977; Neumeister, *Caliche*, 1929, 11, 488.

2. See Blasdale, *J. Ind. Eng. Chem.*, 1918, **10**, 344.

3. It is important that the student should himself prepare the graphs referred to in this chapter, using a moderately large scale.

4. If the evaporation is carried out at some other temperature, say 100°, the corresponding isothermal solubility curve must, of course, be constructed.

5. Blasdale, *J. Ind. Eng. Chem.*, 1918, **10**, 344.

6. See Turrentine and Tanner, *J. Ind. Eng. Chem.*, 1924, **16**, 242.

7. Blasdale, loc. cit.

8. Rec. trav. chim., 1924, **43**, 475.

9. The student should prepare a graph showing the course of the separation.

10. Hamid, *J. Chem. Soc.*, 1926, pp. 199, 206; *J. Soc. Chem. Ind.*, 1926, **45**, 315 T. For other cases, see Blasdale, *J. Ind. Eng. Chem.*, 1918, **10**, 344.

11. *Compt. rend.*, 1917, **165**, 787; 1918, **166**, 115, 686; *Annales Chim. Phys.*, 1918, **9**, 251.

12. *J. Chem. Soc.*, 1918, **113**, 675.

13. Freeth, Rec. trav. chim., 1924, **43**, 475.

14. See also the previous discussion of this system, p. 369.

15. Freeth, loc. cit. Leiden, 1924.

16. The direction of the line CA is, of course, obtained by joining the angle of the triangle representing pure water (Fig. 193) with the point C and producing to A.

SECTION 5: SYSTEMS OF MORE THAN THREE COMPONENTS

CHAPTER XIX

FOUR-COMPONENT SYSTEMS

In the systems which have so far been studied we have met with cases where two or three components could enter into combination; but in no case did we find double decomposition occurring.[1] The reason for this is that in the systems previously studied, in which double decomposition might have been possible, namely, in those systems in which two salts acted as components, the restriction was imposed that either the basic or the acid constituent of these salts must be the same; a restriction imposed, indeed, for the very purpose of excluding double decomposition. A system formed of water and three salts with a common ion will constitute a four-component or quaternary system; and, if the restriction that the salts have a common ion be allowed to drop, two salts along with water will give rise to a four-component system for double decomposition between the salts is then possible.

Hitherto, in connection with four-component systems, the attention has been directed chiefly to the study of aqueous solutions of salts, and more especially of the salts which occur in sea-water, *i.e.* chiefly the sulphates and chlorides of magnesium, potassium, and sodium.[2] The importance of these investigations will be recognised when one recollects that by the evaporation of sea-water there have been formed the enormous salt-beds at Stassfurt, which constitute at present the chief source of the sulphates and chlorides of magnesium and potassium. The investigations, therefore, are not only of great geological interest as tending to elucidate the conditions under which these salt-beds have

403

been formed, but are of no less importance for the industrial working of the deposits.

I. Water and Three Salts with Common Ion.

Water and three salts with a common ion constitute a system of four components, and a brief discussion of such systems may be given here for the purpose more especially of explaining the methods by which the composition of such systems can be represented graphically.

Just as we saw (p. 340) that the equilateral triangle can be employed for the isothermal representation of the composition of a ternary system, so, for the isothermal representation of the composition of a quaternary system one may employ a regular tetrahedron, each face of which is an equilateral triangle and the edges of which are all equal (Fig. 195). If the four components A, B, C, D, are represented by the four corners of the tetrahedron then it is clear that points on one of the edges will represent binary systems, points on a triangular face will represent ternary systems, and points within the tetrahedron will represent quaternary systems. Thus, the point a (Fig. 195) represents the composition of a solution of the two components A and D in equilibrium with one solid phase (A); d represents the composition of the ternary solution, containing A, B and D in equilibrium with two solid phases (A and B); and g represents the composition of a quaternary solution in equilibrium with three solid phases A, B and C. The composition represented by g can be obtained by drawing from g a line, parallel to AC or AB or AD, so as to cut the face BCD of the tetrahedron. The length of this line gives the proportional (percentage) amount of A in the quaternary solution g. Similarly, by drawing lines parallel to BA or BC or BD and to CA or CB or CD, so as to cut the faces ADC and ADB respectively, the length of the lines so obtained gives the proportional amounts of B and C. Lastly, by drawing from g a line parallel to DA, DB, or DC, so as to cut the face ABC, the amount of D in the quaternary mixture is obtained.

In Fig. 195, it may be mentioned, the curves dg, eg and fg represent quaternary solutions in equilibrium with two solid phases, while the areas *adgf*, *bdge* and *cegf* represent quaternary solutions in equilibrium with a single solid phase A, B, or C.[3]

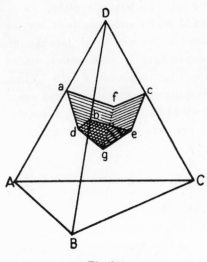

Fig. 195

Although a three-dimensional method of representation is necessary in order to give a complete picture of the isothermal conditions in a quaternary system, it is very convenient, for practical purposes, to make use of a plane diagram. Such a diagram can be obtained by projecting the curves in Fig. 195 *perpendicularly* on the base of the tetrahedron. The vertex of the tetrahedron (D) then comes to lie at the centre D of the triangle ABC (Fig. 196), and the edges AD, BD and CD find their projections in the three medians AD, BD and CD.

In order to plot the results of experiment in the plane triangular diagram it has to be borne in mind that while the composition of the quaternary solution is expressed in terms of the four components, namely, x per cent. A, y per cent. B, z per cent. C, w per cent. D, the projection of this point in the tetrahedron can represent only the relative proportions, x', y', and z' of the three components A, B, and C. To obtain the position of this point in the triangular diagram, therefore, $w/3$ is added to the actual percentages x, y, and z, and we fix a point x', y', z' in the triangle such that $x' = x + w/3$, $y' = y + w/3$, and $z' = z + w/3$.

The same diagram can be obtained without adding $w/3$ to each percentage if x, y and z are plotted directly on axes at $120°$ to each other, that is, by measuring off x along DA, then y from this point parallel to DB, then z from this point parallel to DC.

It should be noted that unless other information is appended to the diagram such as the water content at each point, it is impossible to "read back" the composition of each point from the diagram, except for points which are known to be on the surface of the tetrahedron (and therefore belong only to a ternary system).

Instead of projecting the solid model *orthogonally* it may be projected *perspectively* according to the method of Jänecke (cf. pp. 341 and 421). To plot compositions by this method means finding the percentage of each salt *in the dissolved salts*. Thus, in the above example, the percentage of A actually plotted would be $100x/(x + y + z)$, that of B would be $100y/(x + y + z)$ and that of C $100z/(x + y + z)$, these percentages being plotted in the

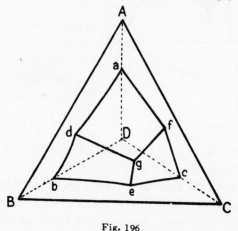

Fig. 196

usual way on an equilateral triangle. It would still be necessary, of course, to know the water content for each point and these may be given as data accompanying the diagram or indicated graphically on a vertical axis erected on the triangle.

Instead of using the regular tetrahedron to represent isothermal behaviour in such quaternary systems Lodochnikov[4] has proposed a right-angled isosceles triangle, in which quaternary solutions are represented by *vectors*. The method of plotting is illustrated in Fig. 197 in which AD equals AB. Any point within the triangle ABD represents one or a hundred grams or moles of solution. A solution containing, for instance, 0.1 moles of the first component, 0.4 of the second, 0.3 of the third and 0.2 of the fourth is represented by the vector FG where EF = 0.1, FG = 0.4, GH = 0.3 and HJ = EA = 0.2. Thus a quaternary solution is denoted by a vector. Analogously, a series of solutions, such as would be represented in the usual tetrahedron by lines, is denoted by an area enclosing a group of these vectors such as $wxyz$ in the figure. In like manner a surface within the tetrahedron becomes two overlapping areas.

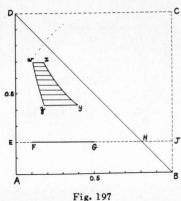

Fig. 197

It will be seen that the complete isotherm is a difficult one to interpret and this constitutes a major disadvantage of it. The method is not in common use for this and other reasons. It has been shown[5] that the Lodochnikov method, modified so that the triangle ABD is equilateral, is really equivalent to two simultaneous projections of the usual tetrahedron on one face of the latter.

Lithium Sulphate–Ammonium Sulphate–Ferrous Sulphate–Water. The equilibria in quaternary systems in which three salts with a common ion together with water are the components have been investigated by Schreinemakers,[6] and the results obtained for the system water — lithium sulphate — ammonium sulphate — ferrous sulphate at 30° are represented by the orthogonal projection method in Fig. 198, and summarised in the table on p. 408.

The solid phases which occur are $(NH_4)_2SO_4$; $Li_2SO_4 \cdot H_2O$; $FeSO_4 \cdot 7H_2O$; $LiNH_4SO_4$ (= D_{Li}); and $Fe(NH_4)_2(SO_4)_2 \cdot 6H_2O$ (= D_{Fe}). Since the double salt D_{Li} is anhydrous it is represented by a point on the side of the triangle Li—NH4; but the hydrated salts are represented by points within the triangle, as indicated in Fig. 198.

PERCENTAGE COMPOSITION OF SOLUTIONS AT 30°.

Point.	Solid phase.	Per cent. FeSO₄.	Per cent. Li₂SO₄.	Per cent. (NH₄)₂SO₄.
a	$FeSO_4 . 7H_2O$	24·87	—	—
b	$Li_2SO_4 . H_2O$	—	25·1	—
c	$(NH_4)_2SO_4$	—	—	44·27
d	$FeSO_4 . 7H_2O + Li_2SO_4 . H_2O$	16·1	16·5	—
e	$Li_2SO_4 . H_2O + D_{Li}$	—	21·88	12·46
f	$(NH_4)_2SO_4 + D_{Li}$	—	6·59	39·55
g	$(NH_4)_2SO_4 + D_{Fe}$	0·79	—	43·86
h	$FeSO_4 . 7H_2O + D_{Fe}$	25·22	—	5·93
k	$FeSO_4 . 7H_2O + Li_2SO_4 . H_2O + D_{Fe}$	16·85	15·62	4·82
l	$Li_2SO_4 . H_2O + D_{Fe} + D_{Li}$	4·15	20·03	12·32
m	$(NH_4)_2SO_4 + D_{Fe} + D_{Li}$	0·61	6·23	40·48
p	D_{Fe}	13·13	—	11·45
q	D_{Li}	—	16·58	19·29

The different areas *adkh, bdke,* etc., of the projection figure represent the composition of solutions with which the single solid phases $FeSO_4 \cdot 7H_2O$, $Li_2SO_4 \cdot H_2O$, etc., can exist. Since the curves separating two areas represent solutions in equilibrium

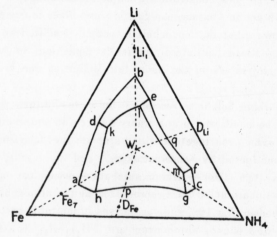

Fig. 198

with the two solid phases belonging to these areas, it follows that solid phases belonging to adjacent areas can coexist with solution, but solid phases belonging to areas which are not adjacent cannot coexist with solution. Thus $FeSO_4 \cdot 7H_2O$ can coexist with $Li_2SO_4 \cdot H_2O$ and with D_{Fe}, but it cannot coexist with D_{Li} or with $(NH_4)_2SO_4$. From the figure we see that D_{Fe} can coexist with all the other solid phases in contact with solution.

II. Reciprocal Salt-Pairs.

Choice of Components. When two salts undergo double decomposition the interaction can be expressed by an equation such as

$$NH_4Cl + NaNO_3 \rightleftharpoons NaCl + NH_4NO_3.$$

Since one pair of salts — $NaCl + NH_4NO_3$ — is formed from the other pair — $NH_4Cl + NaNO_3$ — by double decomposition, the two pairs of salts are known as *reciprocal salt-pairs*.[7] It is with systems in which the component salts form reciprocal salt-pairs that we have now to deal.

It must be noted that the four salts formed by two reciprocal salt-pairs do not constitute a system of four, but only of three components. This will be understood if it is recalled that only so many constituents are taken as components as are necessary to *express* the composition of all the phases present (p. 11); and it will be seen that the composition of each of the four salts which can be present together can be expressed in terms of three of them. Thus, for example, with NH_4Cl, $NaNO_3$, NH_4NO_3, $NaCl$, we can express the composition of NH_4Cl by $NH_4NO_3 + NaCl - NaNO_3$; or of $NaNO_3$ by $NH_4NO_3 + NaCl - NH_4Cl$. In all these examples it will be seen that negative quantities of one of the components must be employed; but that we have seen to be quite permissible (p. 11). The *number* of components is, therefore, three; and any three of the four salts can be chosen.

Since, then, two reciprocal salt-pairs constitute only three components or independently variable constituents, another component is necessary in order to obtain a four-component system. As such, we shall choose water.

Transition Point. In the formation of double salts from two single salts we saw that there was a point—the *quintuple point*—at which five phases could coexist. This point we also saw to be a transition point, on one side of which the double salt, on the other side the two single salts in contact with solution, were found to be the stable system. A similar behaviour is found in the case of reciprocal salt-pairs. The four-component system, two reciprocal salt-pairs and water, can give rise to an invariant system in which the six phases, four salts, solution, vapour, can coexist; the temperature at which this is possible constitutes a *sextuple point*. This sextuple point is also a transition point, on the one side of which the one salt-pair, on the other side the reciprocal salt-pair, is stable in contact with solution.

The sextuple point is the point of intersection of the curves of six univariant systems, viz. four solubility curves with three solid phases each, a vapour-pressure curve for the system: two reciprocal salt-pairs—vapour; and a transition curve for the condensed system: two reciprocal salt-pairs—solution. If we omit the vapour phase and work under atmospheric pressure (in open vessels), we find that the transition point is the point of intersection of four solubility curves.

Just as with three-component systems we saw that the presence of one of the single salts along with the double salt was necessary in order to give a univariant system, so in the four-component systems the presence of a third salt is necessary as solid phase along with one of the salt-pairs. In the reciprocal salt-pairs mentioned above the transition point would be the point of intersection of the solubility curves of the systems with the following groups of salts as solid phases. Below the transition point:

$$NH_4Cl + NaNO_3 + NaCl; \quad NH_4Cl + NaNO_3 + NH_4NO_3;$$

above the transition point:

$$NaCl + NH_4NO_3 + NaNO_3; \quad NaCl + NH_4NO_3 + NH_4Cl,$$

and at the transition point the phase reaction on withdrawal of heat from the system would be $NaCl + NH_4NO_3 \rightarrow NH_4Cl + NaNO_3$. From this we see that the two salts NH_4Cl and $NaNO_3$ would be able to exist together with solution below the transition point, but not above it. This transition point has not been determined.

Solubility and Transition Point. The transition point, we have seen, is the point of intersection of four solubility curves (absence of vapour and constant pressure being assumed), and it has been shown by van't Hoff[8] that at this point the products of the solubilities of the salts of the two salt-pairs are equal. At any other temperature, the salt-pair with the lower solubility product will be the stable salt-pair. Thus, from the solubility values of the single salts at a given temperature, it is possible to state which of the salt-pairs is stable at that temperature.

For the reciprocal salt-pairs $NaCl + NH_4HCO_3$ and $NaHCO_3 + NH_4Cl$, to be discussed later (p. 431), the solubilities of the four single salts, in moles per litre, at $0°$, are 6.1, 1.5, 0.82 and 5.57 respectively. We have, therefore, 6.1 ✗ 1.5(= 9.15) > 0.82 ✗ 5.57 (= 4.57). At $0°$, therefore, the stable salt-pair is $NaHCO_3 + NH_4Cl$; and the two salts $NaCl$ and NH_4HCO_3 cannot coexist in presence of solution.

For the reciprocal salt-pairs[9] $Na_2Cl_2 + (NH_4)_2B_4O_7$ and $(NH_4)_2Cl_2 + Na_2B_4O_7$, the salts Na_2Cl_2 and $(NH_4)_2Cl_2$ yield, on complete ionisation, four ions, while the borates yield only three. In calculating the products of concentrations, therefore, the solubility values (in moles) for the two chlorides must be raised to the fourth power, and those for the borates to the third power.[10] At $0°$, we have,

$$C^4_{Na_2Cl_2} \times C^3_{(NH_4)_2B_4O_7} = 3.035^4 \times 0.203^3 = 0.7098$$
$$C^4_{(NH_4)_2Cl_2} \times C^3_{Na_2B_4O_7} = 2.761^4 \times 0.0549^3 = 0.00962.$$

The stable salt-pair is therefore $NH_4Cl + Na_2B_4O_7$.

Formation of Double Salts. In many four-component systems the transition point is not a point at which one salt-pair passes into its reciprocal, but one at which a double salt is formed. Thus, at $4.4°$, Glauber's salt and potassium chloride form glaserite and sodium chloride with the absorption of heat, according to the equation

$$2Na_2SO_4, 10H_2O + 3KCl \rightarrow K_3Na(SO_4)_2 + 3NaCl + 20H_2O,$$

the water formed then giving saturated solution. Above the transition point, therefore, there could be $K_3Na(SO_4)_2$ and $NaCl$ coexisting with KCl and solution; and it may be considered that at a higher temperature the double salt would interact with the potassium chloride according to the equation

$$K_3Na(SO_4)_2 + KCl \rightarrow 2K_2SO_4 + NaCl,$$

thus giving the reciprocal of the original salt-pair. This point has, however, not been experimentally realised.[11]

Transition Interval. A double salt, we learned (p. 351), when brought in contact with water at the transition point, undergoes partial decomposition with separation of one of the constituent salts; and only after a certain range of temperature (transition interval) has been passed, can a pure saturated solution of the double salt be obtained. A similar behaviour is also found with reciprocal salt-pairs. For each salt-pair there will be a certain range of temperature, called the transition interval, within which, if excess of the salt-pair is brought into contact with water, interaction will occur and one of the salts of the reciprocal salt-pair will be deposited. For the salt-pair which is stable below the transition point the transition interval will extend down to a certain temperature below the transition point, and for the salt-pair which is stable above the transition point the transition interval will extend up to a certain temperature above the transition point. Only when the temperature is below the lower limit or above the upper limit of the transition interval will it be possible to prepare a solution saturated only for the one salt-pair. For ammonium chloride and sodium nitrate the lower limit of the transition interval is $5.5°$, so that above this temperature and up to that of the transition point (unknown) ammonium chloride and sodium nitrate in contact with water will give rise to a third salt by double decomposition, viz., sodium chloride.[12]

Graphic Representation. For the graphic representation of the isothermal equilibria in systems formed by two reciprocal salt-pairs and water two methods are commonly employed, one due to Löwenherz and the other to Jänecke.[13] In these systems, it may be recalled, an isotherm can be represented completely only by a three-dimensional model.

A. According to the (original) method of Löwenherz[14] four axes are chosen intersecting at a point like the edges of a regular tetrahedral pyramid (Fig. 199). Along each of the four edges is measured the number of equivalent gram-molecules of the four salts in a fixed amount of water. The salts with a common ion must be measured along adjacent axes. Thus, if we consider the reciprocal salt-pairs (Na, K)—(NO$_3$, Cl), we may measure moles of NaNO$_3$ along OA, moles of KNO$_3$ along OB, moles of KCl along OC and moles of NaCl along OD. If we consider the salt-pairs (Na, K)—(SO$_4$, Cl) we may measure moles of Na$_2$SO$_4$ along OA, moles of K$_2$SO$_4$ along OB, moles of K$_2$Cl$_2$ along OC and moles of Na$_2$Cl$_2$ along OD, the formulae of the latter two being doubled to retain the property of equivalence to the first two. It is in the sense of such equivalent gram-molecules that we shall thenceforth use the term 'mole'.

To represent the composition x moles of B, y of C and z of D per 1000 moles of water, say, we measure off along OB and OC the lengths Ob and Oc equal to x and y respectively. From the points b and c lines ba and ca are drawn parallel to OC and OB. The point of intersection a (Fig. 199) then represents a solution containing xB and yC ($ab = y$; $ac = x$). From a a line aP is drawn parallel to OD and equal to z. P then represents the solution of the above composition.

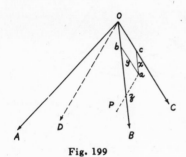

Fig. 199

It will be understood from the general method of construction that the same point, P, will be reached if one first of all measures off on OC and OD lengths equal to y and z respectively, draws from the points so obtained lines parallel to OD and OC respectively, and then, from the point of intersection draws a line of length x, parallel to the edge OB.

It should be pointed out here that the composition of each of the four anhydrous salts is represented by a point an infinite distance from O along the corresponding edge of the pyramid so that the model extends downwards to infinity. As the model has no definite dimensions extrapolation to the composition of the solid phases is impossible with this method of plotting.

The difficulty just referred to can be avoided by using the
method of Schreinemakers[15] according to which the concentration
of the salts is plotted in terms of the number of moles of salt in
100 moles of total mixture (including water.)[16] This gives a regular tetrahedral pyramid of finite dimensions in which the base is
a square and the altitude is equal to one half the diagonal of the
base as in Fig. 200. Points may be plotted in the manner described for Fig. 199.

Fig. 200 shows a typical isotherm for a reciprocal salt-pair

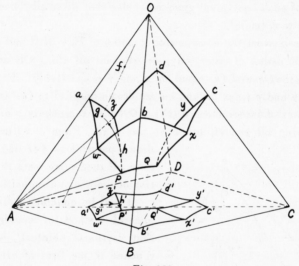

Fig. 200

(Schreinemakers' method). It is seen to consist of four surfaces,
$awPz$, $bxQPw$, $cyQx$ and $dzPQy$, representing solutions saturated
with A, B, C and D respectively. It may therefore be imagined
that every point on, say, $awPz$ is joined by a tie line to A and
similarly for the other surfaces. There is thus a sheaf of tie lines
for each surface, each sheaf filling an element of volume within
the pyramid. The triangular faces of the pyramid, it will be seen,
correspond to the four ternary systems comprising the quaternary
system (cf. Fig. 156, p. 342). The lines of intersection of adjacent
surfaces, wP, xQ, yQ, zP and PQ, denote solutions saturated with the
two corresponding solids and the points P and Q liquids saturated with

three solids. The volume above the four surfaces represents unsaturated solutions which are trivariant at the temperature and pressure of the diagram. Similarly the equilibria represented by the surfaces are bivariant, those by the lines univariant and those by the points invariant. There are seven more elements of volume representing solid-liquid equilibria in addition to the four mentioned above. These are, of course, also situated below the saturation surfaces, and are all irregularly shaped tetrahedra. Five of the seven denote liquids saturated with two solids and two denote liquids saturated with three solids. Their location can readily be visualised. It is to be noticed that, according to this diagram, B and D, but not A and C, can coexist with solution: B and D are therefore the stable salt-pair.

If the data are plotted according to the original Löwenherz method the general aspect of the figure is not greatly altered. The tie-lines of each sheaf which radiate from A, B, C and D, however, are all effectively parallel, for A, B, C and D are at infinity.

We may briefly refer here to the process of isothermal evaporation and postpone more detailed discussion of it until a better method of graphical representation has been described. Suppose a quaternary liquid f is evaporated at the temperature of the isotherm. The total composition of the system will follow the prolongation of Of away from O. When g, on the surface $awPz$ is reached, solid A will begin to separate, and as the complex passes below this surface the composition of the liquid alters along the curved line gh which is the locus of the ends of the tie lines (radiating from A) which the complex successively intersects. When the solution reaches h, solid D, as well as solid A, is deposited and the liquid follows hP. At P the solution dries up while depositing A, D and B. The curve gh is a "one-solid" crystallisation path. Obviously there are an infinite number of such paths lying on the surface $awPz$ and radiating from A. In a similar manner it can be shown that the other three surfaces are crossed by imaginary curves radiating from b, c and d.

It is more convenient, however, not to employ the three-dimensional figure, but its vertical or orthogonal projection on the base of the pyramid. This is shown in Fig. 201, the points being lettered to correspond with those on the solid model. The relation of the projection to the pyramid is shown by including a pictorial projection in Fig. 200 which is also lettered to correspond. The projection of the edges of the pyramid form two axes at right angles and give rise to four quadrants similar to those employed for the representation of ternary solutions (p. 340). The significance of each point is obvious. All the lines in this projection, including the crystallisation paths such as $g'h'$ will normally be slightly curved, although, for lack of data, they are commonly drawn straight.

Many systems are known which do not follow the simple behaviour portrayed in Figs. 200 and 201. There may be more than four surfaces as a result of the formation of additional solid phases such as double salts, but the principles discussed are readily extended to them. It may be observed that if, on the

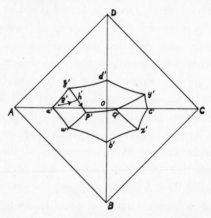

Fig. 201

orthogonal projection, the point representing the composition of the solid phase lies outside of the field for liquids saturated with that solid, it does not by any means follow that this solid is incongruently saturating. Point A, for example, lies outside of the area $a'w'P'z'$ but A is not incongruently saturating. This is to be contrasted with the perspective projection to be described later.

The orthogonal projection of the original Löwenherz solid model presents a similar appearance except, of course, that there are no limits to the figure. Its interpretation should present no difficulty.

The method of plotting data on such orthogonal projections is a matter which deserves special consideration for it can present real difficulties to the student. The Schreinemakers modification of the Löwenherz method is not, surprisingly, in common use, so we shall suppose that our data are expressed in moles of each of the salts in 1000 moles of water, bearing in mind the special meaning attributed to 'mole of salt' on p. 413. Let us again represent the salts by A, B, C and D so that $A + C \rightleftharpoons B + D$. Consider a solution which contains 10 moles of A, 30 of C and 40 of D in 1000 moles of water. In order to plot this composition we measure 10 moles along OA (Fig. 202), 30 back toward C (i.e.,

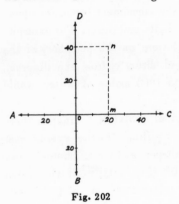

Fig. 202

to m), and finally 40 from m parallel to OD to give n. It will be realised that x moles of A corresponds *graphically* to $-x$ moles of C and *vice versa*, and that y moles of B corresponds to $-y$ moles of D and *vice versa*. We can express, therefore, this same composition as 10 moles of B, 20 of C and 50 of D (per 1000 moles of water). Or we can express it either as 50 moles of A, -40 of B and 70 of C or as -20 of A, 30 of B and 70 of D. There are thus four sets of three independent concentration variables which can express the composition of this solution, two sets of which will involve only positive quantities and two sets of which will involve a negative quantity, any of which will give the same point (n) when plotted. It is obviously desirable, in tabulating data, to express the concentrations in positive quantities. Of the two sets which give positive quantities it is generally preferable to use that set which includes the salt-pair which is stable at that particular temperature.

In spite of the ease with which such data can be plotted one must not lose sight of the fact that it is not possible to "read back" the composition of the solution from the position of the point on the projection. This is because any number of concentrations can give the same point, thus emphasising the inadequacy of two dimensions for the representation of three independent variables. Any of the following sets of data, for instance, will give point n on the projection: 20 moles of C, 40 of D and none of A or B; 20 of A, 40 of C and 40 of D; 30 of B, 20 of C and 70 of D. Thus any such projection, in order to be completely informative, must be accompanied by additional data, such as the total number of moles of salt per 1000 moles of water, from which the correct set of data can be found. This is not true, however, for points which are on the periphery of the pyramid, such as points w, x, y and z of Fig. 200, for these are in the component ternary systems and therefore must contain only two salts and water. For example, if it were known that n (Fig. 202) were on the periphery of the projection its composition, as read directly from the diagram, viz., 20 moles of C and 40 of D to 1000 moles of water, would be unequivocal.

As an example of the orthogonal projection diagram there may be given one representing the equilibria in the system composed of water and the reciprocal salt-pair sodium sulphate—potassium chloride for the temperature 0° (Fig. 203)[17] which is just below the transition temperature referred to on p. 411. The amounts of the different salts are measured along the four axes and the composition of the solution is expressed in moles per 1000 moles of water.

The outline of this figure represents four ternary solutions in which the component salts have a common acid or basic constituent; viz. sodium chloride—sodium sulphate, sodium sulphate—potassium sulphate, potassium sulphate—potassium- chloride, potassium chloride—sodium chloride. These four sets of curves are therefore similar to those discussed in Chapter XVII. Under particular conditions the "compound" glaserite, $K_3Na(SO_4)_2$, is formed. According to van't Hoff and Barschall[18] glaserite is an isomorphous mixture, but Gossner[19] considers it to be a definite compound having the formula $K_3Na(SO_4)_2$. More recent work,[20] however, confirms the opinion that its composition is somewhat variable: it should not, therefore, be called a compound. Point X gives the composition of the solution saturated for Glauber's salt, potassium sulphate and glaserite; point XI gives the composition of the solution saturated for Glauber's salt, potassium chloride and glaserite, and point XII the composition of the solution saturated for potassium sulphate, potassium chloride and glaserite.

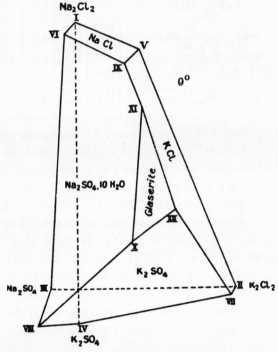

Fig. 203

The lines which pass inwards from the boundary curves represent solutions containing three salts in contact with only two solid phases; and the points where three lines meet, or where three fields meet, represent solutions in equilibrium with three solid phases, with the phases, namely, belonging to the three concurrent fields.

The numerical data from which Fig. 203 was constructed are contained in the table below, which gives the composition of the different solutions at 0°.

Point.	Solid phases.	Composition of solution in gram-mols. per 1000 gram-mols. water.				Total number of salt-molecules.
		Na_2Cl_2.	K_2Cl_2.	Na_2SO_4.	K_2SO_4.	
I.	NaCl	53·84	—	—	—	53·84
II.	KCl	—	34·05	—	—	34·05
III.	Na_2SO_4, $10H_2O$	—	—	5·85	—	5·85
IV.	K_2SO_4	—	—	—	7·47	7·47
V.	NaCl ; KCl	48·58	12·75	—	—	61·33
VI.	NaCl ; Na_2SO_4, $10H_2O$	53·28	—	2·32	—	55·60
VII.	KCl ; K_2SO_4	—	33·66	—	1·25	34·91
VIII.	K_2SO_4 ; Na_2SO_4, $10H_2O$	—	—	7·99	9·30	17·29
IX.	NaCl ; KCl ; Na_2SO_4, $10H_2O$	49·44	9·43	—	3·75	62·62
X.	K_2SO_4 ; Glaserite ; Na_2SO_4, $10H_2O$	11·50	16·00	6·0	—	33·50
XI.	KCl ; Na_2SO_4, $10H_2O$; Glaserite	41·71	12·15	—	3·35	57·21
XII.	KCl ; K_2SO_4 ; Glaserite	19·41	21·48	2·87	—	43·76

From the aspect of these diagrams the conditions under which the salts can coexist can be read at a glance. Thus, for example, Fig. 203 shows that at 0° Glauber's salt and potassium chloride can exist together with solution; namely, in contact with solutions having the composition IX — XI. This temperature must therefore be below the transition point of this salt-pair (p. 411). On raising the temperature to 4.4° it is found that the curve X — XI moves so that the point XI coincides with point IX.[21] At this point, therefore, there will be *four* concurrent fields, viz. Glauber's salt, potassium chloride, glaserite and sodium chloride. But these four salts can coexist with solution only at the transition point; so that 4.4° is the transition temperature of the salt-pair: Glauber's salt — potassium chloride. At higher temperatures the lines VIII — X — XI move still further to the left, so that the field for Glauber's salt becomes entirely separated from the field for potassium chloride. This shows that at temperatures above the transition point the salt-pair Glauber's salt — potassium chloride cannot coexist in presence of solution.[22]

If it is desired to indicate only the mutual relationships of the different components and the conditions for their coexistence (*paragenesis*), a simpler diagram than Fig. 203 can be employed. Thus if the boundary curves of Fig. 203 are drawn so that they cut one another at right angles, a figure such as Fig. 204 is obtained, the Roman numerals here corresponding with those in Fig. 203.

B. According to the method of *Jänecke and Le Chatelier*[23], which possesses certain advantages over the method employed by Löwenherz, the composition of the solutions is expressed not in terms of salts, but in terms of ions, or of acid and basic radicals. Thus the composition of aqueous solutions formed from the

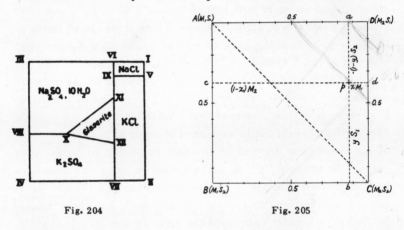

Fig. 204   Fig. 205

salt-pair $M_1S_1 + M_2S_2$ and its reciprocal pair, $M_1S_2 + M_2S_1$, can be represented in accordance with the scheme

$$xM_1, (1-x)M_2, yS_1, (1-y)S_2, mH_2O$$

where x, $(1-x)$, y, $(1-y)$ are the number of moles of the ions dissolved in m moles of water. The quantity x is thus the mole fraction of the ion M_1 in the total amount of dissolved basic radicals, y is the mole fraction of the ion S_1 in the total amount of dissolved acid radicals and m is the number of moles of water per mole of dissolved salt. These data are then plotted on a solid model (isotherm) consisting of a rectangular column on a square base. The four corners of the base represent the pure salts, salts with a common ion being placed at adjacent corners of the square

(Fig. 205). The sides AD and BC of the square will represent solutions containing different proportions of M_1 and M_2, and by dividing these sides in the ratio of x to $(1 - x)$, and joining the points a and b so obtained, the line ab will represent quaternary solutions in all of which the ratio of M_1 to M_2 is as x is to $(1 - x)$. Similarly, the line cd represents the composition of solutions in which the radicals S_1 and S_2 are present in the ratio y to $(1 - y)$. The point of intersection p will then, obviously, represent the solution having the composition xM_1, $(1 - x)M_2$, yS_1, $(1 - y)S_2$ dissolved in m moles of water.

We shall illustrate by plotting the composition of a solution containing 10 moles of M_1S_1, 30 of M_2S_2 and 40 of M_2S_1 per 1000 moles of water (cf. p. 413). In terms of ions there are 10 moles of M_1, $30 + 40 = 70$ of M_2, $10 + 40 = 50$ of S_1 and 30 of S_2 per 1000 moles of water, giving $x = 10/80 = 0.125$, $y = 50/80 = 0.625$ and $m = 1000/80 = 12.5$. This composition, insofar as the relative amounts of dissolved salts are concerned is plotted as point p in Fig. 205. It will be observed that p must lie within the triangle ADC for its composition is expressed in terms of positive amounts of the three salts denoted by the corners of that triangle; it is also in the triangle BCD so that its composition could also have been expressed in terms of positive quantities of B, C and D. It may be seen further that the same point p could have been located by finding the mole fraction of the *salts* in the dissolved salts, viz., 0.125 for M_1S_1, 0.375 for M_2S_2 and 0.50 for M_2S_1, and measuring off a distance 0.125 from D toward A and a distance 0.375 downward, parallel to the sides of the square. The distance of p thus found, from the diagonal AC, measured parallel to either side of the square, is seen to be 0.50, the amount of M_2S_1 in the solution. To represent the amount of water a perpendicular is erected at O, and a length corresponding with m moles is measured off; or better, a length $N = 100m/100 + m$ (see p. 342). The point in space so obtained represents the solution of the composition

$$xM_1 + (1 - x)M_2 + yS_1 + (1 - y)S_2 + mH_2O.$$

Generally, however, only the plane quadrangular diagram is employed, only the relative proportions of the salts being represented graphically, the amounts of water being indicated, when desired, by numerals.

It will be helpful to indicate the relation of this type of plot to the Löwenherz model described earlier. The Jänecke square is, in fact, the *perspective* projection of the Löwenherz tetragonal pyramid projected on the base, assuming that, according to the Schreinemakers procedure, the concentrations in the pyramid have been plotted in moles of each salt per fixed number of moles of total mixture. The Jänecke square is thus the pyramidal model viewed with the eye at the apex. It has certain definite advantages over the orthogonal projection which will become apparent later, not least among which is the fact that having plotted a point, its composition (apart from water content) can be "read back" from the diagram.

With reciprocal salt-pairs the simplest kind of behaviour is typified by Fig. 206 which should be compared with the typical orthogonal projection of Fig. 201 (p. 416). The metathesis is again, of course, represented by $A + C \rightleftharpoons B + D$, and lines within the square denote liquids saturated with two solids. In Fig. 206 B and D are obviously the stable salt-pair. The univariant lines are drawn straight in such diagrams because, as a rule, only their end points are determined experimentally. Sufficient data, however, would doubtless show that they are actually curved. It is to be observed that P is a congruently saturated solution (cf. p. 348) for it lies within the composition triangle formed by joining the compositions of the three solids with which it is in equilibrium. The same applies to Q. The fact that PQ, denoting liquids saturated with B and D, intersects the line joining B and D means that excess B and D and water can be mixed without a third salt separating. Alternatively, the three substances B, D and water form a stable ternary system at this temperature.

The representative behaviour just described may well alter with a change in the temperature of the system; it may, for instance, pass into the type of Fig. 207 where Q has now become an incongruently saturated solution and the system B-D-water is no longer a stable ternary one. Adding excess B and D to water, even

though these are still the stable salt-pair, must now result in the
formation of another solid, namely C. Further temperature change

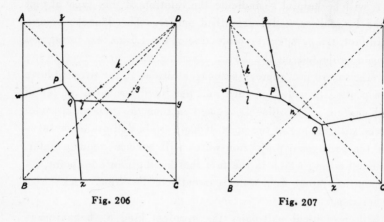

Fig. 206   Fig. 207

can result in Fig. 208 where P and Q have moved so as to coincide
at S. Point S is a solution saturated with the four solids A, B, C
and D; and, if vapour is present, there are six phases so that S
is a sextuple point referred to on p. 410). Obviously this can
occur only at a fixed temperature and pressure or, if the vessel is
open to the atmosphere, only at a fixed temperature. Continued
change of temperature may now give Fig. 209 where A and C are
now the stable salt-pair and G is an incongruently saturated solution. Still further change in temperature could result in FG intersecting AC making both **F and G** congruently saturated solutions.
A study of the changes wrought by altering the temperature and
shown in Figs. 206 to 209 will now make clear the meaning of
transition interval defined earlier (p. 412). The transition interval
for the salt-pair BD, for instance, is seen to be the interval between the temperature at which Q in Fig. 206 just crosses the
diagonal BD and the temperature of Fig. 208 (transition temperature).

As mentioned, the sequence of changes just described is the
simplest possible kind of behaviour, but, even so, the authors are
not aware of any salt systems which have been studied over a
large enough temperature range to bring out all the phenomena

referred to. Not infrequently there are complications arising from the formation of hydrates or double salts and this will mean additional fields in the diagram for liquids saturated with these solids. The system $Na_2SO_4 - KCl - H_2O$ (see p. 411) is such an example. Sometimes a *tetragene salt*, that is, one containing two different basic and two different acid radicals is formed. For example, in the system $MgSO_4 - KCl - H_2O$ at $85°$[24] kainite, $MgSO_4 \cdot KCl \cdot 3H_2O$, is found as a stable solid.[25] In addition there is the possibility of solid solution formation as in the system $NH_4Fe(SO_4)_2 - KAl(SO_4)_2 - H_2O$ at $25°$.[26]

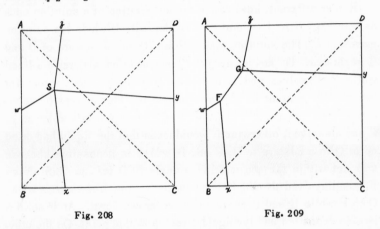

Fig. 208   Fig. 209

Isothermal Evaporation. The Jänecke projection is especially adapted to the study of the isothermal evaporation of solutions. Suppose, for instance, that in Fig. 206 the liquid k is evaporated at the temperature of the isotherm. As k lies within the field for liquids saturated with A, the latter will first be deposited. Loss of A from the solution will cause the liquid composition to follow the prolongation of Ak to l. On arrival at l the solution is now saturated with both A and B and will deposit both of these while following lP to P where it will remain constant in composition while drying up to a mixture of A, B and D. The evaporation of other solutions in the same figure is similarly treated and the direction of movement of the solution compositions is indicated by arrows. The line kl, it is to be noted, is straight, and herein lies another advantage of the Jänecke projection, for crystallisation paths, during the separation of a single solid, are straight lines on such a plot whereas they are curved lines on the orthogonal projection.[27] Each field on the Jänecke diagram is therefore crossed by straight lines, "one-solid" crystallisation paths, radiating from the point representing the composition of the corresponding solid phase. The latter points, it will be seen, can never lie outside of the diagram; on the orthogonal projection, however, they frequently radiate from some point outside of the boundaries of the areas for liquid.

Rather different, however, is the evaporation of a solution such as k in Fig. 207. Evaporation first deposits D while the solution moves to l. The solution then follows lQ and a mixture of D and C separates. On arrival at Q the concentration will remain fixed while C dissolves and B and more D separate, the composition being held constant by the presence of the four phases (constant atmospheric pressure). There will still be liquid left when all of C has dissolved, otherwise it would mean that the liquid had dried up at Q to a mixture to B, C and D, which is impossible because k is not within the composition triangle BCD (cf. p. 280). When C has dissolved the liquid composition is now free to move along Q to P while B and D continue to be thrown down. At P solid A is also deposited and the liquid dries up at that point. On the other hand, were the solution g evaporated it would dry up at Q, otherwise the series of changes would not be greatly different.[28]

The reader is reminded that we have assumed in the foregoing that any solids deposited in the evaporation have not been removed as deposited, but have been left available for re-solution if the equilibrium behaviour of the system at fixed total composition has demanded it. We shall describe an example later (p. 440) in which the solids, once deposited, are no longer available for re-solution.

Conversion Saltpetre. To illustrate the use of Jänecke's method of representation we may consider briefly the equilibria formed by the reciprocal salt-pairs $(Na,K) \rightarrow (NO_3,Cl)$ and water, which are of importance for the manufacture of conversion saltpetre, and which have been studied by Uyeda[29] and by Reinders.[30]

In this system no compounds or salt hydrates are formed.

In Fig. 210 is shown the projection isothermal for 25°, the faint-drawn lines representing *isohydrores* or lines of equal water content. At the four corners of the square are the pure salts, the numerals within brackets giving the-number of moles of water in which one mole of the salt dissolves. At A we have a solution

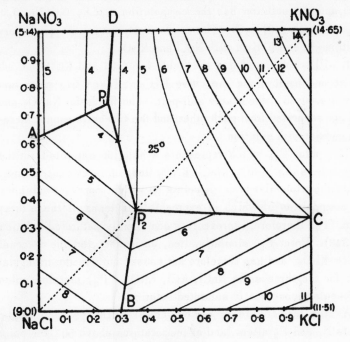

Fig. 210

which is saturated for both $NaNO_3$ and $NaCl$. Its composition is given by $1.00\,Na$, $0.624\,NO_3$, $0.376\,Cl$, $5.08\,H_2O$. At B the solution is in equilibrium with $NaCl$ and KCl as solid phases, and its composition is given by $0.303\,K$, $0.697\,Na$, $1.00\,Cl$, $7.63\,H_2O$. At C the solution has the composition represented by $1.00\,K$, $0.325\,NO_3$, $0.675\,Cl$, $8.00\,H_2O$, and is saturated for KCl and KNO_3; while at D the solution is in equilibrium with solid KNO_3 and $NaNO_3$, and has the composition $0.278\,K$, $0.722\,Na$, $1.00\,NO_3$, 3.38 H_2O.

The curves AP_1, DP_1, BP_2, and CP_2 represent the composition of quaternary solutions in equilibrium with two solid salts, and the points P_1 and P_2 solutions in equilibrium with three solid salts. At P_1 the solid phases are NaCl, KNO_3, $NaNO_3$, and the composition of the solution is given by 0.26 K, 0.74 Na, 0.74 NO_3, 0.26 Cl, 3.54 H_2O; and at P_2 the solid phases are NaCl, KNO_3, KCl, and the solution has the composition 0.36 K, 0.64 Na, 0.36 NO_3, 0.64 Cl, 5.01 H_2O. The curve P_1P_2 gives the quaternary solutions in equilibrium with NaCl and KNO_3.

It will be observed that the fields for NaCl and KNO_3 are adjacent and meet along the curve P_1P_2. These two salts are, therefore, at 25°, the stable salt-pair. The fields for $NaNO_3$ and KCl are separated from each other, and the two salts cannot therefore coexist with solution.

The point P_1, which represents a solution saturated for the three solid salts $NaNO_3$, NaCl, KNO_3 lies, as is evident, entirely within the triangular area all points on which represent solutions the composition of which is expressible in terms of these three salts. P_1, therefore, represents a congruently saturated solution (p. 348). Point P_2, similarly, lies, as is seen, on the diagonal NaCl—KNO_3, and has therefore not passed outside the triangular area for the three salts NaCl, KCl, KNO_3. P_2, therefore, also represents a congruently saturated solution.

As the temperature is raised, however, the position of the points P_1 and P_2 alters, and at temperatures above 50° the point P_2 passes outside the triangular area NaCl, KCl, KNO_3 into the triangular area NaCl, $NaNO_3$, KNO_3. Although the solution, therefore, is in equilibrium with the three salts NaCl, KCl, KNO_3, its composition is not expressible in positive quantities of these salts. Thus, at 100°, the solution saturated for NaCl, KCl, KNO_3 has the composition 35.9 grams NaCl, 47.0 grams $NaNO_3$, and 192.2 grams KNO_3 in 100 grams of water. The solution is thus incongruently saturated (p. 348). The solubilities at 5° and 100° are given in the following table, (p. 429).

From the information yielded by the isothermal diagrams based on the solubility data it is possible to decide the conditions under

Temperature.	Solid phases.	Composition of the solution.						
		Grams of salt in 100 grams of water.				xK, $(1-x)$Na, y NO$_3$, $(1-y)$Cl, m H$_2$O.		
		NaCl.	KCl.	NaNO$_3$.	KNO$_3$.	x.	y.	m.
5°	NaNO$_3$; KNO$_3$	—	—	82·10	18·1	0·155	1·00	4·80
	NaNO$_3$; KNO$_3$; NaCl	29·1	—	44·3	14·0	0·12	0·57	4·80
	NaCl; KCl; KNO$_3$	38·5	0·64	—	20·7	0·23	0·22	6·50
	NaCl; KCl	31·50	10·40	—	—	0·207	0	8·19
100°	NaNO$_3$; KNO$_3$	—	—	233·6	218·0	0·44	1·00	1·13
	NaNO$_3$; KNO$_3$; NaCl	6·5	—	207·5	194·6	0·43	0·975	1·24
	NaCl; KCl; KNO$_3$	35·9	—	47·0	192·2	0·62	0·80	1·81
	NaCl; KCl	27·3	36·2	—	—	0·51	0	5·83

which potassium nitrate can best be prepared by double decomposition between potassium chloride and sodium nitrate. Thus Reinders has found that the best yield of potassium nitrate, working between the temperatures 5° and 100°, is obtained in the following manner: 0.80 mole of sodium nitrate, 0.62 mole of potassium chloride and 1.81 moles of water are mixed together at 100°. There is deposited from the solution 0.42 mole of sodium chloride and a mother liquor is produced having the composition 0.38 Na, 0.62 K, 0.20 Cl, 0.80 NO$_3$, 1.81 H$_2$O. This solution is saturated for sodium chloride, and also for potassium nitrate and potassium chloride. Its composition corresponds to the point P$_2$ on the isotherm for 100°, and lies above the dotted line shown in Fig. 210.[31] The mother liquor is separated from the solid sodium chloride and cooled down to 5°. Since, however, at this temperature, the above solution would deposit not only potassium nitrate but also sodium chloride and sodium nitrate, 0.371 mole of water is added to the solution, so as to give the composition 0.62 K, 0.38 Na, 0.80 NO$_3$, 0.20 Cl, 2.181 H$_2$O. From this solution there crystallises out at 5°, 0.563 KNO$_3$ and a solution is left having the composition 0.057 K, 0.38 Na, 0.24 NO$_3$, 0.20 Cl, 2.18 H$_2$O. The cycle is then repeated by heating this solution to 100°, adding a mixture of 0.563 KCl + 0.563 NaNO$_3$ and evaporating off 0.371 H$_2$O. During the evaporation there separates out 0.563 NaCl. This is removed, the solution is diluted by addition of $0.371 H_2O$, and again cooled down to $5°$.

During the first cycle, therefore, $0.563 ✖ 100/0.62 = 90.8$ per cent. of the potassium chloride is recovered as potassium nitrate and, thereafter, 100 per cent. is recovered; from each 100 grams of solution at $100°$ there are obtained 0.461 mole or 46.6 grams of potassium nitrate.

General Description of the Method. Having discussed the process which may be employed for the production of potassium nitrate from potassium chloride and sodium nitrate, a general statement may now be given of the conditions under which one pair of salts belonging to a reciprocal salt-pair may be most efficiently obtained from the other salt-pair. Calling the salts forming the unstable or incompatible salt-pair the reactants, and the salts forming the stable or compatible salt-pair the resultants, we may state the general conditions for successful and efficient working by a multiple temperature cycle as follows.

To a solution, which is frequently called a *nucleus solution*, and which is used over and over again, equivalent quantities of the reactants are added in such amount as will produce a solution saturated with respect to one resultant only, at the upper limit of temperature used in the process, the other resultant remaining in solution. The mother liquor obtained, after separation of the solid resultant, is cooled down to such a temperature that the quantity of the second resultant deposited is equivalent to the amount of the first resultant removed at the higher temperature. After separation of the second resultant, the mother liquor will have the composition of the original nucleus solution, and the cycle of processes can then be repeated. If, at any stage of the cycle, water has to be added in order to adjust the composition of the solutions, this water is removed at a later stage of the cycle.

A consideration of the above conditions will show that the point in the equilibrium diagram representing saturation with respect to the one resultant, at the *higher* temperature, lies well within the saturation field of the second resultant at the *lower* temperature. From this it follows that an infinite number of nucleus solutions are theoretically possible, but since the object of the manufacturer is to obtain, during each operation, as large an amount of salt as possible per unit of volume of liquor, it usually happens that, for a particular pair of temperatures between which the process is carried out, there is a unique nucleus solution which gives the best results. This solution has almost always a composition such that when the appropriate equivalent amounts[32] of the reactants have been added to it at the higher temperature, and one of the resultants has separated out, a solution is obtained which is represented by a characterised point in the diagram, that is, by a point representing a solution saturated for three solid phases. Thus, in the case of the production of conversion saltpetre referred to above, the nucleus solution has the composition $0.057 K$, $0.38 Na$, $0.24 NO_3$, $0.20 Cl$, $2.18 H_2O$. On addition to this solution of a mixture of $0.563 KCl + 0.563 NaNO_3$ at $100°$, and after the evaporation of $0.371 H_2O$, a mother liquor is obtained having the composition $0.38 Na$, $0.62 K$, $0.20 Cl$, $0.80 NO_3$, $1.81 H_2O$. This solution is, as we have seen, saturated for sodium chloride, potassium nitrate and potassium chloride. During the evaporation, $0.563 NaCl$ separates out.

Ammonia - Soda Process. One of the most important applications of the Phase Rule to systems of four components with reciprocal salt-pairs has been made by Fedotieff[33] in his investigations of the conditions for the formation of sodium carbonate by the so-called ammonia-soda (Solvay) process.[34] This process consists, as is well known, in passing carbon dioxide through a solution of common salt saturated with ammonia.

Whatever differences of detail there may be in the process as carried out in different manufactories, the reaction which forms the basis of the process is that represented by the equation[35]

$$NaCl + NH_4HCO_3 \rightleftharpoons NaHCO_3 + NH_4Cl$$

We are dealing here, therefore, with reciprocal salt-pairs, the behaviour of which has just been discussed in the preceding pages. Since the study of the reaction is rendered more difficult on account of the fact that ammonium bicarbonate in solution, when under atmospheric pressure, undergoes decomposition at temperatures above $15°$, this temperature was the one chosen for the detailed

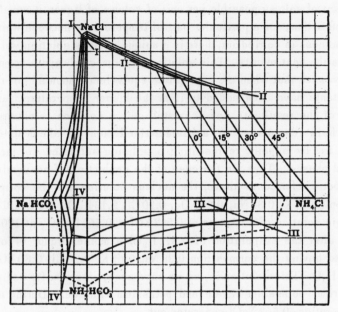

Fig. 211

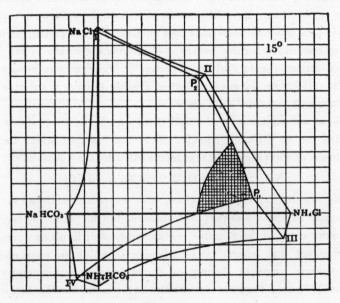

Fig. 212

investigation of the conditions of equilibrium. Since, further, it has been shown by Bodländer[36] that the bicarbonates possess a definite solubility only when the pressure of carbon dioxide in the solution has a definite value, the measurements were carried out in solutions saturated with this gas. While this really constitutes another component, the variance of the system remains unaltered because of the maintenance of the carbon dioxide pressure at a constant value.

In order to obtain the data necessary for a discussion of the conditions of soda formation by the ammonia-soda process, solubility determinations with the four salts, NaCl, NH_4Cl, NH_4HCO_3 and $NaHCO_3$ were made, first with the single salts and then with the salts in pairs. The results obtained are represented graphically in Fig. 211, which is an isotherm similar to that given in Fig. 203. The points I, II, III, IV represent the composition of solutions in equilibrium with two solid salts. We have, however, seen (p. 410) that the transition point, when the experiment is carried out under constant pressure (atmospheric pressure), is the point of intersection of four solubility curves, each of which represents the composition of solutions in equilibrium with three salts, viz. one of the reciprocal salt-pairs along with a third salt. Since it was found that the stable salt-pair at temperatures between $0°$ and $30°$ is sodium bicarbonate and ammonium chloride, determinations were made of the composition of solutions in equilibrium with $NaHCO_3 + NH_4Cl + NH_4HCO_3$ and with $NaHCO_3 + NH_4Cl + NaCl$ as solid

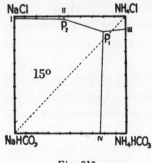

Fig. 213

phases. Under the conditions of experiment (temperature = $15°$) sodium chloride and ammonium bicarbonate cannot coexist in contact with solution. These determinations gave the data necessary for the construction of the complete isotherm (Fig. 212). For the sake of comparison, the results are also represented in the quadrangular diagram of Jänecke (Fig. 213). The most important of these data are given in the following table (temperature 15°):

Point.	Solid phases.	Composition of the solution in moles to 1000 grams of water.			
		NaHCO₃.	NaCl.	NH₄HCO₃.	NH₄Cl.
—	NaHCO₃	1·08	—	—	—
—	NaCl	—	6·12	—	—
—	NH₄HCO₃	—	—	2·36	—
—	NH₄Cl	—	—	—	6·64
I.	NaHCO₃; NaCl	0·12	6·06	—	—
II.	NaCl; NH₄Cl	—	4·55	—	3·72
III.	NH₄Cl; NH₄HCO₃	—	—	0·81	6·40
IV.	NaHCO₃; NH₄HCO₃	0·71	—	2·16	—
P₁	NaHCO₃; NH₄HCO₃; NH₄Cl	0·93	0·51	—	6·28
P₂	NaHCO₃; NaCl; NH₄Cl	0·18	4·44	—	3·73

With reference to the solution represented by the point P_1, it may be remarked that it is an incongruently saturated solution (p. 348); it lies, as we see from Fig. 213, in the triangular area, the points on which represent solutions the composition of which can be expressed in terms of the three salts $NaHCO_3$, $NaCl$, NH_4Cl, although the solid phases with which the solution is in equilibrium are $NaHCO_3$, NH_4HCO_3, NH_4Cl. If sodium chloride is added to this solution the composition of the latter undergoes change; and if a sufficient amount of the salt is added the solution P_2 is obtained.

Turning now to the practical application of the data so obtained, consider first what is the influence of concentration on the yield of soda. Since the reaction consists essentially of a double decomposition between sodium chloride and ammonium bicarbonate, then, after the deposition of the sodium bicarbonate, we obtain a solution containing sodium chloride, ammonium chloride and sodium bicarbonate. In order to ascertain to what extent the sodium chloride has been converted into solid sodium bicarbonate it is necessary to examine the composition of the solution which is obtained with definite amounts of sodium chloride and ammonium bicarbonate.

Consider, in the first place, the solutions represented by the curve P_2P_1. With the help of this curve we can state the conditions under which a solution, saturated for ammonium chloride, is obtained, after deposition of sodium bicarbonate. In the table below there is given the composition of the solutions which are obtained with different initial amounts of sodium chloride and ammonium bicarbonate. The last two columns give the percentage amount of the sodium used, which is deposited as solid sodium bicarbonate (U_{Na}); and likewise the percentage amount of ammonium bicarbonate which is usefully converted into sodium bicarbonate, that is to say, the amount of the radical HCO_3 deposited (U_{NH_4}):

Point.	Initial composition of the solutions: grams of salt to 1000 grams of water.		Composition of solutions obtained: moles per 1000 grams of water.				U_{Na} per cent.	U_{NH_4} per cent.
	NaCl.	NH₄HCO₃.	HCO₃.	Cl.	Na.	NH₄.		
P_2	479	295	0·18	8·17	4·62	3·73	43·4	95·1
—	448	360	0·31	7·65	3·39	4·56	55·7	93·4
—	417	431	0·51	7·13	2·19	5·45	69·2	90·5
P_1	397	496	0·92	6·79	1·44	6·28	78·8	85·1

This table shows that the greater the excess of sodium chloride, the greater is the percentage utilisation of ammonia (Point P_2); and the more the amount of sodium chloride decreases, the greater is the percentage amount of sodium chloride converted into bicarbonate. In the latter case, however, the percentage utilisation of the ammonium bicarbonate decreases; that is to say, less sodium bicarbonate is deposited, or more of it remains in solution.

Consider, in the same manner, the relations for solutions represented by the curve P_1IV, which gives the composition of solutions saturated with respect to sodium bicarbonate and ammonium bicarbonate. In this case we obtain the results given in the following table, (p. 436).

As is evident from this table, diminution in the relative amount of sodium chloride exercises only a slight influence on the utilisation of this salt, but is accompanied by a rapid diminution of the effective transformation of the ammonium bicarbonate. So far as the efficient conversion of the sodium is concerned we see that it reaches its maximum at the point P_1, and that it decreases both with increase and with decrease of the relative amount of sodium chloride employed; and faster, indeed, in the former than in the latter case. On the other hand, the effective transformation of the ammonium bicarbonate reaches its maximum at the point P_2, and diminishes with increase in the relative amount of ammonium bicarbonate employed. Since sodium chloride is, in comparison with ammonia—even when this is regenerated—a cheap material, it is evidently more advantageous to work with solutions which are relatively rich in sodium chloride (solutions represented by the curve P_1P_2). This fact has also been established empirically.

Point.	Initial composition of the solutions: grams of salt to 1000 grams of water.		Composition of solutions obtained: in moles per 1000 grams of water.				$U_{Na}.$	$U_{NH_4}.$
	NaCl.	NH₄HCO₃.	HCO₃.	Cl.	Na.	NH₄.		
P_1	397	496	0·92	6·79	1·44	6·28	78·8	85·1
—	351	446	0·99	6·00	1·34	5·65	77·7	82·5
—	316	412	1·07	5·41	1·27	5·21	76·4	79·5
—	294	389	1·12	5·03	1·23	4·92	75·5	75·1
—	234	327	1·30	4·00	1·16	4·14	71·0	68·6

When, as is the case in industrial practice, we are dealing with solutions wihch are saturated not for two salts but only for sodium bicarbonate, it is evident that we have then to do with solutions the composition of which is represented by points in the area P_1P_2I, IV. Since, in the commercial manufacture, the aim must be to obtain as complete a utilisation of the materials as possible, the solutions employed industrially must lie in the neighbourhood of the curves P_2P_1IV ,as is indicated by the shaded portion in Fig. 212.[37] The best results, from the manufacturer's standpoint, will be obtained, as already stated, when the composition of the solutions approaches that given by a point on the curve P_2P_1. Considered from the chemical standpoint, the results of the experiments lead to the conclusion that the Solvay process, i.e. passage of carbon dioxide through a solution of sodium chloride saturated with ammonia, is not so good as the newer method of Schlösing, which consists in bringing together sodium chloride and ammonium bicarbonate with water.[38]

A modification of the ammonia-soda process in which sodium nitrate or sodium sulphate is used in place of sodium chloride has been suggested and studied from the point of view of the Phase Rule by Fedotieff and Koltunoff.[39]

Oceanic Salts. The behaviour of reciprocal salt-pairs is of especial importance in connection with the study of the conditions governing the deposition of oceanic salts such as has taken place at Stassfurt. In sea water there are present a number of ions, *e.g.* sodium, potassium, magnesium, calcium, chloride and sulphate ions, which, on evaporation of the water, can give rise to deposits of single salts or double salts in large numbers, the nature of the deposit depending on the concentration of the solution and the temperature of evaporation. To obtain an insight into the conditions under which the different salts can be deposited van't Hoff and his pupils[40] carried out a large number of solubility determinations and investigated the conditions under which the different salts and mixtures of salts exist in equilibrium with solution.

Leaving out of consideration the calcium salts, the relative molecular proportions of the sodium, potassium, and magnesium salts in sea water are expressed by the numbers

$$100 \, NaCl, \; 2.2 \, KCl, \; 7.8 \, MgCl_2, \; 3.8 \, MgSO_4.$$

The equilibrium conditions for the two salts with a common ion, KCl and $MgCl_2$, have already been discussed (p. 370), and we shall consider briefly here the conditions for equilibrium in the systems formed by the reciprocal salt-pairs $(K, Mg) \rightarrow (Cl, SO_4)$. Besides the four single salts there exist the double salts carnallite $(KMgCl_3 \cdot 6H_2O)$ and schoenite $(K_2Mg(SO_4)_2 \cdot 6H_2O)$.

The solubility data for these salt-pairs at 25° are as given in the table on p. 438. These data are represented in Fig. 214 by the graphic method of Löwenherz (p. 412), and in Fig. 215, by the method of Jänecke (p. 421). These two figures are lettered so as to correspond with each other and with the data given in

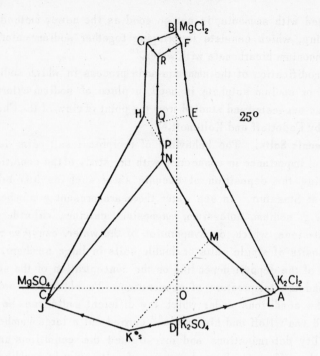

Fig. 214

Point.	Solid phases.	Moles of salt to 1000 moles of water.			
		K₂Cl₂.	MgCl₂.	MgSO₄.	K₂SO₄.
A	KCl	44	—	—	—
B	MgCl₂ . 6H₂O	—	108	—	—
C	MgSO₄ . 7H₂O	—	—	55	—
D	K₂SO₄	—	—	—	12
E	KCl + carnallite	5·5	72·5	—	—
F	MgCl₂ . 6H₂O + carnallite	1	105	—	—
G	MgCl₂ . 6H₂O + MgSO₄ . 6H₂O	—	104	14	—
H	MgSO₄ . 7H₂O + MgSO₄ . 6H₂O	—	73	15	—
J	MgSO₄ . 7H₂O + .schoenite	—	—	58·5	5·5
K	K₂SO₄ + schoenite	—	—	22	16
L	K₂SO₄ + KCl	42	—	—	1·5
M	KCl + K₂SO₄ + schoenite	25	21	11	—
N	KCl + MgSO₄ . 7H₂O + schoenite	9	55	16	—
P	KCl + MgSO₄ . 7H₂O + MgSO₄ . 6H₂O	8	62	15	—
Q	KCl + carnallite + MgSO₄ . 6H₂O	4·5	70	13·5	—
R	MgCl₂ . 6H₂O + carnallite + MgSO₄ . 6H₂O	2	99	12	—

the table. In Figs. 214 and 215 the different areas represent solutions in equilibrium with only one salt, as indicated in the following table:

Area.	Salt.
ALMNPQE	KCl
EQRF	Carnallite
FRGB	$MgCl_2 . 6H_2O$
GHPQR	$MgSO_4 . 6H_2O$
PHCJN	$MgSO_4 . 7H_2O$
JKMN	Schoenite
LDKM	K_2SO_4

The curves EQ, FR, GR, HP, JN, KM, LM, MN, NP, PQ, QR represent quaternary solutions saturated for two solid salts, namely, for those belonging to the areas adjacent to the curve (*e.g.* curve MN represents quaternary solutions in equilibrium with KCl and schoenite). The dotted curves EQ, HP, and KM represent incongruently saturated solutions.

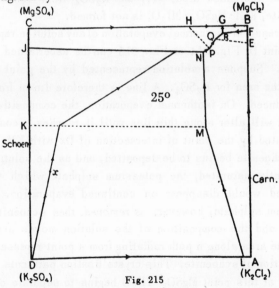

Fig. 215

Attention may be drawn to the fact that although the solutions corresponding with the points M and N are in equilibrium with three solid salts, of which potassium sulphate or schoenite is one, the composition of the solution is expressed in terms only of KCl, $MgCl_2$, and $MgSO_4$. This shows that the points M and N represent incongruently saturated solutions (*cf.* p. 348). This is clearly indicated also by the fact that in Fig. 215 the points M and N lie above the diagonal AC, and consequently outside the triangular area for the salts KCl, K_2SO_4, $MgSO_4$ (*cf.* p. 423).

This system has also been studied at $100°$,[41] and it is interesting to compare the behaviour at this temperature with that found at $25°$. A comparison with the $25°$ isotherm of Löwenherz shows that: (1) the field of $MgSO_4 \cdot 7H_2O$ has altered to that of $MgSO_4 \cdot H_2O$ without changing greatly in area; (2) the field of $MgSO_4 \cdot 6H_2O$ has become that of $MgSO_4$ anhydrous, and decreased in area; (3) the field of $MgCl_2 \cdot 6H_2O$ has decreased considerably in area; (4) the carnallite field alters in contour but not much in area; (5) the KCl field has shrunk a little; (6) the schoenite field has given place to that of langbeinite, $K_2Mg_2(SO_4)_3$ with a somewhat increased area; (7) the K_2SO_4 field remains large; (8) kainite, $KCl \cdot MgSO_4 \cdot 3H_2O$, is not formed.

The result of isothermal evaporation of any solution represented by a point in Fig. 214 or Fig. 215 can be ascertained from the diagram. Suppose a solution represented by the point x. This lies in the area for K_2SO_4. A line is therefore drawn from D to x and produced. On isothermal evaporation, the composition of the solution will alter along this line until it reaches a composition represented by the point of intersection of Dx with KM. At this point schoenite begins to be deposited, and as the solution is incongruently saturated, the potassium sulphate which was first deposited would disappear on continued evaporation. If this potassium sulphate, however, *is removed*, then schoenite is deposited and the composition of the solution moves across the schoenite area along a path radiating from a point representing the composition of schoenite. This crystallisation path cuts the curve JN, and at this point $MgSO_4 \cdot 7H_2O$ begins to separate out. The composition of the solution then alters towards N, at which point potassium chloride is deposited, then to P, when $MgSO_4 \cdot 7H_2O$ passes into $MgSO_4 \cdot 6H_2O$; the crystallisation path then leads to Q, where carnallite separates, and so on to R, where $MgCl_2 \cdot 6H_2O$ is deposited, and the solution dries up to a mixture of $MgSO_4 \cdot$

$6H_2O$, $MgCl_2 \cdot 6H_2O$ and carnallite. R is the end-point of crystallisation.

With the help of the solubility data given on page 438, it is also possible to follow the crystallisation process in a quantitative manner,[42] and to calculate the amounts of the salts successively deposited on isothermal evaporation. Thus, when a solution containing 1 mole of potassium sulphate (174.3 grams) and 1 mole of magnesium chloride hexahydrate (203.4 grams) was evaporated at 25°, potassium sulphate was first deposited because the above mixture corresponds with a point in the potassium sulphate area. The composition of the solution then alters away from D until schoenite begins to separate out. The potassium sulphate first deposited was not removed from the solution, and so the deposition of schoenite was accompanied by a corresponding disappearance of potassium sulphate, until the point M was reached when potassium chloride just began to be deposited. The evaporation was then discontinued and the amounts of potassium sulphate and of schoenite determined by analysis. The result was 25 grams of K_2SO_4 and 120 grams of $K_2Mg(SO_4)_2 \cdot 6H_2O$. The calculated amounts of these salts can be obtained as follows:

The composition of the solution at the point M is given by the expression

$$1000\,H_2O + 25\,K_2Cl_2 + 11\,MgSO_4 + 21\,MgCl_2.$$

If, therefore, one starts with a solution $K_2SO_4 + MgCl_2 + aH_2O$, then, on evaporating the solution until point M is reached, a certain amount of potassium sulphate, say, xK_2SO_4, and a certain amount of schoenite, say, $yK_2Mg(SO_4)_2 \cdot 6H_2O$, will have been deposited, and a certain amount of solution of the above composition will remain, say, $w(1000\,H_2O,\ 25\,K_2Cl_2,\ 11\,MgSO_4,\ 21\,MgCl_2)$. Since 1 mole of chloride (Cl_2) was taken to start with, and since the whole of the chloride radical remains in the residual solution, there must be 1 mole of chloride in the solution. Since in the expression ($1000\,H_2O$, $25\,K_2Cl_2$, $11\,MgSO_4$, $21\,MgCl_2$) there are 46 moles Cl_2, it follows that $w \times 46 = 1$ or $w = 1/46$. Similarly, if we consider the amount of the magnesium radical, the original gram-atom of Mg is divided between the solid schoenite and the magnesium salts in the residual solution. We have, therefore, for Mg, $1 = y + 32w$, and, therefore, $y = 7/23$. Also, for K_2 we have $1 = x + y + 25w$, and, therefore, $x = 7/46$. Consequently, the amount of potassium sulphate deposited is equal to xK_2SO_4, or $(7/46 \times 174.3)$ grams = 26.5 grams; and the amount of schoenite deposited will be $yK_2Mg(SO_4)_2 \cdot 6H_2O = 7/23 \times 402.8$ grams, or 122.6 grams. These two amounts, 26.5 grams and 122.6 grams, agree well with the experimentally determined amounts (25 grams and 120 grams respectively), especially when one considers the difficulty of freeing the deposited salts from the mother liquor.

NOTES

1. An exception to this statement will be found on p. 380.

2. See, however, the researches of Schreinemakers, *Z. physikal. Chem.*, 1907, **59**, 641; 1910, **71**, 109. Studies of quaternary systems of four oxides are also by no means rare. For a table of quaternary liquid systems studied see J. C. Smith, *Ind. Eng. Chem.*, 1949, **41**, 2936.

3. The composition of these solid phases can be determined indirectly by extrapolation according to Schreinemakers' method of wet residues previously discussed on p. 378. See Schreinemakers, *Z. physikal. Chem.*, 1907, **59**, 641, and, for a simpler method, Bell, *J. Phys. Chem.*, 1907, **11**, 394. See also Pozner, *J. Phys. Chem.* (U.S.S.R.), 1947, **21**, 377, 389 for relationships among the concentrations in these systems.

4. Lodochnikov, *Ann. inst. anal. phys.-chim.* (U.S.S.R.), 1924, **2**, 255; *Z. anorg. allgem. Chem.*, 1926, **151**, 185. For the extension of the method to more complex systems see Lodochnikov, *Z. anorg. allgem. Chem.*, 1928, **169**, 177. For still another method see Sayre, *J. Amer. Chem. Soc.*, 1949, **71**, 3284.

5. Randall and Longtin, *J. Phys. Chem.*, 1938, **42**, 1157.

6. *Z. physikal. Chem.*, 1908, **65**, 586; 1910, **71**, 109.

7. See especially Meyerhoffer, *Sitzungsber. Wien. Akad.*, 1895, **104**, II. *b*, 840; Meyerhoffer and Saunders, *Z. physikal. Chem.*, 1899, **28**, 453; **31**, 370; Uyeda, *Mem. Coll. Sci. Eng. Kyoto*, 1910, **2**, 245. The investi-

gation of the equilibria between reciprocal salt-pairs alone (three-component systems) is of great importance for the artificial preparation of minerals, as also in analytical chemistry for the proper understanding of the methods of conversion of insoluble systems into soluble by fusion (see Meyerhoffer, *Z. physikal. Chem.*, 1901, **38**, 307;   Jänecke, *ibid.*, 1908, **64**, 305, 343;   1912, **80**, 1;   1913, **82**, 1).

8. Van't Hoff and Reicher, *Z. physikal. Chem.*, 1889, **3**, 482.

9. The formulæ for sodium chloride and ammonium chloride are doubled in order to express their equivalence with the salts of boric acid. (See p. 413 and Sborgi and Franco, *Gazzetta*, 1921, **51**, II., 1.)

10. See also Meyerhoffer, *Z. physikal. Chem.*, 1905, **53**, 513.

11. See Meyerhoffer, *Z. physikal. Chem.*, 1899, **28**, 459.

12. Compare the reciprocal salt-pair $NaCl-NH_4HCO_3$ (p. **431**). In this case the upper limit of the transition interval was found by extrapolation of the solubility curve for $NaHCO_3 + NH_4Cl + NH_4HCO_3$ and $NaHCO_3 + NH_4Cl + NaCl$ to be $32°$ (Fedotieff, *Z. physikal. Chem.*, 1904, **49**, 179).

13. A convenient two-dimensional method of representation is described by Sayre, *J. Amer. Chem. Soc.*, 1949, **71**, 3284.

14. *Z. physikal. Chem.*, 1894, **13**, 459.

15. Schreinemakers, *Z. physikal. Chem.*, 1909, **69**, 557.

16. An alternative to this method, described by Ricci and Loucks, *J. Chem. Education*, 1938, **15**, 329, is to plot moles of salt in 100 *grams* of total mixture.

17. Blasdale, *J. Ind. Eng. Chem.*, 1918, **10**, 344.

18. *Sitz.-Ber. der kgl. preuss. Akad. der Wiss.*, 1903, p. 359; van't Hoff, *Zur Bildung der ozeanischen Salzablagerungen*, I., p. 34 (Brunswick, 1905);   van't Hoff and Barschall, *Z. physikal. Chem.*, 1906, **56**, 212.

19. *Z. Krist.*, 1904, **39**, 155.

20. Blasdale, *J. Ind. Eng. Chem.*, 1918, **10**, 344;   Hamid, *J. Chem. Soc.*, 1926, 199.

21. This was determined by Meyerhoffer and Saunders, *Z. physikal.*

Chem., 1899, **28**, 479. The equilibria at 0° determined by these workers, however, do not agree with those obtained by Blasdale. Blasdale did not determine the equilibria at 4.4°.

22. For the equilibria at higher temperatures see Blasdale, *J. Ind. Eng. Chem.*, 1918, **10**, 344.

23. Jänecke, *Z. anorgan. Chem.*, 1906, 51, 132; 1911, **71**, 1; Le Chatelier, *Compt. rend.*, 1894; **118**, 415; 1921, **172**, 345.

24. Meyerhoffer, *Z. anorg. Chem.*, 1902, **34**, 147.

25. For a discussion of tetragene salts see Blasdale, Equilibria in Saturated Salt Solutions, *Chemical Catalogue Co.*, New York, 1927, p. 149.

26. For a partial study of this system see Hill, Smith and Ricci, *J. Amer. Chem. Soc.*, 1940, **62**, 858.

27. For other advantages of the Jänecke method of plotting see Purdon and Slater, Aqueous Solution and the Phase Diagram, *Edward Arnold and Co.*, London, 1946, p. 96.

28. See Purdon and Slater (*loc. cit.*), p. 102, for a more detailed discussion of this topic.

29. *Mem. Coll. Sci. Kyoto*, 1909, II., 245.

30. *Proc. K. Akad. Wetensch. Amsterdam*, 1914, **16**, 1065; *Z. anorgan. Chem.*, 1915, **93**, 202.

31. The student should construct the equilibrium diagram from the data given above.

32. These are the amounts of the two salts which are deposited during each cycle of the process.

33. *Z. physikal. Chem.*, 1904, **49**, 162. See also Toporescu, *Compt. rend.*, 1922, **174**, 870; 1922, **175**, 268; Le Chatelier, *ibid.*, 1922, **174**, 836.

34. Other commercial processes in the study of which good service is done by the Phase Rule are: the caustification of the alkali salts (G. Bodländer, *Z. Elektrochem.*, 1905, **11**, 186; J. Herold, *ibid.*, 418; Le Blanc and Novotny, *Z. anorgan. Chem.*, 1906, **51**, 181; Fedotieff, *ibid.*, 1913, **82**, 341), the production of borax by the double decomposi-

tion between ammonium borate and sodium chloride (Sborgi and Franco, *Gazzetta*, 1921, **51**, II, 1), and the formation of saltpetre from sodium nitrate and potassium carbonate (Kremann and Zitek, *Sitzungsber. Wien. Akad. math.-naturwiss Klasse*, 1909, **118**, II., b). The production of calcium nitrate from calcium chloride and sodium nitrate has been worked out by Gilbert (British Patent. 1917, No. **124,780**) and the production of ammonium nitrate from ammonium sulphate and sodium nitrate by Freeth and Cocksedge (British Patent, 1917, No. **126,678**; see also *Chem. Met. Eng.*, **20**, 320). For the preparation of ammonium nitrate from ammonium chloride and sodium nitrate, see Mlle. Wurmser, *Compt. rend.*, 1922, **174**, 1466. For the preparation of barium nitrite from barium chloride and sodium nitrite see Witt and Ludwig, *Ber.*, 1903, **36**, 4384; Meyerhoffer, *ibid.*, 1904, **37**, 261, 1116; Matuschek, *ibid.*, 1907, **40**, 990. The reciprocal salt-pair $(Na,Mg) \rightleftharpoons (Cl,SO_4)$ has been studied by Takegami (*Mem. Coll. Sci. Kyoto*, 1921, **4**, 317).

35. According to W. Mason (*Chem., Z.*, 1914, **38**, 513), the reaction which takes place in practice is represented by $2NaCl + (NH_4)_2CO_3 \rightleftharpoons Na_2CO_3 + 2NH_4Cl$.

36. *Z. physikal. Chem.*, 1900, **35**, 32.

37. More recent information on this topic may be found in Hou, Manufacture of Soda, *Reinhold Publishing Corp.*, New York, 1942.

38. See also Jänecke, *Z. angew. Chem.*, 1907, **20**, 1559.

39. *Z. anorgan. Chem.*, 1914, **85**, 247; 1923, **103**, 39.

40. *Untersuchungen über die Bildungsverhältnisse der ozeanischen Salzablagerungen*, edited by Precht and Cohen (Akadem. Verlagsgesellschaft, 1912); van't Hoff, *Zur Bildung der ozeanischen Salzablagerungen*, Parts I. and II. (Vieweg, 1905 and 1909). A summary of the investigations is given by E. F. Armstrong in the *Reports of the British Association* for 1901, p. 262.

41. Campbell, Downes and Samis, *J. Amer. Chem. Soc.*, 1934, **56**, 2507.

42. See van't Hoff, *Zur Bildung der ozeanischen Salzablagerungen*, I., p. 26.

CHAPTER XX

SYSTEMS OF MORE THAN FOUR COMPONENTS

The systematic study of systems of five and six components
has so far been confined to those consisting of salts and water.
This is readily understandable, for the phase relations are very
complex and the necessary analyses laborious. Studies have been
directed, as one would expect, to the soluble salts of common
occurrence in nature, such as the chlorides, sulphates and nitrates
of the alkali and alkaline earth metals, and we shall attempt only
to outline the equilibria and indicate some of the methods available for their graphical representation. For a more detailed account the reader is referred to other works on the subject[1] and to
the original literature.

I. Five-Component Systems

Aqueous five-component (quinary) salt systems are of at least
two kinds: those comprising water and four salts with a common
ion, and those involving reciprocal salt-pairs (*cf.* the two kinds
of quaternary systems of the previous chapter). Even four dimensions are inadequate for the representation of the concentration variables in such systems at constant temperature and pressure, and a variety of methods may be resorted to in order to sur-
mount the difficulty. For the first-mentioned kind of quinary system
it is convenient to omit the water variable from the diagram completely and to represent the four remaining salt variables by means
of a regular tetrahedron such as that shown in Fig. 195 (p. 405),
any point within which represents one or a hundred moles or grams
of *dissolved salts* and each corner of which therefore represents
a *saturated solution* of one of the component salts. Solutions
saturated with one solid are denoted by volumes. The latter are
separated by surfaces denoting liquids saturated with two solids,

these surfaces intersect along lines denoting liquids saturated with three solids, and the lines intersect at points denoting liquids saturated with four solids. Such systems are not of sufficient importance for further discussion; we turn immediately, therefore, to the more important type, namely those involving reciprocal salt-pairs.

Aqueous quinary salt systems with metathesis may consist of water, three cations and two anions; or water, two cations and three anions; that is, they consist of water and three electrolytes which yield only five ions. Thus the systems $(A, B, C)-(X, Y)-H_2O$ and $(A,B)-(X, Y, Z)-H_2O$, (where A, B and C are cations and X, Y and Z are anions) are typical. In terms of salts the first of these may be called the system $AX-BX-CY-H_2O$ or the system $AX-BY-CY-H_2O$, *etc.*, although, of course, being a quinary system five quantities (of water and four salts) must be stated in defining the composition of the solutions. To represent the equilibria at constant temperature and pressure it is convenient, as in the type discussed in the previous paragraph, to disregard the water content of the solutions and plot only the concentrations of the components in the *dissolved salts*. For this purpose one can use a regular triangular prism[2] whose base is an equilateral triangle and the three vertical faces of which are squares as shown in Fig. 216, which is for a system composed of water, three

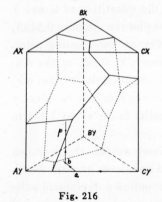

Fig. 216

cations and two anions. Clearly, all the edges of the prism are of equal length. The corners of the prism again denote saturated solutions of each of the six possible component salts from which the three salts, chosen along with water as components, are selected. The six possible salts are assigned to the corners of the model in such a way that each of the two triangular faces refers to three salts with a common ion and each of the three square faces refers to reciprocal salt-pairs. In this way each of the nine edges refers at its ends to two salts with a common ion.

Any point within the model represents one (or a hundred) moles of dissolved salts, the term 'mole' meaning 'equivalent gram molecule' as in the previous chapter. Points for solutions belonging to either of the quaternary systems AX-BX-CX-H_2O or AY-BY-CY-H_2O, and therefore expressible in terms of water and three salts with a common ion, lie on the triangular faces of the prism, and the data, after converting to mole fraction of dissolved salts, are plotted thereon by the usual method for triangular coordinates. Similarly, points for solutions belonging to any of the quaternary reciprocal salt-pair systems AX-CY-H_2O, BX-AY-H_2O, CX-BY-H_2O lie on the square faces of the prism, and the data are plotted thereon according to the Jänecke method (p. 421).

To plot the composition of a quinary solution the procedure is slightly more involved. Suppose the composition to be plotted is 10 moles of AX, 20 of BX, 50 of AY and 30 of CY in 1000 of water, which, incidentally, could have been equally well expressed as 30 moles of AX, 20 of BY, 30 of CY and 30 of AY in 1000 of H_2O. This becomes, on reducing to one mole of dissolved salts, 0.091 AX, 0.182 BX, 0.455 AY, 0.273 CY and 9.09 H_2O, or, in terms of ions, 0.546A, 0.182B, 0.273C, 0.273X, 0.728Y and 9.09 H_2O. Of these six quantities the water must be neglected and two of the remaining quantities are reduntant. If the quantities of C and Y are chosen as the reduntant quantities we plot the amounts 0.546A, 0.182B, 0.273X, and use the CY corner as our starting point. Point a is first found by measuring, from CY, 0.546 of the distance to AY. Then from a a distance 0.182 towards BY, but parallel to the edge CY-BY is measured thereby reaching b. Finally from b a distance 0.273 is measured parallel to the edge CY-CX to give the required point p.

In the simplest kind of such a quinary system that one can envision, in which no double salts, solid solutions, $etc.$ are found, each of the square faces presents the ordinary reciprocal salt-pair type of diagram having four fields, one for each salt, and showing a stable and an unstable salt-pair. Each triangular face consists of three lines proceeding inwards from some point on each edge to a common point of contact representing a quaternary solution saturated with three solids. There is a point on each of the nine edges at which two lines, lying in the plane of the adjacent surfaces, originate, as shown in the figure. From each of the invariant points on the five faces other lines proceed inwards (not shown in the figure) and meet in various points within the model; ordinarily only four of such lines meet in any one point. The whole model is thus divided into elements of volume by these intersecting lines, the volumes denoting quinary liquids saturated with one solid. The surfaces separating adjacent volumes denote quinary solutions saturated with the two corresponding solids, the edges of such volumes (lying within the model) quinary solutions saturated with three solids, and the points of intersection of these edges quinary solutions saturated with four solids. The number and shape of the elements of volume will, of course, alter as the temperature is altered and, at unique temperatures for a given pressure, two (or three)univariant points within the model can merge and become the point of contact of five volumes, thereby denoting at this point a liquid saturated with five solids. For example, in the system $(Na, K)—(Cl, SO_4, NO_3)—H_2O$ (*vide infra*), there has been found, at $55°$, a solution saturated with $NaNO_3$, $NaCl$, Na_2SO_4, KNO_3 and $Na_3NO_3SO_4 \cdot H_2O$. (The latter system obviously shows double salt formation but the principles just discussed for the simpler type are equally pertinent).

Examples which may be cited for reference are the oceanic salt system $(Na, K, Mg)—(Cl, SO_4)—H_2O$ studied by van't Hoff (*loc. cit.*)[3] and the system $(Na, K)—(Cl, SO_4, NO_3)—H_2O$.[4]

Oceanic Salts. Sea water, we have seen (p. 437), is really a five-component system. The investigation of this system, however, and the graphic representation of the equilibria are simplified by the fact that, owing to the predominance of sodium chloride, deposition of the other salts has always taken place in presence of excess of sodium chloride. In the graphic representation, therefore, we may leave the sodium chloride out of consideration, providing we bear in mind that all the equilibria represented are equilibria in the presence of solid sodium chloride, as a result of which there is a loss of one degree of freedom.

The graphic construction used by van't Hoff[5] to describe the equilibria is shown for 25° in Fig. 217. The composition of all solutions in this system can be expressed in terms of H_2O, NaCl and the salts of the reciprocal salt-pair $(K, Mg) - (Cl, SO_4)$, even though negative quantities may be required. Thus point S, the composition of which is given in the accompanying table in terms of Na_2SO_4 and other salts can also be expressed as 1000 moles of water, 48 of Na_2Cl_2, 2 of K_2Cl_2, 16 of $MgSO_4$ and 6 of K_2SO_4. As the Na_2Cl_2 content is not being represented, the diagram reduces to the orthogonal projection of the Löwenherz tetragonal pyramid for the system $(K, Mg) - (Cl, SO_4) - H_2O$, as seen in the figure. For purposes of convenience, however, it is desirable to tabulate some of the data in terms of Na_2SO_4 (see

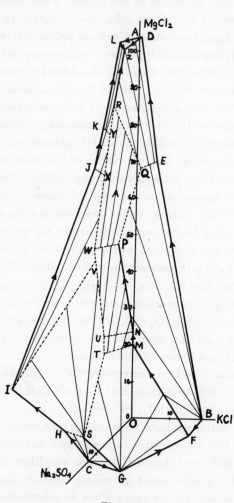

Fig. 217

the table), but the latter is expressible in terms of three other salts thus: $Na_2SO_4 = Na_2Cl_2 + MgSO_4 - MgCl_2$. As the Na_2Cl_2 content is being ignored this amounts to measuring a quantity of Na_2SO_4 as the same quantity of $MgSO_4$, *i.e.*, horizontally to the left of O, and an equal but negative quantity of $MgCl_2$, *i.e.* vertically downward. This will always give a point on the line OC which halves the right angle opposite to AOB. This line, therefore, becomes an axis along which Na_2SO_4 may be measured directly, and is used whenever concentrations are expressed in terms of Na_2SO_4 as one of the quantities. In connection with this model it should be mentioned that potassium sulphate does not occur as such, but, in presence of excess of sodium chloride, is deposited as glaserite,

$$K_4Na_2(SO_4)_3.[6]$$

The presence of the NaCl in solution also permits the formation of other solids containing Na_2SO_4 such as Na_2SO_4 itself and astracanite.

The solid phases, in addition to sodium chloride, which correspond to the different areas are as follows:

Area.	Solid phase.	Mineralogical name.
ALZD	$MgCl_2 . 6H_2O$	Bischofite
BFMNPQE	KCl	Sylvin
CGSH	Na_2SO_4	Thenardite
DZRQE	$KMgCl_3 . 6H_2O$	Carnallite
FMTSG	$Na_2K_4(SO_4)_3$	Glaserite
SHIVUT	$Na_2Mg(SO_4)_2 . 4H_2O$	Astracanite
JXWVI	$MgSO_4 . 7H_2O$	Reichardtite
JXYK	$MgSO_4 . 6H_2O$	—
KYRZL	$MgSO_4 . H_2O$	Kieserite
TUNM	$K_2Mg(SO_4)_2 . 6H_2O$	Schoenite
NUVWP	$(K, Na)Mg(SO_4)_2 . 4H_2O$	Leonite
PWXYRQ	$KCl . MgSO_4 . 3H_2O$	Kainite

The relations met with here, as can be seen from a glance at the diagram, Fig. 217, are considerably more complex than those found in the absence of sodium chloride. The discussion of the simpler systems, however, will enable us to understand the relations shown graphically in Fig. 217 where also the crystallisation paths are indicated by arrowheads and the lightly drawn lines radiating from different points in the diagram and crossing the fields for the different solid phases. The experimental data on which the graphic representation is based, are given in the table which follows:[7]

Point.	Solutions saturated with NaCl and	Moles of salt to 1000 moles water.				
		Na_2Cl_2.	K_2Cl_2.	$MgCl_2$.	$MgSO_4$.	Na_2SO_4.
O	—	55·5	—	—	—	—
A	$MgCl_2 . 6H_2O$	1	—	106	—	—
B	KCl	44·5	19·5	—	—	—
C	Na_2SO_4	51	—	—	—	12.5
D	$MgCl_2 . 6H_2O$; carnallite	1	0·5	105	—	—
E	KCl ; carnallite	2	5·5	70·5	—	—
F	KCl ; glaserite	44	20	—	—	4·5
G	Na_2SO_4 ; glaserite	44	10·5	—	—	14·5
H	Na_2SO_4 ; astracanite	46	—	—	16·5	3
I	$MgSO_4 . 7H_2O$; astracanite	26	—	7	34	—
J	$MgSO_4 . 7H_2O$; $MgSO_4 . 6H_2O$	4	—	67·5	12	—
K	$MgSO_4 . 6H_2O$; kieserite	2·5	—	79	9·5	—
L	Kieserite ; $MgCl_2 . 6H_2O$	1	—	101	5	—
M	KCl ; glaserite ; schoenite	23	14	21·5	14	—
N	KCl ; schoenite ; leonite	19·5	14·5	25·5	14·5	—
P	KCl ; leonite ; kainite	9·5	9·5	47	14·5	—
Q	KCl ; kainite ; carnallite	2·5	6	68	5	—
R	Carnallite ; kainite ; kieserite	1*	1	85·5	8	—
S	Na_2SO_4 ; glaserite ; astracanite	42	8	—	16	6
T	Glaserite ; astracanite ; schoenite	27·5	10·5	16·5	18·5	—
U	Leonite ; astracanite ; schoenite	22	10·5	23	19	—
V	Leonite ; astracanite ; $MgSO_4 . 7H_2O$	10·5	7·5	42	19	—
W	Leonite ; kainite ; $MgSO_4 . 7H_2O$	9	7·5	45	19·5	—
X	{ $MgSO_4 . 6H_2O$; kainite ; $MgSO_4 . 7H_2O$ }	3·5	4	65·5	13	—
Y	$MgSO_4 . 6H_2O$; kainite ; kieserite	1·5	2	77	10	—
Z	Carnallite ; $MgCl_2 . 6H_2O$; kieserite	1	0·5	100	5	—

The one-solid crystallisation paths (two solids including NaCl) may require a word of explanation. Those crossing the field JXWVI for $MgSO_4 \cdot 7H_2O$, for instance, radiate from the point of intersection of JI produced and BO produced; those crossing the field FMTSG for glaserite radiate from the point of intersection of FG and the line representing $2K_2SO_4 : 1Na_2SO_4$, etc.

The equilibria represented in the diagram, Fig. 217, are the stable equilibria. On evaporation of a solution of sea-water, however, super-saturation occurs, in some cases, with great ease, and the stable phase may be entirely missed.

Fig. 217 gives a picture of the relations between the different salts only at 25°. As the temperature is altered the solubility relations also alter; and the areas for the different solid salts change and may entirely disappear, while new salts, represented by new areas in the diagram, make their appearance. Thus schoenite, which at 25° is stable, becomes at 26° unstable, and the schoenite area entirely disappears from the isotherm. The areas for leonite and glaserite then become adjacent, and these two salts can exist in contact with solution. From determinations of the solubilities at a number of different temperatures a series of paragenetic diagrams (p. 421) can be constructed; and from these and a knowledge of the salts occurring together in the salt-deposits, it is possible to tell the temperature at which deposition of the salts had taken place. The different salt layers, therefore, constitute a "geological thermometer".

Diagrams similar to that shown in Fig. 217 may also be used in order to ascertain the best conditions for obtaining different salts from solution by crystallisation.[8]

II. Six-Component Systems

Little need be said here of six-component systems, and, in any case, relatively few studies have ever been undertaken. If one takes into account, for example, the calcium ion present in sea water, thereby considering water and the six ions Na, K, Ca, Mg, Cl, SO_4, the study of oceanic salts becomes one of six components. As for five-component systems, certain simplifying assumptions are necessary in order to form intelligible phase diagrams, but we do not propose to consider these further, although reference to them may be found in the literature[9] and a discussion of them in Blasdale's monograph (*loc. cit.*).

NOTES

1. See, for example, Blasdale, Equilibria in Saturated Salt Solutions, *Chemical Catalogue Co.*, New York, 1927; Purdon and Slater, Aqueous Solution and the Phase Diagram, *Edward Arnold & Co.*, London, 1946.

2. This method of representation was devised by Jänecke, Z. *anorg. allgem. Chem.*, 1907, 53, 319.

3. For the equilibrium diagram at 25° according to the method just described, see D'Ans, *Kali*, 1915, **9**, 249, reproduced by Blasdale (*loc. cit.*), p. 167.

4. Cornec and Krombach, *Ann. chim.*, 1929, [10], **12**, 203; Cornec, Krombach and Spack, *ibid.*, 1930, **13**, 525.

5. Jänecke has re-calculated the data obtained by van't Hoff and his co-workers, and has represented them graphically by the method already described. (See *Z. anorgan. Chem.*, 1917, **100**, 161, 176; 1918, **102**, 41; **103**, 1.) See also F.C. Phillips, Oceanic Salt Deposits, *Quarterly Rev.*, 1947, I, p. 91.

6. With regard to the nature of glaserite, see p. 419.

7. More recent investigations of this system (D'Ans, *Kali*, 1915, **9**, 148, 161, 177, 193, 217, 229) yield a somewhat different diagram from the one shown here, particularly in the shape of the astracanite and $MgSO_4 \cdot 7H_2O$ fields.

8. See, for example, the discussion of the conditions for obtaining potash and other constituents from sea-water bittern, by Hildebrand, *J. Ind. Eng. Chem.*, 1918, **10**, 96.

9. See, for example, D'Ans, *Kali*, 1915, **9**, 261.

SOME THERMODYNAMIC DEDUCTIONS

It is customary in text-books on Phase Rule to give typical equilibrium diagrams, and particular experimental studies of these, without showing how these typical diagrams are obtained, beyond, perhaps, the statement that they rest on thermodynamics and the treatment of equilibrium proposed by Willard Gibbs. This leaves the student with the impression that the deduction of the diagrams is a matter of difficulty, but this is not so. In this chapter a few of the simpler (graphical) derivations are given. The treatment is that of Roozeboom[1], although a graphical method of treating the problem was introduced by van Alkemade.[2]

I. Solid Solutions are Not Formed.

(a) Two-Component Systems.

Since, at constant pressure and temperature, the molar free energy (F) of a solution of two given components is a function of concentration only, it is possible to represent its molar free energy by means of a system of plane rectangular coordinates. Fig. 218 shows that the graph is convex toward the concentration axis, a being the molar free energy of molten A and b that for molten B. The absolute values of the free energy are not, of course, known, but this is immaterial. The curve could not be concave for molten A and molten B are assumed to dissolve each other spontaneously. For any given concentration c, say, it is well known that the partial molar free energy or chemical potential (μ) of each component[3] is given by the intercepts, on the A and B axes respectively, of the tangent to the curve at that concentration.[4] Thus the point μ_A gives the chemical potential of A in the solution of concentration c. Only one such tangent can be drawn since the curve must always be convex downwards

APPENDIX

and non-reentrant unless the liquid forms two layers.

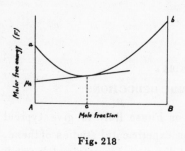

Fig. 218

It was shown by Gibbs that a heterogeneous system is in equilibrium, at constant temperature and pressure, when the chemical potential of each component is the same in all the phases that contain that component. Solution c, therefore, will be in equilibrium with solid A only if the molar free energy of solid A equals the ordinate μ_A^*. Conversely, if μ_A represents the molar free energy of solid A at the temperature and pressure of the diagram, the composition of the solution with which it is in equilibrium is found by drawing the tangent to the curve which passes through μ_A.

If a third temperature axis is added to the above plane diagram, there is obtained, instead of the F-curve for solutions of different composition at fixed temperature, a F-surface for different temperatures (but at constant pressure.) This F-surface will be lower at higher temperatures, as will also be the molar free energies of solid A and B, for, according to a well-known thermodynamic relation, the temperature coefficient of free energy at constant pressure equals the negative of the entropy, and the entropy is a positive quantity. The molar free energies of the solid components will, however, in general, decrease more slowly than that of the solution for the latter has the greater entropy. For each of these temperatures, we can determine the point of contact of the tangent drawn from the points which give the F-values of one or the other solid phases. The projection of these points of contact on the horizontal plane will then give the compositions of the solutions coexisting with these phases at different temperatures, *i.e.* they form the curves of saturated solution. Concentration is best represented as mole fraction or mole per cent, since, in this way, one hundred per cent of both components can be represented on a finite diagram.

The solid model is represented in Fig. 219.

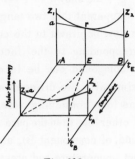

Fig. 219

In the solid model, the free energy curve of the solutions now extends for each temperature between the axes AZ_1 and BZ_2, whose distance apart equals one (or one hundred). The curve touches the axes at points Z_1 and Z_2, whose heights equal the free energy for a mole of each substance, respectively, in the liquid state.

In the simplest possible case, the only solid phases are the two components, and for every temperature the vertical Aa and Bb must be taken equal to the free energy values of the solid phases and tangents drawn to the solution curve from a and b. The projections on the t-x plane of the points of contact will then form the two solubility curves, as shown.

In the direction of increasing temperature the curves will extend to the melting-points of A and B, *viz.* t_A and t_B. At these points, a and Z_1 or b and Z_2 coincide. In the direction of falling temperature the curves will extend to t_E, where the tangents from a and b coincide and hence only one point of contact, r, and one solution, E, exist. This is the eutectic temperature. At still lower temperatures, the line ab will run below the solution curve, which means that the stable system is the mixture of the two solid components. The two solubility curves must always meet, since it is an experimental fact that in any two-component system complete solidification will eventually occur, if the temperature be lowered sufficiently. Fig. 219, with two curves, expresses the simplest type of the solubility relations of two substances, (*cf.* Fig. 38, p. 135).

If the two components are capable of forming a solid compound, A_xB_y, the simple plane free energy diagram (constant temperature and pressure) must be modified to include representa-

tion of the free energy of the compound. This is done by erect-
ing a vertical on the axis of composition, whose height represents
the free energy of the compound $\mu_{A_xB_y}$, as shown in Fig. 220.

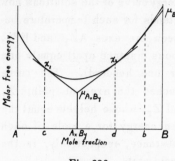

It is apparent that two tangents
can now be drawn to the curve,
corresponding to the fact that
the compound can be in equilibrium with two different solutions (one containing more and
the other less than the pure compound, of component B), at constant temperature and pressure.
When to the above plane diagram
an axis of temperature is added

Fig. 220

and a solid model produced, the projection of such points as x_1
and x_2 on the plane of temperature-composition gives rise to a
(double) solubility curve of the compound. Hence, the solubility
curves of A and B cannot meet directly, but each meets the solubility curve of the compound, giving rise to the well-known diagram of Fig. 40 (p. 145). We then have two eutectic points, where
the solution solidifies to a mixture of the two solid substances,
whose curves meet in these points. If several compounds, such
as A_xB_y, exist, several curves such as CDE occur between the
curves for the two components.

In Fig. 40 it is assumed that the compound is congruently melting. It may happen, however, that the compound melts incongruently. In terms of chemical potential, this is represented graphically in Fig. 221. Here the tangent from μ_B intersects one of
the tangents from $\mu_{A_xB_y}$. This means that all total compositions
lying to the right of A_xB_y represent entirely solid systems consisting of A_xB_y and B. This behaviour persists up to a temperature at which a common tangent can be drawn from $\mu_{A_xB_y}$ and
μ_B to the curve for liquid, the point of contact lying to the left
of A_xB_y, so that the series of solutions represented by d never
has a stable existence. Above this temperature, the transition
temperature, solid A_xB_y cannot be in equilibrium with liquid, but

solid B can. This is the familiar phenomenon of incongruent melting or transition point, and gives rise to the *t-x* diagram of Fig. 42 (p. 149).

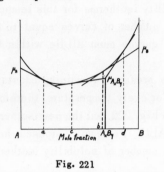

Fig. 221

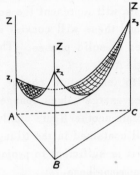

Fig. 222

(b) Three-Component Systems.

In a three-component system, as previously described (Chap. XIII), composition is represented by means of an equilateral triangle. Molar free energy is then measured along an axis at right-angles to this plane, giving rise to a solid model. Such a model, however, refers only to one temperature and pressure and in order to represent the variation of free energy with temperature, a number of such models is necessary. For components which are completely miscible in the liquid state, the free energy surface is continuous and convex downwards. In Fig. 222 A, B and C represent the three pure components and we erect from A, B and C three perpendicular axes, on which the free energy of pure liquid A, B and C are measured off, as the vertical distances Az_1, Bz_2 and Cz_3. Then the free energy surface of the solution is entirely contained by the planes ABZ, ACZ and BCZ.

The solution coexisting with a solid phase will be found, as before, by the point of contact of a tangent with the free energy surface of the solutions drawn from the point which expresses the free energy value of the solid phase. If the solid phase is a pure component the point will lie on one of the vertical axes, if the solid phase is a binary compound it will lie in one of the side planes, and finally if the solid phase is a ternary compound the point expressing its chemical potential will lie in the space above ABC. The projections on the ABC plane of the points of contact for the solid phases existing at a given temperature will represent the solubility isotherms for this temperature and these will consist of a number of curves equal to the number of solid phases. These curves must all lie within the triangle ABC.

With temperature change (the pressure remaining constant) all free energy values change. For every temperature, therefore, we obtain another figure similar to Fig. 222, but the new isotherms are all contained in the triangle ABC. For many purposes, however, it is sufficient to project a number of solubility isotherms on a common base.

(i) The Components are the only Solid Phases.

The simplest possible case is that in which only the components occur as solid phases.

Turning again to Fig. 222, we erect the molar free energies of the solid components Aa, Bb and Cc on the vertical axes (a, b, c are not shown in the Figure). Let C be the highest melting component. At the melting point of C, the free energy of 1 mole of solid and 1 mole of liquid C are equal. On lowering the temperature, Cc will become smaller than Cz_3, and tangents can then be drawn to the potential surface of solutions. Their points of contact will form a curve, which begins at the point of contact of the tangent from c with the curve $z_1 z_3$ and ends in the point of contact with the curve $z_2 z_3$. The projection of the curve of contact will represent all solutions which can be in equilibrium with C; it also forms a curve (1, Fig. 223), which, in the triangle ABC, runs from CA to CB and hence comprehends the solutions which contain both C and A, and C and B, that is, solutions containing all three components C, A and B.

In general, with progressive fall of temperature, the curve of contact will move away from the CZ axis and hence its projection will move away from C. When the temperature has been lowered below the melting-point of B, curves will arise in the same way which represent saturated solutions of B, and which will extend between AB and CB. At such temperatures therefore, the isotherm will consist of two separate curves (2, 2). The lower the temperature, the more these will approach until finally they touch (3, 3). This happens at that temperature at which, in Fig. 222, the straight line bc touches the curve z_2z_3. This point is a temperature minimum for solutions containing B and C only, because the solubility curves for this binary system cut there.

On lowering the temperature still further two of the three curves (4, 4, 4 of Fig. 223) of the isotherm will cut, before they have reached BC. Such points of intersection will therefore represent solutions which coexist with both B and C as solid phases (at different temperatures). They form the curve DG.

At temperatures below the melting-point of A solutions with A as solid phase can also occur. A curve for this will extend between AB and AC. These curves also will in general depart from A as the temperature is lowered. With continued fall of temperature these curves will meet analogous curves relating to B and C. It is assumed in Fig. 223 that this meeting first takes place with curves from C, in E, and then with curves from B, in F. From these two points space curves then proceed towards lower temperatures, EG for solutions coexisting with A and C, FG for solutions coexisting with A and B. Finally, these curves also meet in the point G, which represents the solution which is simultaneously

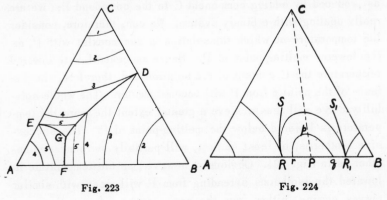

Fig. 223   Fig. 224

in equilibrium with the three solid phases, at a temperature which

is also the minimum temperature for the region of solutions
(ternary eutectic temperature, *cf.* Fig. 135 p. 315).
(ii) Binary Compounds as Solid Phases.

Consider a compound whose composition is expressed by the
point P (Fig. 224) on the side AB. If now we imagine, in Fig.
224, a perpendicular erected from such a point, on which the free
energy value PP′ is measured for a mole of the compound, a
series of tangents can be drawn from P′ to the free energy
surface of the solutions. The projection of the curve of contact
on ABC will form a curve, surrounding the point P, such as *rpq*
(Fig. 224), and representing all solutions, which can coexist at
the given temperature and pressure with the solid phase P.   The
points *q* and *r* in this figure are the projections of the points of
contact of tangents from P′ to z_1 z_2 and hence represent the two
solutions which can coexist with P, if the solutions contain no
other component. The line CP cuts the isotherm *rpq* in *p*, which
point, therefore, gives the solution with the same ratio A/B as in
the solid phase. Solutions *rp* have a greater, solutions *pq* a
smaller, ratio A/B than P.

The change in the form of the curves with temperature can
be predicted to some extent. In general, on lowering the temperature the points *q* and *r* are displaced further from one another and
from P. The same applies to *p*. Solution *p* can be considered
as produced by adding component C to the compound P: we are
really dealing with a binary system. We can, therefore, consider
the temperature at which the solution *p* can coexist with P, as
the lowered melting-point of P. Hence in general with lowered
temperature the C content of the solution and, therefore, the distance of the point *p* from P will become greater. The whole solubility curve will thus achieve a greater extent the more the temperature is lowered below the melting-point of P. The successive isotherms, at least at first, will partially surround one another as in Fig. 224. Obviously, however, as the temperature is
lowered the isotherms spreading from P will meet with similar
curves coming either from the components or from other compounds, in a manner similar to that described in the previous sec-

tion. Just as in the domain of two-component systems the curve
for P, in a *t-x* diagram, meets on both sides the curves for the components A and B or for other compounds of these, the isotherms
of solutions of three components in equilibrium with solid P will
also meet on the right and left sides with similar isotherms for
other components or compounds.

The further working out of the temperature-composition models
can now be left to the reader, since the detailed description of
such models has already been given under three-component systems, but a few more points should be made clear. If a binary
compound of the same two components exists, two cases must be
discriminated. In one case, the isotherms spreading out from the
melting-point of the compound may intersect on opposite sides
those from the two components or other compounds giving rise,
first to a binary eutectic and then to a eutectic trough *cf*. Fig.
139 (p. 323). On the other hand, it may happen that the isotherm
from a component has already spread beyond the composition of
the compound before the melting temperature of the compound is
reached. This is equivalent to saying that the compound cannot
exist stably in equilibrium with a solution of its own composition, *i.e.* the compound has no true melting-point. In this case
intersection of the isotherms is only possible on corresponding
sides, and in the binary system we have a peritectic or transition point, and in the ternary system a transition curve (*cf*. Fig.
142, p. 326).

The case also occurs where the isotherms of a binary compound meet the isotherms of the third component or of a compound in which it occurs. In this way curves now arise for two
solid phases (which are different from curves like RS, Fig. 224 ,
for two phases neither of which contains the third component).
Let us consider the meeting of the isotherms from a compound
of A and B, represented by P (Fig. 226) with the isotherms
from Q, a compound of C and A. At temperatures such as T_1, a
little below their melting-points T_P and T_Q, the solution curves
are still independent. Hence the two binary compounds cannot yet

coexist with solution. At T_2 the two solution curves touch, and
P and Q can now exist in contact with the single solution R. At

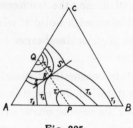

Fig. 225

still lower temperatures such as T_3,
the solution isotherms will cut one
another and we obtain two points of
intersection, S and S′. The curve
SRS′ will hence represent the solutions coexisting with P and Q, at
different temperatures. The point
of contact R of the isotherms must
lie on the line PQ. This is proved

as follows: In the solid model (Fig. 222), representing free energy
as a function of composition at constant temperature and pressure,
the straight line joining the free energies of solid P and solid
Q will cut the convex surface representing free energy of solutions at all temperatures above that of R. As the temperature
falls, since the free energy of solids rises more slowly than that
of solutions the straight line joining P and Q eventually emerges
entirely from the convex surface. As it emerges from the surface,
this straight line forms a common tangent from P and Q to the
surface of free energy. This means that the temperature of this
isotherm is the highest temperature at which both solid P and
solid Q can be in equilibrium with the same solution, and there
is only one such solution whose composition is represented by R,
the point of contact of the straight line joining P and Q with
the surface of free energy. Hence R lies on PQ. At temperatures lower than this, PQ lies entirely below the surface, that is,
all solutions whose compositions are represented by points on
this line are metastable with respect to a mixture of solid P and
Q. Nevertheless, separate tangents can be drawn from P and from
Q to the curved surface, but the curves representing the projections of the points of contact will now intersect in two points
(at a given temperature). These two points of intersection give
the compositions of the two solutions each of which can coexist
with both solid P and Q (at constant temperature). Hence the
curve SRS′ (Fig. 225), which is the locus of these points, has its

maximum temperature at R, where the solution can be formed from the two solid phases P and Q (only), in suitable proportions. For the solutions of the two branches RS and RS' this is no longer true; the former contain an excess of A, the latter less A.

(iii) Congruently Melting Ternary Compounds as Solid Phases.

In the triangle ABC (Fig. 226), A, B and C represent, as usual, the three pure components, and S the composition of a ternary compound. We now imagine this triangle to be the base of Fig. 222, and erect from S a perpendicular SS', the height of which is chosen equal to the free energy of one mole of the solid phase S. At the melting-point T of this phase the point S' will be in the free energy surface of the solutions. At a lower temperature T_1 the point S' will lie below this surface, and hence a series of tangents can be drawn to the surface, whose points of contact, on account of its convex form, will together form a closed curve. Their projection on the plane ABC will also form a curve around the point S   This curve will represent all solutions which can

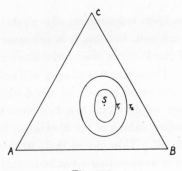

Fig. 226

exist at T_1 with the solid phase S.

On lowering the temperature still further below the melting-point T, this curve will, in general, attain greater extent. Hence successive isotherms will be ringed around S. These isotherms will, of course, meet isotherms coming from other

solid phases and thus the region of stable existence of the ternary compound will be limited in the manner which has been described in the discussion of three-component systems (*cf.* Fig. 141, p. 326).

II. Formation of Solid Solutions.

(a) *Two-Component Systems.*[5]

(i) The Solid Components form Solid Solutions in all Proportions.

In this case, the curve of free energy as a function of composition will also be a continuous curve for the solid phase, and, like that of the liquid phase, it will be convex downwards. Even with the above limitation, however, three types must be discriminated.

Type I. The freezing-points of all mixtures lie between those of the two components.

Consider an entirely liquid mixture above the melting-point of the higher melting component B. At temperatures above this melting-point, since only the liquid phase can exist, the molar free energy (F)-composition curve of the solid phase, hereinafter called the S-curve must lie entirely above the corresponding curve of the liquid (L-curve). At the melting-point of B both curves have a common point of contact on the right hand vertical axis. In Fig. 227, I, S represents the curve for the mix-crystals, L that for the liquid phase. The whole S-curve, except at the extreme right, still lies above the L-curve, so that only pure B can exist in contact with melt.

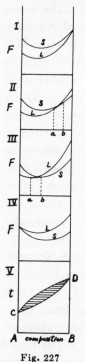

Fig. 227

At a somewhat lower temperature, mix-crystals can deposit from the melt. For this it is necessary that a portion of the L-curve must have risen above the S-curve. The coexisting phases will now be found as the points of contact of the double tangent which can be drawn to the two curves. Let the corresponding values of the abscissae be a and b, Fig. 227, II. This means that, at this temperature, a homogeneous liquid of composition a can be in equilibrium with a homogeneous solid of composition b.

At still lower temperatures the L-curve rises still higher above the S-curve, Fig. 227, III. There is always one liquid phase existing in equilibrium with a solid phase of different composition. Finally, at the melting-point of A, Fig. 227, IV, only the last point of the L-curve is stable. Plotting the abscissae of the points of contact as abscissae, against the corresponding temperatures as ordinates, Fig. 227, V, the well-known equilibrium curve, is obtained (*cf.* Fig. 45, I, p. 159). This type of equilibrium diagram has already been discussed.

Type II. The freezing-point curve shows a maximum.

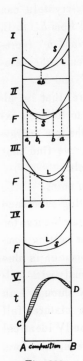

In the previous case it was assumed that the liquid was always completely stable above the melting-point of B, and entirely metastable below the melting-point of A. But this can only be true for a certain curvature of the two curves, and with a different curvature contact will occur somewhere between the end-points before contact at the melting-point of the higher melting component is reached. This case is shown in Fig. 228, I. At a somewhat lower temperature, but still above the melting-point of B, a part of the S-curve has become stable (Fig. 228, II). The two curves then cut in two points and two double tangents can be drawn; these determine the concentrations of co-existing liquid and solid phases a_1 and b_1 and of a second set a and b. The following Figure 228, III, is drawn for the temperature of the melting-point of B; the next again, 228, IV, for the temperature of the melting-point of A. From now on, the solid state is entirely stable. If the abscissae of the points of contact are plotted against the corresponding temperatures, Fig. 228, V, which has previously been discussed, is obtained (*cf.* Fig. 45, II, p. 159).

Fig. 228

Type III. The continuous curve of freezing-points exhibits a minimum.

This case occurs if the L-curve has the greater curvature, so that the L-curve has not risen entirely above the S-curve by the time contact at the two ends has taken place. The stages of the deduction, leading to the Type III of Roozeboom, can now be left to the reader.

(ii) The Solid Components form Solid Solutions to a Limited Extent.

In this case the S-curve is re-entrant and shows two minima, as indicated in Fig. 229. The points of contact, *a* and *b*,

of the double tangent then determine the limits a' and b' of miscibility at the temperature of the isothermal diagram.   This means

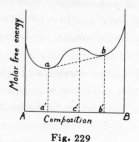

Fig. 229

that homogeneous mix-crystals can
exist from A to a', and from b' to B.
All points between a' and b' represent equilibrium mixtures of the saturated solid solutions a' and b'.

Proceeding as before, that is, allowing the temperature to fall and examining the changes in the free energy-
concentration diagram, we find that
two principal types result:

Type IV. The freezing curve shows a transition point.

Here, at the melting temperature of the high melting substance
B, the whole L-curve still lies completely below the S-curve for
the solid, but at the melting temperature of the lower melting component (A) it has moved entirely above it. The assumption is also
made that, as the two curves change shape continuously with falling temperature, curve S is displaced continuously through L in
such a manner that the freezing temperatures of the mixtures fall
in the direction B to A. This assumption makes type IV identical
with type I in many respects. Fig. 230, I and II, agrees, therefore,
with Fig. 227, I and II, all of which represent the state of affairs
at the melting-point of B and at a somewhat lower temperature.
This continues as long as the double tangent to the S-curve lies
above the double tangent to the L- and S-curves. As, however, the
displacement of the L- and S-curves upwards continues, there must
come a time when these two tangents coincide. In Fig. 230, III,
this is represented in such a manner that both points of contact
with the S-curve lie on the same side of the point of contact with
the L-curve. Only in this way can the freezing curve fall progressively from B to A. At this temperature, therefore, the liquid mixture a is in equilibrium with both solid b and solid b_1. At a still
lower temperature, the double tangent to S no longer coincides with
that which can be drawn from L to the stable part of the S-curve
towards B. The possibility, however, now arises of drawing a

double tangent to L and the part of the stable S-curve towards A, as in Fig. 230, IV, so that at this temperature we have liquid mixture a coexisting with solid solution b_1'. There has been, however,

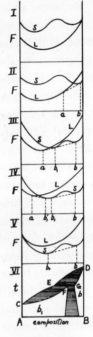

Fig. 230

a discontinuous change in composition from solid solutions of the b type to the b_1 series. This state of affairs lasts down to the freezing temperature of component A, where the last liquid mixture is able to exist. When, as usual, the abscissae of the points of contact of the tangents are plotted against temperature, the usual t-x diagram, in this case Roozeboom's Type IV previously discussed, arises (*cf.* Fig. 51, p. 167).

Type V. The freezing curve has a eutectic point.

This type (Fig. 231) arises when the L-curve passes through the S-curve with falling temperature, in a manner different from that given in Fig. 230, viz., at the temperature t (Fig. 231, IV), at which the two double tangents coincide, the two points of contact of the S-curve fall on opposite sides of the points of contact of the L-curve. This means that already at temperatures higher than t, the left-hand portion of the S-curve is below the L-curve, so that a double tangent on the left-hand side to L and S is already possible (Fig. 231, III), and therefore a second pair of phases can coexist. This behaviour commences at the melting-point of substance A, so that Fig. 231, III, is the type for all temperatures between this melting-point and t.

Above this melting-point, therefore, only one pair of phases, on the B side, coexist. Figs. 231, I and II, are therefore not essentially different from Fig. 230, I and II. Below the temperature t, the more stable portions of the S-curve, and their tangents, lie below the L-curve, Fig. 231, V. No liquid mixture is any longer stable; only solid solutions can now exist. Plotting in the usual way, the equilibrium diagram of Fig. 231, VI results (*cf.* Fig. 53, p. 169).

(b) Three-Component Systems.

The method of treatment here is essentially the same as in two-component systems, except that *both* solid and liquid solutions have free energy values represented by surfaces, which touch the vertical sides of the solid model. If both liquid and solid components are miscible in all proportions both these surfaces will be convex downwards. At high temperatures the free energy surface of the solid solutions will lie entirely above

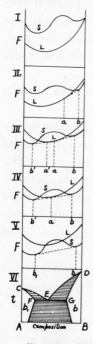

Fig. 231

that of liquid solutions and only liquid solutions will be stable, while at low temperatures the converse will be true and only solid solutions will be stable. At intermediate temperatures, one surface will interpenetrate the other and common tangents can be drawn to the two surfaces. The projection of the points of contact of these tangents gives an isotherm in the form of two continuous curves, representing equilibrium liquid and solid solutions. If the solid components are not miscible in all proportions the surface of chemical potential for the solid state is re-entrant (both convex and concave downwards), and two sets of common tangents can be drawn, separated by a gap, that is, two solubility curves, separated by a gap, are produced on the concentration isotherm. Since, however, numerous examples of the graphical method have now been given, it is unnecessary to go further into detail. The five types of Roozeboom (three-component systems) were arrived at on the basis of an osmotic analogy[6] and, therefore, do not merit consideration here.

NOTES

1. *Z. physikal, Chem.*, 1893, **12**, 359.

2. *ibid.*, 11, 289.

3. For a pure substance the molar free energy and the chemical potential are identical.

4. For a proof of this see Lewis and Randall, *Thermodynamics and the Free Energy of Chemical Substances*, McGraw-Hill, N. Y., 1923, p. 38.

5. Roozeboom, *Z. physikal. Chem.*, 1899, **30**, 387 *et seq.*

6. Roozeboom, *Z. physikal, Chem.*, 1891, **8**, 521.

APPENDIX II

DETERMINATION OF BINARY SOLID-LIQUID EQUILIBRIA

Chapter VIII has dealt with the interpretation of the equilibrium curves for binary systems when solids and liquids are present. The present chapter discusses the establishment of those curves for a previously uninvestigated system. The oldest, and still perhaps the most powerful, method is that of thermal analysis.

Thermal Analysis.

The principle of this method consists in the fact that a phase change must necessarily produce an energy transformation, which usually manifests itself as an evolution or absorption of heat.

When a pure substance cools without change of state, the curve connecting its temperature with time is continuous and exponential in form, when the surroundings are at a constant temperature, in accordance with Newton's law of cooling. If, however, the cooling substance is a pure molten solid it will commence to freeze at a characteristic temperature. In the process of freezing heat is evolved, and usually the rate of freezing is conditioned by the rate of loss of heat by radiation, so that the temperature remains constant. This behaviour manifests itself on the cooling curve as a horizontal straight line at the temperature of freezing. If the rate of crystallisation is low or the rate of cooling large, crystallisation may not take place fast enough to supply the heat lost by radiation and the horizontal then becomes a point of inflection or an S-shaped curve. The rate of cooling should, however, be kept sufficiently small, by controlling the temperature of the environment, so that crystallisation evolves heat fast enough to keep the temperature constant.

We now consider the cooling of a liquid mixture of two substances which are completely miscible in the liquid state, completely immiscible in the solid state, and do not form a compound, that is, a system of the simple eutectic type. This will cool until primary crystallisation of A or B occurs. Since, however, a solution does not freeze at a constant temperature, the temperature continues to fall, but not so rapidly, until the eutectic temperature is reached, when separation of the other component commences, and the temperature remains constant at the eutectic temperature until all is solid. Hence the appearance of the cooling curve is that of Fig. 232.

In the Figure, *ab* represents free cooling of the liquid (the temperature corresponding to *b* is the freezing temperature of the solution, that is, the temperature at which A (or B) first separates), *bc* represents delayed cooling due to continuous separation of pure solid A (or B), the temperature of the horizontal *cd* is the eutectic temperature, while *de* represents

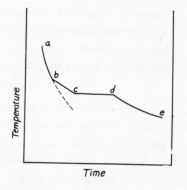

Fig. 232

cooling of the completely solidified system. For a fixed weight of system the length of *bc* will depend on the amount of excess B or A over the eutectic composition. Thus, as the eutectic composition is approached (with successive mixtures) the primary crystallisation will be less and the eutectic crystallisation greater. With a mixture exactly of the eutectic composition there will be no primary crystallisation, and the eutectic halt will be a maximum. This is the principle of Tammann's method[1] of finding the eutectic composition. According to this method, the duration of eutectic halt is plotted as ordinate against the composition of the mixture as abscissa, as shown in Fig. 233. The intersection of the two curves representing eutectic halt times gives the maximum eutectic halt time and hence the eutectic composition. Tammann's method is rarely employed nowadays, because of many possible sources of error in the experimental determination of the halt time.

The method of thermal analysis is applicable to all systems, however complicated, for instance, to those systems in which congruently or incongruently melting compounds are formed. In every case, the cooling curve gives the freezing temperature, that is, a point on the liquidus curve for the given total composition, and the temperature of eutectic freezing. In addition, if an incongruently

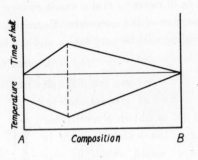

Fig. 233

melting compound is formed, there will be a peritectic halt for all mixtures richer in the higher melting component than the peritectic composition.

It is not always easy to obtain from the freezing-point curve the exact composition of a congruently or incongruently melting compound, due in the first case to dissociation in the molten state, which flattens the maximum, and in the second to dissociation of the compound at the transition or peritectic point. In these cases, Tammann's method may sometimes be employed with advantage. If the eutectic halt time is plotted, it will be zero for the pure components, but it will also be zero for a composition corresponding to that of the compound. Thus the composition of a congruently melting compound may be obtained as shown in Fig. 234.

If the compound is incongruently melting and the eutectic and peritectic halts are plotted, as in Fig. 235, the hidden maximum corresponding to the composition of the compound may be obtained through the same process of reasoning since the peritectic halt will be a maximum and the eutectic halt zero for the exact composition of the compound.

Types of Cooling Curves Employed.

(a) Free Cooling.

As previously indicated, free cooling, *i.e.* allowing the system to cool naturally by radiation from a higher temperature to a lower one, yields an exponential curve. The disadvantage of this type of curve is that a small change in slope can easily be missed because of the curvature. Moreover, if the temperature is high, the cooling will be very rapid, and the heat effect may be missed.

(b) Graduated Cooling.

To overcome the difficulty mentioned above Plato[2] suggested a method of gradual cooling, so as to obtain a rectilinear curve, on which changes in slope would show up very easily. Since heating is now usually electrical, the cooling can be carried out progressively and regularly by reducing the current. Plato did this by means of a resistance wire wound on a porcelain cylinder and rotated slowly by a motor. Many methods have been employed for this purpose, ranging from very complicated machinery to simple rheostats.

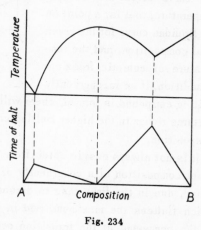

Fig. 234

Formation of Solid Solutions. The problem here is that of determining the temperature at which a cooling system of given composition passes the liquidus and solidus lines. These two temperatures, determined for each of several mixtures, permit of the complete plot of liquidus and solidus. For experimental work of this kind the method of graduated cooling is indispensible. In the absence of transformation in the melt, the plot of temperature against time has the appearance of Fig. 236 (a), namely, a straight line. For a pure substance in which a transformation occurs at a temperature T_1, linear cooling produces the cooling curve shown in Fig. 236 (b). The temperature of the melt follows that of the furnace linearly to f (the freezing point), where the first appearance of solid phase produces a change in the cooling rate of the melt.

During the time interval represented by the straight horizontal portion *fm*, solid deposits continuously, until at *m* (the melting-point), where the material is completely solid, the rate of cooling increases abruptly. Cooling of the solid is very rapid along *mb*, since during the time of freezing (*fm*) the furnace has cooled along *fb*, while the temperature of transformation has remained constant at T_1. At the time instant *m*, therefore, the difference in temperature between the solid and the furnace is considerable. At point *b*, the solid once more resumes the cooling rate of the furnace and cooling proceeds linearly along the original path.

During the liquid-solid transformation of a system which forms *solid solutions*, the temperature does not remain invariable, but gradually decreases as the solid solution deposits. The ideal linear cooling curve for such a system is shown in Fig. 236 (*c*). The cooling gradient remains constant along *f′ m′* from the freezing point (T_1) to the melting-point (T_2), where a sharp break in the cool-

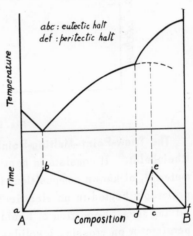

Fig. 235

ing curve marks the disappearance of the liquid phase. The solid solution cools rapidly from *m′*, finally assuming the cooling rate of the furnace at *b′*. In actual experience, the curve obtained usually shows a pronounced curvature as the freezing approaches completion; the last portion of freezing liquid does not release enough heat to maintain a constant temperature gradient. Fig. 236 (*d*) represents an experimentally determined curve where the melting point is not defined by a sharp break in the cooling curve. Tammann[3] has shown that the extensions of portions of the curve *f″m″* and *m″b″* intersect at the true melting-point. Therefore, as long as *f″m″* and *m″b″* have a reasonably linear portion, it is possible to arrive at melting-points with accuracy. The experimental technique necessary for accurate results has been developed recently.[4]

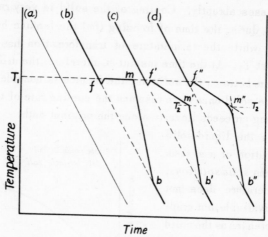

Fig. 236

The Thaw-Point–Melting-Point Method. This method is due to Rheinboldt.[5] It consists in heating a small quantity of solidified material, of known composition, in a capillary melting-point tube, preferably heated in an electrical apparatus provided with a magnifying lens. Formation of liquid occurs either at a eutectic temperature or on crossing a solidus line. This is known as "thawing" and is readily detectible in the magnified image. This temperature is noted and the temperature slowly raised, the amount of liquid increasing continuously. The temperature at which the last crystal skeleton disappears (melting-point) is observed. It is shown by Rheinboldt and Kircheisen[6] that every type of equilibrium diagram can be investigated by this method. The method is not capable of the highest accuracy but it is to be recommended for a rapid survey of the nature of a system, and for investigation of rare, expensive or explosive substances.

The Quenching Method. This method was devised for the investigation of systems which supercool obstinately, for instance, the naturally occurring silicates. Many molten silicates when cooled cannot be caused to crystallise: they become more and more viscous and are finally described as glasses: such substances have no melting-point. It is, however, possible to obtain these silicates in the crystalline condition, either by prolonged heating at a temperature below the melting-point (devitrification) or by treatment with a catalyst, or as naturally occurring substances. If a mixture of such substances is heated it will commence to liquefy on passing a eutectic temperature or a solidus line. If this mixture is kept at a temperature a little above the temperature at which liquid forms, it will come into equilibrium as a heterogeneous mixture of liquid and solid. If the temperature is still further raised and kept constant, the mixture will become homogeneous liquid. It should be noticed that while liquids readily enter the metastable state, *i.e.* remain supercooled, there is no well-authenticated instance of a solid being heated, metastably, above its melting-point. In practice the method is as follows: the completely solidified and crystalline mass is heated to a temperature below that at which liquefaction is expected to occur, and kept at that temperature for a sufficient length of time for equilibrium to be established. The mass is then quenched, that is, cooled rapidly to room temperature, and a thin section examined in the polarising microscope. The complete absence of isotropic material will show that no melting has occurred. The experiment is then repeated at a slightly higher temperature. As soon as a thin section reveals the presence of isotropic material (glass), it is evident that a solidus line has been passed. From here on, as the experiment is repeated at successively higher temperatures, the amount of isotropic material visible in the thin section increases until finally a completely isotropic mass is obtained. The temperature of this last observation will be slightly above the freezing-point. The method is laborious but it is the only one which can be used with systems which will not crystallise fast enough to permit of the application of thermal analysis.

The Isothermal Method. If the temperature is not very far removed from room temperature and the composition of the liquid phase is such that the amount of one component considerably exceeds the other, it is customary to describe the curve of the equilibrium liquid-solid as a solubility curve, although, as stated earlier, there is no theoretical difference whatever between a freezing curve and a solubility curve (in the absence of solid solution). There is, however, some practical difference if freezing curves are considered to run to high temperatures and high concentrations. In the former case, the course of the equilibrium curve can be defined readily and accurately by the methods of solubility determination, *i.e.* the temperature is held constant, excess of solid phase added, and, after equilibrium has been attained, a sample of the solution removed and analysed. By altering the temperature of experiment by small amounts and repeating the determination, a curve is obtained when the results are plotted as a function of temperature. If the solid phase does not change its nature abruptly the curve will be smooth, exhibiting no breaks. Conversely, a break or sharp change in the slope of the curve indicates that the nature of the solid phase has changed. The question of the nature of the solid phase is one by no means easy to answer when the system is binary. The obvious method of removing a sample of the solid phase and analysing it is very crude, because of the difficulty of freeing the solid phase entirely from adhering mother liquor: the solid phase cannot be washed because of the danger of changing its nature, neither can it be dried, for the same reason, although some success has been attained by centrifuging. This method of working has led to numerous errors in the older literature. Strangely enough, this ambiguity is lacking in three-component systems, studied isothermally, where the Schreinemakers method of the "wet residue" can be applied (see p. 378). When there is any doubt as to the nature of the solid phase it is advisable to convert the two-component system into a three-component one by addition of an inert solute, and apply the Schreinemakers method.

It has occasionally been suggested that the isothermal method could be advantageously applied to high temperature systems and curves of high concentration, for instance in the study of alloys, where the method hitherto has been almost exclusively that of thermal analysis. The difficulties are two in number, *viz.*, that of maintaining a constant high temperature, and that of separating the solid phase from the liquid phase at high temperature. The former difficulty has now been overcome since there are many designs of thermostatic control of high temperature furnaces.[7] The difficulty of filtering at high temperature is more serious. When the solid phase is much heavier than the liquid gravitational separation is possible. A sample of the liquid phase can then be withdrawn for analysis, but the nature of the solid phase must still be determined by other means. When, however, the nature of the solid phase is known, this method may be applied with advantage to determine the exact form of the liquidus.[8]

NOTES

1. Tammann, *Z. anorg. Chem.*, 1903, **37**, 303.

2. Plato, *Z. physik. Chem.*, 1906, **55**, 721.

3. G. Tammann, *Z. anorg. Chem.*, 1905, **43**, 218; **47**, 290.

4. Campbell and Prodan, *J. Am. Chem. Soc.*, 1948, **70**, 553.

5. Rheinboldt, *J. pr. Chem.*, 1925, (2), **111**, 242.

6. Rheinboldt and Kircheisen, *J. pr. Chem.*, 1926 (2), **112**, 187; **113**, 199, 348.

7. *Cf.* for example Lutz and Wood, *Can. J. Res.*, 1948, **26A**, 145.

8. *Cf.* for example, the system iron — tin: Campbell, Wood and Skinner, *J. Amer. Chem. Soc.*, 1949, **71**, 1729.

Abbott, 208.
Adams, 55, 56, 87, 231.
Adriani, 186, 208,
Alexander, 389.
Allen, 210.
Allison, 232.
Allmand, 387.
Amadori, 388.
Andersen, 210.
Andrew, 201.
Andrews, 194.
Andrusov, 215.
Armstrong, 445.
Ashley, 295.
Aten, 185, 275, 276.
Atkins, 275.
Aulich, 132.
Awerbach, 219.

de Baat, 385.
Bailey, 105.
Bain, 209.
Bancroft, 185, 227, 231, 385, 387, 388.
Barbaudy, 313.
Barnes, 56.
Barnett, 231.
Barrell, 313.
Barschall, 419, 443.
Baur, 57, 210.
Beckmann, 276.
Beech, 295.
Bell, 389, 442.
Bernal, 58.
Berthollet, 2,
Berthoud, 58.

Bidwell, 260.
Bigelow, 19, 58.
Biltz, 216, 231.
Binnie, 201.
Blasdale, 385, 386, 387, 401, 402, 443, 444, 453, 454.
Bloch, 58.
Blumenthal, 388.
Bodländer, 295, 433, 444.
Boeseken, 82.
Bogojawlenski, 51, 59.
Bogue, 329.
Bokhorst, 57, 72, 73, 74, 81, 82.
Booge, 185.
Booth, 260.
Bornemann, 209.
Bosch, 60.
Butari, 105.
Bouvier, 231.
Bowen, 185, 210, 211, 339.
Bragg, 229, 232.
Brauns, 57.
Bridgman, 27, 55, 56, 57, 60, 62, 64, 71, 78, 79, 80, 82, 83.
Brings, 58.
Briscoe, 187.
Brönsted, 59, 81.
Brown, 295.
de Bruin, 60.
Bruins, 58, 60.
Bruni, 186.
Bružs, 231.
Buchner, 105, 389.
Buddington, 197.
Bunn, 231.
Burwell, 80.
Bussen, 339.

Butler, 19, 132.

Cailletet, 95.
Cameron, 275.
Campbell, A.J.R., 45, 79, 94, 105, 187.
Campbell, A.N., 45, 58, 59, 79, 82, 94, 105, 173, 186, 187, 208, 209, 259, 295, 339, 445, 480.
Carpenter, 206.
Carrington, 106.
Carson, 81, 275, 276.
Carveth, 275, 338.
Centnerszwer, 215, 219, 231, 243.
Cernatescu, 106.
Chapman, 81.
Chattaway, 59, 60.
Chrétien, 385.
Christie, 208
Churchill, 186.
Clapeyron, 100.
Clark, 231.
Clendinnen, 187, 387, 388.
Clifford, 231.
Cocksedge, 445.
Cohen, 46, 53, 56, 57, 58, 60, 69, 81, 179, 187, 188, 232, 445.
Compton, 232.
Cook, 58.
Cornec, 454.
Cox, 105.
Creighton, 132.
Cretcher, 105.

Daniels, 231.
D'Ans, 387, 454.
Davis, 105.
Dawson, 385, 386, 387, 398.
Day, 210, 211.
Debye, 229.
Deffet, 56.
Degens, 81.
Dehlinger, 232.
Deleano, 211.
Denham, 389.
Desch, 209.
De Witt, 81.
Dickinson, 186.
Dingemans, 260.

Dobinski, 82.
Doelter, 210.
Dolique, 106.
Doscher, 82, 389.
Downes, 445.
Drucker, 105.
Duckett, 102, 106.
Dulmage, 313.
Dundon, 58.
Durham, 388.
Dutilh, 208.
Dutoit, 275.

Early, 56.
Edwards, 209.
Ehret, 199.
Eisenhut, 209.
Eitel, 339.
Elbrächter, 59.
Engel, 276.
Epstein, 209, 210.
Estis, 208.
Euwen, 187.
Eyring, 45.

Fahrenheit, 43.
Faht, 275.
Falk, 219.
Faraday, 215, 226.
Fedotieff, 431, 437, 443, 444.
Ferguson, 187.
Fife, 389.
Findlay, 60, 104, 132, 185, 208, 275.
Fischer, 185.
Fiske, 186.
Flaschner, 105.
Foote, 59, 231.
Fortey, 132.
Fouquet, 187.
Franco, 443, 445.
Frankforter, 389.
Frary, 389.
Freeman, 281.
Freeth, 187, 397, 398, 400, 401, 402, 445.
Frost, 70, 81.
Freundlich, 51.

Gapon, 188.

Gayler, 210.
Geer, 339.
Gernez, 48.
Gibbs, 7, 15, 19, 281, 455, 456.
Gibbs-Konovalov, 114.
Gilbert, 445.
Gilson, 232.
Gingrich, 82.
Githens, 132.
Glasstone, 295.
Goerens, 201, 209, 210.
Gomolka, 81.
Gossner, 419.
Grahmann, 187.
Grebenschtschikov, 184.
Greig, 210, 339.
Guertler, 59.
Guldberg, 7.
Gurinsky, 199.
Gurtler, 105.
Guthrie, 139, 140, 210.

Hagg, 229, 230.
Hall, 187.
Hamid, 401, 402, 443.
Hammick, 275.
Hansen, 209.
Hartley, 187.
Hautefeuille, 76.
Helderman, 56, 57, 60.
Heller, 60.
Helmholz, 73, 74, 81.
Hendricks, 78.
Hermann, 82.
Herold, 444.
Hetterschij, 187.
Heycock, 209, 232.
Hickmans, 185, 208.
Hickson, 106.
Higman, 185.
Hildebrand, 401, 454.
Hill, 105, 187, 254, 295, 386, 388, 444.
Hissink, 187.
Hollmann, 275.
Holmes, 81, 295.
Holt, 232.
Honda, 206, 209, 210.

Horsley, 132, 313.
Hostetter, 59, 231.
Hou, 445.
Howard, 106.
Howells, 387.
Hulett, 19, 56, 58, 74, 82.
Hull, 132.
Hultgren, 82.
Hume-Rothery, 199.
Humphrey, 210.
Hutchinson, 187.
Hüttig, 231, 232.

Igelsrud, 387.
Inouye, 187.
Ipatiev, 70, 71, 81.
Isasc, 186, 187.
Ishikawa, 187.

Jaffé, 187.
Jänecke, 56, 57, 186, 209, 339, 422, 433, 437, 421, 443, 444, 445, 453, 454.
Jeffreys, 59.
Jellinghaus, 59.
Jenkins, 210.
Johansson, 269.
Johnston, 55, 56, 59, 194, 231.
Jolibois, 81, 231.
Jones, 187, 209.
Joseph, 187.

Kaplan, 388.
Kastle, 52, 59.
Katz, 82.
Kaufmann, 187.
Kaupp, 209.
Keeling, 206.
Kendall, 185.
Kenrick, 386, 388.
Kettner, 275.
Kipping, 208.
Kircheisen, 477, 480.
Klesper, 209.
Kohnstamm, 100, 105.
Koltunoff, 437.
Kondoguri, 58.
Kooy, 56, 57, 60.

Koppel, 388.
Kordes, 185, 186.
Korvezee, 259, 260.
Kracek, 78.
Kremann, 185, 387, 445.
Kremers, 209.
Krombach, 454.
Krummacher, 82.
Kruyt, 81, 276.
Kuhn, 58.
Kultascheff, 210.
Kurakov, 185.
Küster, 49, 58.

Lagerqvist, 339.
Lambert, 59, 60.
Lattey, 105.
von Laue, 229.
Lautz, 60.
Laybourn, 281.
Lebedeff, 210.
Le Blanc, 444.
Lecat, 313.
Le Chatelier, 22, 25, 26, 35, 38, 67,
    100, 107, 179, 181, 210, 234, 237,
    264, 421, 444.
Lee, 389.
de Leeuw, 81, 82, 271, 276.
Lehmann, 77.
Lennox, 388.
von Lepkowski, 186.
Lewis, 57, 132, 471.
Liesche, 276.
Lightfoot, 387.
Linck, 82.
Lodochnikov, 281, 442.
Logan, 231.
Longtin, 442.
Losana, 57, 59.
Loucks, 388, 443.
Löwenherz, 412, 421, 437.
Löwenstein, 232.
Lowry, 56, 187, 275.
Loyd, 231.
Ludwig, 445.
Lussana, 57.
Lutz, 480.

Maass, 55.
MacDougall, 19.
MacRae, 72, 74, 81.
Macrae, 82.
Mack, 56, 58,
Madgin, 187, 281.
Malisoff, 105.
Marc, 51
Marckwald, 73, 74, 81.
Markley, 105, 187.
Maron, 132.
Mason, 445.
Mathias, 95.
Matignon, 387, 398.
Matt, 209.
Matuschek, 445.
Maurer, 210.
May, 82.
Mazzotto, 338.
McBain, 389.
McEwen, 105.
McKay, 185.
McKenzie, 208.
de Meester, 81, 187.
Menzies, 66.
Merwin, 59 , 231.
Meusser, 186.
Meyer, 260, 387, 388, 398.
Meyerhoffer, 210, 385, 386, 387, 442,
    443, 444, 445.
Miers, 45, 58, 186, 187.
Miller, 388.
Millican, 187.
Mlodziejowski, 209.
Mochels, 132.
Moesveld, 56, 58, 60, 187.
Morey, 59.
Morningstar, 59.
Müller, 58, 60, 187, 209, 386.
Mylius, 186.

Nabot, 105.
Nelson, 105.
Nernst, 132, 276.
Neumeister, 401.
Neville, 209, 232.
Novotny, 444.

Occleshaw, 386.
Offer, 140.
Olander, 209.
Oppenheimer, 51.
Osmond, 209.
Ostwald, 54, 275.
Othmer, 58.
Owen, 209.

Padoa, 186.
Pampini, 388.
Papafil, 106.
Parks, 50, 59.
Parsons, 57.
Partington, 187.
Parvatiker, 105.
Pasteur, 189.
Patterson, 102, 106.
Paul, 276.
Pawloff, 19, 58.
Perman, 387.
Peterson, 209.
Pfaundler, 140.
Phillips, 454.
Phragmen, 209.
Plato, 475, 480.
Pollatschek, 49, 58.
Pope, 208.
Posnjak, 78.
Pozner, 385, 388, 442.
Precht, 385, 445.
Pritchard, 59.
Prodan, 186, 339, 480.
Prutton, 132, 385, 387.
Purdon, 444, 453.
Puschin, 184.

Rabe, 187.
Randall, 57, 82, 132, 232, 442, 471.
Rankin, 339.
Rastall, 211.
Read, 184.
Reed, 52, 59.
Reicher, 386, 443.
Reinders, 49, 52, 186, 388, 401, 426.
Reinitzer, 76.
Reiter, 210.
Rheinboldt, 477, 480.

Rhodes, 105, 187.
Ricci, 187, 386, 388, 443, 444.
Richards, 186.
Rinck, 186.
Rivett, 187, 385, 387.
Roberts-Austen, 209.
Robson, 386.
Rooksby, 82.
Roozeboom, 55, 56, 57, 185, 208, 254,
     260, 281, 295, 338, 339, 385, 386,
     387, 455, 470, 471.
Rose, 209.
Ross, 185, 208.
Roth, 81.
Rothmund, 105.
Royster, 214.
Ruer, 201, 209, 210.

Sachs, 187.
Sahmen, 339, 388.
Saldaou, 210.
Samis, 445.
Sato, 209.
Saunders, 442, 443.
Sayer, 442, 443.
Sborgi, 443, 445.
Scatchard, 132.
Schairer, 211.
Schenck, 82.
Schenker, 57.
Scherrer, 229.
Schischakow, 59.
Schlösing, 401, 437.
Schneider, 339.
Schoevers, 275.
Schreinemakers, 295, 313, 385, 386, 388,
     407, 414, 442, 443.
Schukareff, 105.
Schut, 187.
Seljakow, 80.
Seltz, 160, 186.
Shen, 132.
Shepherd, 210.
Sherman, 45.
Sichling, 57.
Sicklen, 58.
Sinnige, 187.
Skinner, 209, 480.

Slater, 444, 453.
Smith, A., 81, 272, 275, 276.
Smith, J.C., 294, 389, 442.
Smith, N.O., 187, 386, 388, 444.
Smits, 41, 57, 72, 73, 74, 81, 82, 259, 260, 271, 275, 276.
Smyth, 231.
Solovev, 185.
Sommerville, 185, 208.
Sosman, 59, 231.
Soth, 388.
Southard, 214.
Spack, 454.
Stamm, 81.
Steacie, 55.
Stenzel, 209.
Stock, 81.
Stockhardt, 132.
Stoffel, 185.
Stokes, 281.
Stollenwerk, 216, 231.
Stortenbeker, 185, 246, 387, 388.
Sypiena, 387.

Takegami, 445.
Tammann, 39, 48, 49, 54, 55, 56, 57, 58, 59, 60, 61, 62, 65, 74, 80, 81, 186, 208, 228, 275, 480.
Tanner, 402.
Taylor, 45.
Terwen, 57.
Thomas, 313.
Thomas, Smeath, 57.
Thompson, 387.
Thönnessen, 46.
Thorvaldson, 339.
Timmermans, 56, 100, 105, 162, 186.
Tomassi, 132.
Toporescu, 444.
Tower, 385.
Traube, 386.
Trevor, 19.
Trimble, 19, 58.
Troost, 76.
Turrentine, 402.

Uyeda, 426, 442.

Van Alkemade, 455.
van den Berg, 260.
van den Bosch, 56, 187.
van Deventer, 386.
van Eyk, 56.
van Klooster, 81.
van Laar, 184, 186, 208, 261.
van Leeuwin, 386.
van Liempt, 57.
van Lieshout, 69, 81.
Vanstone, 209
van't Hoff, 51, 56, 59, 132, 156, 187, 385, 386, 387, 411, 419, 437, 443, 445, 450, 454.
van Wyk, 186.
Vedinskii, 70, 81.
von Vegesack, 339, 388.
Vogt, 210.
Vold, 82, 389.
Voller, 187.
Volmer, 45.
Voorhis, 72, 74, 81, 82.
Vorländer, 82.

Waage, 7.
Wagner, 105.
Wahl, 74.
Walden, 243, 246.
Wallace, 295.
Wallerant, 79.
Wallmark, 339.
Walters, 338.
Waring, 56.
Warren, 59, 80, 82.
Washburn, 184.
Weber, 45.
Webster, 58.
Wegelius, 19.
von Weimarn, 58.
Wells, 186.
Wenzel, 2.
Werner, 275.
West, 66, 209.
Westgren, 209, 339.
Weston, 388.
Wigand, 276.
Williamson, 59.

Witt, 445.
Wittjen, 385.
Wood, J., 209, 480.
Wood, S.E., 132.
Woodman, 294.
Wooster, 58.
Wrede, 186.
Wright, C.R.A., 295.
Wright, F.E., 57, 339.
von Wrochem, 186.

Wuite, 242, 259.
Wurmser, 445.
Wyckoff, 232.

Yaffe, 294.
Young, S., 132, 313.
Young, S.W., 58.

Zawidski, 56, 132.
Zitek, 445.

SUBJECT INDEX

Absorption Coefficient, 107.
Acetaldehyde, 270.
-- and paraldehyde, 270.
Acetic acid-toluene-water, 283.
Acetone-carbon disulphide, 114
  — chloroform, 115.
Acid salt, 388.
Akermanite-gehlenite, 162.
Alkemade, theorem of, 327.
Allotropic transition, effect of solvent on, 184.
Allotropy, 35, 79, 80, 182.
  — of components, 143.
  — Smits' theory of, 41.
Alloys, 193
  — study of, 479
Amalgams, 197.
Ammonia compounds of metal chlorides, 215.
Ammonia-soda process, 431.
Ammoniates, 215.
Ammonium nitrate, 78.
  — — effect of potassium nitrate on transition point of, 170.
  — — equilibrium diagram of, 79.
  — — - water, 183.
Ammonium perchlorate-ammonium sulphate-water, 397.
Ammonium sulphate-lithium sulphate - ferrous sulphate-water, 407.
  — — - sodium sulphate-water, 398.
  — — - ammonium perchlorate-water, 397.
Aniline-phenol-water, 292.
  — - sulphur dioxide, 254.
Anisotropic, 77
  — liquids, 76.

Antipodes, optical, 190.
Astracanite, 352, 358, 362.
Atomic heats, 194.
Austenite, 203.
Azeotropic maximum, 302.
  — minimum, 304, 306.
  — solution,
      117, 119, 121, 301, 302, 304, 306.

Basic salt, 380.
Benzaldoxime, 262, 269.
Benzaldoximes, 269.
Benzene, fusion pressure of, 28.
Benzoic acid - water, 175, 176.
Binary equilibria at lower temperatures, 176.
Binary systems, 84, 455, 465.
  — — classification of, 87
Binodal curve, 289,
  — surface, 289.
Bittern, sea-water, 454.
Bivariant, 14.
  — systems, 32, 237, 249.
Bleaching powder, 231.
Boiling-point, 21.
  — curves, 118.
  — maximum, 301.
  — minimum, 304, 305.
  — of saturated solutions, 238.
Brasses, 196.
Break in solubility curve, 154, 181, 182.
Broken series of solid solutions, 164.
Bubble-cap, 122.
n-Butyl alcohol-water, 125.
sec-Butyl alcohol-water, effect of pressure on, 101.

Cadmium carbonate, dissociation pressure of, 215.

Calcium carbonate, dissociation pressure of, 214.

Calcium sulphate - strontium sulphate, 171.

Carbon disulphide - acetone, 114.

Carbon dioxide, solubility of, in water, 108.

Carbon tetrachloride - cyclohexane, 113.

Carvoxime, 161.

Cementite, 203.

Ceramics, 207.

Changes at the triple point, effect of addition of heat on, 33.

— — — — — effect of change of volume on, 34.

Chemical potential, 126, 455.

Chloroform - acetone, 115.

Clapeyron equation, 100.

Clausius-Clapeyron equation, 23.

Colloids, as one- or two-phase systems, 383.

Commercial processes, quaternary, Phase Rule study of, 444.

Common ion effect, 385.

Common ion, three salts with, 404.

Complex ion, effect on solubility of, 385.

Complex molecules, presence of, 24.

Components, 9.

— allotropy of, 143.

— choice of, 409.

— number of, 11.

Composition triangle, 322.

Concealed maximum, 185.

Concentration, graphical representation of, 278.

— - temperature diagram, 246.

Condensed system, 27, 100, 134, 237.

Conglomerate, 168, 190.

Congruent melting-point, 144.

— — pressure and composition in the neighbourhood of, 254,

Congruent point, 385.

— solution, 375, 385.

Congruently melting binary compound, 321.

— — ternary compound, 325, 465.

— saturating, 346, 348.

Conjugate solutions, 93.

— — solid, 167.

— — ternary, 283.

Consolute, 91, 94.

Constant boiling mixture, 117, 119.

Conversion saltpetre, 426.

Cooling curve, 473, 476.

— — with solid solutions, 476.

— curves, types of, 474.

— free, 472, 474.

— graduated, 475.

Copper sulphate - water, solid model for, 224.

Coring, 197, 208.

Cricondentherm, 260.

Critical composition, 94.

— curve, 251, 257, 289.

— phenomena, 236.

— — in binary systems, 257.

— — in salt solutions, 243.

— point, isothermal, 285.

— — ternary, 284.

— — variance at, 100.

— pressure, 22.

— solution temperature, 94, 164.

— — — effect of impurities on, 101.

— — — influence of foreign substances on, 101.

— — — influence of pressure on, 99.

— temperature, 22.

— temperatures of solutions, 257.

Cryohydrate, 140.

Cryohydric point, 139.

Curd-fibres, 384.

Curve, of fusion, 26.

— transition, 38.

Cyclic process, general conditions for, 430.

Cyclic processes, examples of, 394, 397, 398, 429.

Cyclohexane - carbon tetrachloride, 113.

Degree of subdivision, effect of, on

equilibrium, 9.

Dehydration, 220.

— by means of anhydrous sodium sulphate, 154.

Deliquescence, 237, 257.

Deuterium oxide, 64.

Devitrification, 50, 478.

dl-mixture, 190.

Dimorphism, 35.

Discontinuous series of solid solutions, 164.

Dissociation, effect of degree of, on melting-point curve, 145.

— pressure, 213.

— — constancy of, 216.

— — equation for, 223.

Distillation, 115, 118, 121, 126, 128.

— cold to hot, 76.

— isobaric, 118.

— isothermal, 115.

— with steam, 129.

Distribution of liquids, 285.

— — salts in ternary systems, 374.

Double decomposition, 409.

Double salts, formation of, 411.

Drying up point, 344.

Dynamic allotropy, 272.

Dystectic, 144.

Efflorescence, 224, 226.

Electrical conductivity, 194.

Electrode potential, 194.

Enantiotropy, 39, 182.

— combined with monotropy, 42.

Equilibrium, apparent, 4, 5.

— between liquid and vapour, 21.

— between solid and liquid, 26.

— between solid and vapour, 25.

— between solid, liquid and vapour, 29.

— binary, at lower temperatures, 176.

— false, 4, 5.

— homogeneous and heterogeneous, 4.

— metastable, 42.

— real and apparent, 5.

— true, 4, 5.

Ether - anthraquinone, critical phenomena in the system, 259.

Ethyl alcohol, dehydration of, 313.

— — - water, 120.

Eutectic composition, 137, 138, 141.

— curves, 315.

— influence of pressure on temperature and concentration of, 184.

— point, 136, 167.

— structure, 136.

— temperature, 136, 141.

— ternary, 315.

— vapour composition at, 250.

Eutectoid, 170, 171.

Evaporation, isothermal, 343.

— —, calculation of quantities in, 392.

Ex-solution, 164.

Extrapolation, algebraic vs. graphical, 379.

Ferric chloride - water, 147.

Ferrite, 200.

Ferrous sulphate - lithium sulphate - ammonium sulphate - water, 407.

Field, 32.

Five-component systems, 446.

Fluid phase, 259.

Formation of double salts, 411.

Four-component systems, 403.

Fractional crystallization, of solid solutions, 162.

Fractional distillation, 298, 300, 304, 307, 311.

— —, industrial, 121.

Fractionating column, 122.

Free cooling, 474.

Freedom, degree of, 13.

Free energy, 455.

Freezing mixtures, 139.

Freezing-point curve, 161, 162.

— curves, miscellaneous examples of, 189.

— effect of concentration on, 135.

— of solutions, 143.

Fuming liquids, 123.

Gases, solubility of, in liquids, 107.
Gehlenite-akermanite, 162.
Geological thermometer, 453.
Gibbs-Konovalov, theorem of, 114, 115.
Glaserite, 418, 451.
Glasses, 50, 478.
Glauber's salt, 151.
Graduated cooling, 475.
Graphical representation, 277, 411.
— — of ternary systems, rectangular plot, 278, 340.
— — of ternary systems, triangular plot, 278, 341.

Halt time, in cooling curve, 473.
Heat of hydration, 223.
— — mixture, 194.
— — solution, 181.
Hemihedry, 189.
Henry's law, 107.
— — constant, 107.
— — deviations from, 108.
Heterogeneity, band of, 291.
Heterogeneous, 4, 5.
Homogeneous, 4, 5.
Hume-Rothery, principle of, 199.
Hydrates, dissociation pressure of, 220.
— metastability of, 226.
— preservation of, 225.
— range of existence of, 226.
Hydration, heat of, 353.
— of double and component salts, 345.
Hydrolysis, 380.
Hylotropic substances, 264.
Hypereutectic, 205.

Ice, fusion pressure of, 28.
— vapour pressure of, 47.
— various forms of, 62.
Ideal solutions, 91, 109.
Immiscible liquids, 129.
Incongruent melting-point, 150.
Incongruently saturating, 346, 347, 348.
Indifferent point, 146.
Industrial fractional distillation, 121.
Inevaporable solutions, 148.

Inoculation, 44.
Insoluble substances, preparation of, for analysis, 443.
Intermetallic compounds, nature and formulae of, 198.
Interrupted series of solid solutions, 164.
Invariant, 14.
Iron - carbon alloys, 200.
— transition points of, 200.
Isobar, 86.
Isobaric distillation, 118, 298, 302, 304, 311.
Isohydrore, 427.
Isomeric transformation, velocity of, 263.
Isomerides, dynamic, 261.
— optical, 190.
Isomorphous, 156.
Isopleth, 86, 118, 298, 302, 303.
Isotherm, 86.
Isothermal distillation, 115, 300.
— evaporation, 148, 425.
— method, 478.
Isotropic material, 478.

Jänecke, graphical method of, 341, 406, 412, 421.
— projection, advantages of, 425.
"Join,", 322.

Lattice, in solid solution, 169.
Le Chatelier, graphical method of, 421.
— —, principle of, 22.
Le Chatelier-Brauns equation, 179.
Ledeburite, 203.
Lime, 213.
Limestone, 213.
Liquid crystals, 76.
— — equilibrium relations for, 77.
Liquid layers, in equilibrium with solid, 173.
— pairs, completely miscible, 110.
— state, complexity of, 82.
Liquid-vapour equilibrium, comparison of types, 130.
Liquidus, 157.
Lithium sulphate - ammonium sul-

phate - ferrous sulphate - water, 407.
Lodochnikov, graphical method of, 406.
Löwenherz, graphical method of, 412.
— Schreinemakers' modification of graphical method of, 473.
Lower critical solution temperature, 98, 99.
Lye, 384.
Lysol, 103.

Magma, 207.
— crystallization of, 328.
Magnetic susceptibility, 194.
— transformations in iron-carbon system, 201, 206.
Manganese-nitrogen, 229.
Mannitol-water, 180.
"Melting" of a hydrate, 24.
"Melting under the solvent", 175.
Melting-point, 26, 31.
— curve, 26.
— — of solutions, 143.
Mercuric iodide, 39, 40.
Mercury, alloys of, 197.
Meritectic point, 166.
Mesomorphous state, 77.
Metallurgy, 194.
Metals, phase diagrams for, 194.
Metastability, 43.
— and solubility, 153.
Metastable state, persistence of, 53.
— systems, vapour pressure of, 240.
— — velocity of transformation of, 48.
Metathesis, 314, 409.
Methylethylketone - water, 97.
"Middle soap," 384.
Minerals, 206.
Miscibility, complete and partial, 90.
— partial or limited, 91.
Mix-crystal, pseudo-racemic, 192.
Mixed melting-points, method of, 142.
Monotropy, 39.
— enantiotropy combined with, 42.
Multiple proportions, law of, 199.
Multi-variant, 14.
Muntz metal, 197.

Naphthalene-tetrachlorethane, 180.
"Natural" freezing-point, 264.
Neat soap, 384.
Nematic, 182.
Newton's law of cooling, 472.
Nickel iodate - water, 155.
Nigre, 384.
Nitrobenzene - water, 129.
Nitrogen - manganese, 229.
Nuclear number, 45.
Nuclei, 44.
Nucleus solution, 430.

Oceanic salts, 437, 449.
One-component systems, 20, 61.
Optically active substances, 189.
Orthogonal projection, 319.
Oxy-carbonates, formation of, 219.

Paragenesis, 421.
Paragenetic diagram, 453.
Paraldehyde, 270.
Parkes process, 287.
Partial liquefaction, purification by, 143.
— miscibility, 91, 282.
— pressures of components and composition of vapour phase, 248.
— solid solubility, 164.
Partially miscible liquids, 283, 290, 293.
— — — in equilibrium with vapour, 125.
Particle size, effect on solubility of, 46.
Pearlite, 204.
Peritectic point, 150, 166, 323.
— ternary, 323.
Perspective projection, 319.
Phase reaction, 33.
— — at dystectic, 146.
— — at eutectic, binary, 136.
— — — — ternary, 315.
— — — eutectoid, 172.
— — — peritectic point, 151, 166.
Phase Rule, 7, 15.
— — classification of systems according to, 15.

— — deduction of, 17.

Phases, 7.
— calculation of quantities of, 96.
— number of, 8.

Phenol and water, solubility of, 94, 95.

Phenol - water, 93, 95, 173.
— — metastability in the system, 175.

Phosphorus, 70.
— black, 75.
— critical point of, 73.
— equilibrium diagram of, 73.
— liquid, vapour pressure of, 72.
— red, 70.
— ruby-violet, 70.
— transition curve of, 74.
— triple points of, 73, 74.
— vapour pressure of, 71, 72.
— white, 70.

Plait point, 285.
— — curve, 289.

Plato, method of, 475.

Polarising microscope, 478.

Polymerism, 262.

Polymorphism, 35.

Polythermal diagram, 319.

Portland cement, 334.

Potassium chloride - potassium sulphate - water, 395.
— — - silver chloride, 138.
— — - sodium chloride - water, 390.

Potassium, fusion pressure of, 28.

Potassium iodide - sulphur dioxide, 243.

Potassium - sodium, 151.

Pressure - temperature - composition, model, 233, 254.
— — plane diagram, 234, 246.

Primary phase, 319.

Proeutectic, 205.

n-Propyl alcohol - water, 119.

Pseudo-binary systems, 261, 274.

Pseudo-components, 24.

Pseudomonotropy, 41.

Pseudo-racemic mix-crystal, 192.

Pseudo-ternary systems, 271.

p, t, x model, generalised, 250.

Purification by partial liquefaction, 143.
— — recrystallisation, 344.

Quadruple point, 153, 233.
— — changes at, 234.
— — metastable, 241.

Quaternary systems, 403.

Quenching method, 477.

Quinary systems, 446.

Quintuple point, 277, 316, 362, 409.

Racemate, 189, 191.
— partial, 191.
— transition interval of, 355.

Racemic mixture, 189.

Raoult's law, 91, 109, 113, 114, 131.
— — positive and negative deviations from, 113, 114.

Reciprocal salt-pairs, 409.

Recrystallisation, 344.
— formation of two liquid layers in, 175.

Rectilinear diameter, law of, 95.

Recurrent crystallisation, 328.

Reflection of light, 194.

Reflux, 123.

Residue lines, 300, 303, 304, 307, 312.

Retrograde solubility, 180, 288.

Ricci and Loucks, graphical method of, 443.

Roozeboom, rule of, 327, 329.

Salt effect, 385.
— separation of, on evaporation, 238

Salting-out, 382.

Saturated solution, 177, 178.
— — nature of solid phase, 178.
— — vapour pressure of, 235.

Saturation, time of approach to, 178.

Schlösung, method of, for production of sodium bicarbonate, 437.

Schoenite, 451.

Schreinemakers' method, 479.

Sections, isobaric, 253.
— isoplethal, 253.
— isothermal, 253.

Seeding, 44.

Separation of salts by a temperature-cycle process, 394.
Sextuple point, 410.
Silicates, 477.
Silver chloride - potassium chloride, 138.
— — - sodium chloride, 158.
Silver nitrate - sodium nitrate, 167.
— — - water, critical phenomena in the system, 258.
Six-component systems, 453.
Smectic, 82.
Soap, 383.
Sodium bicarbonate, manufacture of, 431.
Sodium chloride — potassium chloride
— water, 390.
— — - silver chloride, 158.
— — - water, 139.
Sodium nitrate — silver nitrate, 167.
Sodium — potassium, 151.
Sodium sulphate — water, 151, 239.
— — — critical phenomena in the system, 258.
— — - ammonium sulphate - water, 398.
— — dehydration by means of anhydrous, 154.
Solid and liquid, equilibrium between, 26.
— — vapour, equilibrium between, 25.
— liquid and vapour, equilibrium between, 29.
— phase, determination of, 381, 382, 474, 479.
— solution, 227.
Solid solutions, binary, in binary systems, 156, 465.
— — — — ternary systems, 329, 372.
— — changes in, with temperature, 170.
— — formation of, 465, 475.
— — fractional crystallisation of, 162.
— — freezing-point of, 157.
— — in quaternary systems, 425.
— — melting-point curve of, 157.

— — Roozeboom's classification of, in binary systems, 157, 166, 167, 465.
— — Roozeboom's classification of, in ternary systems, 374, 376.
— — ternary, in ternary systems, 333, 470.
— — theoretical considerations of, 160, 388.
Solidus, 157.
Solubility, 178.
— and transition point, 152, 154, 356, 410.
— coefficient, 107, 132.
— curve, 93, 135, 180.
— — completely closed, 98.
— — determination of, 472.
— — isothermal, 342, 345.
— — upper limit of, 243.
— curves, typical, 181.
— effect of temperature on, 135, 177, 180.
— — — pressure on, 177, 179.
— of metastable form, 183.
Solute, 88.
Solution, definition of, 88.
— saturated, 178.
Solutions, 87.
Solutions, inevaporable, 148.
— with two boiling-points, 238.
Solvay process, 431.
Solvent, 88.
Space curve, 233.
— representation in, 85, 86.
Specific volume, 194.
Spontaneous crystallisation, 44, 45, 188.
Stable and metastable forms, pressure - temperature relations between, 46.
Stassfurt deposits, 370, 403, 437.
Stereoisomerism, 262.
Still, 122.
Strontium sulphate - calcium sulphate, 171.
Structure isomerism, 262.
Sublimation curve, 25.
— pressure, 25.

Sub-system, 321.
Successive reactions, "law" of, 54.
Sulphur, 64, 271.
  — - λ, 272.
  — - μ, 272.
  — - π, 272.
  — bivariant systems, 68.
  — dioxide, 243, 254.
  — equilibrium diagram of, 66.
  — melting-points of, 272.
  — metastability of, 43.
  — metastable systems, 68.
  — monoclinic, 274.
  — mother-of-pearl, 68, 69, 274.
  — nacreous, 68, 69, 274.
  — rhombic, 274.
  — transition curve of, 67.
  — vapour pressure of, 67.
Supercooling, 43.
Superheating, 43.
Supersaturated solution, 178.
Supersaturation, 45, 153, 183.
Surface, 233.
Suspended transformation, 42, 43, 153, 176
  — — and supersaturation, 183.
System, variance of, 13.
Systems of two liquid phases, 90.
  — bivariant, 32.
  — two-component, 84.

Tammann's method of halt time, 473.
Tautomerism, 262.
Temperature - concentration diagram 263.
  — - cycle process, separation of salts by, 394.
Ternary compound, congruently melting, 325, 465.
  — — incongruently melting, 329.
  — systems, 277, 459, 470.
Tetragene salt, 425.
Thallous sulphate — water, 180.
Thaw-point — melting-point method, 477.
Thermal analysis, 194, 472.
Thermodynamics, 9, 455.
Thin section, 478.

Three-component systems, 277, 459, 470.
Tie-line, 94, 284.
Tin, 69.
  — effect of impurities on rate of transformation of, 70.
  — — — low temperature on, 69.
  — grey, 69, 70.
  — white, 69, 70.
  — tetragonal, 69, 70.
  — rhombic, 70.
  — transition point of, 69.
Toluene - water - acetic acid, 283.
Transformation in optically active systems, 193.
Transformation, suspended, 42, 153, 176, 226.
Transition curve, 38.
  — interval, 354, 367, 412.
  — point, 143, 150, 154, 166, 409, 410.
  — — effect of pressure on, 363.
  — — — — solid solution on, 170.
  — — phase reaction at, 151, 353, 355.
  — points, table of in thermometry, 38.
  — — use of, in unary systems, 155.
  — temperature, 38, 154.
Triangular diagram, 278.
Triethylamine - water, 98.
Triple point, 29.
  — — changes at, 32.
  — — S$_1$- S$_2$- V, 37.
Trivariant, 85.
Two-component systems, 84, 455, 465.
  — — classification of, 87.

Unary melting-point, 269.
  — systems, 20, 61.
Univariant, 14.
  . — systems, 236.
Unsaturated solution, 178.
Unstable, 43.
  — and stable forms, transformation of, 267.
Upper critical solution temperature, 94, 98, 99.

Vaporisation curve, 21.

— — upper limit of, 21.

Vapour pressure, 21, 47, 91, 109, 212, 233, 282, 296, 410.

— — constancy of, and formation of compounds, 227.

— — effect of pressure on, 92.

— — of a hydrate, indefiniteness of, 224.

— — — solid-solution-vapour, 235.

— — — supercooled liquid, 47.

Velocity of crystallisation, 48.

— — transformation, effect of solvent on, 52.

— — — — temperature on, 53.

— — — in metastable systems, influence of impurities on, 52.

Viscosity, effect of, on crystallisation velocity, 49.

Vitreous state, 208.

Volatile solids, 212.

Water, 61.

— critical point of, 61.

— equilibrium diagram of, 61, 62, 64.

— melting-point of, 32.

— of crystallisation, salts with, 220, 345, 351, 355, 374.

— other phases of, 61.

— supercooled, 47.

— vapour pressure of supercooled, 47.

"Wet rest", method of, 378.

X-ray analysis, 170, 194, 229.

— — application of, to Phase Rule problems, 229.

Zeolites, 228.

Zoning, 208.